Compendium of Pastoral Hygiene

by

Albert Niedermeyer, M.D., Ph.D., J.C.D.

TRANSLATED BY

FULGENCE BUONANNO, O.F.M., Ph.D.

NEW YORK CITY

JOSEPH F. WAGNER, INC.

HERDER, LONDON

Imprimi Potest:

VERY REV. DONALD HOAG, O.F.M.

Minister Provincial

Nihil Obstat:

DANIEL V. FLYNN, J.C.D.

Censor Librorum

Imprimatur:

✠ FRANCIS CARDINAL SPELLMAN, D.D.

Archbishop of New York ·

NEW YORK, NOVEMBER 27, 1963

(The *nihil obstat* and *imprimatur* are official declarations that a book or pamphlet is free of doctrinal or moral error. No implication is contained therein that those who have granted the *nihil obstat* and *imprimatur* agree with the contents, opinions, or statements expressed.)

English rights have been granted for this translation of *Compendium der Pastoralhygiene* by Verlag Herder & Co., Vienna, Austria.

Preface

The present *Compendium of Pastoral Hygiene* is an important supplement to the *Compendium of Pastoral Medicine*. Topics which belonged more to the field of hygiene rather than to practical medicine were purposely omitted from the *Compendium of Pastoral Medicine*.

Pastoral Medicine would be incomplete without a specific consideration of the basic elements of Pastoral Hygiene. In older works of Pastoral Medicine such a distinction was not common, so that matters pertaining to the field of hygiene were treated inseparably from those associated with practical medicine. Whether this was good or whether the present trend of complete separation is better must be judged by the results.

Even though this book is primarily intended for the spiritual director, nevertheless the interests of the doctor are also taken into consideration.

The problems of Social Hygiene are treated, in detail, in a work entitled *Outline of Social Hygiene,* and published by W. Maudrich. The present *Compendium* is also an addition to this work, since the purpose of the *Outline* is to present a comprehensive "Hygiene of Human Society," and the *Compendium* treats of those problems which are encountered in the field of spiritual direction. Only such questions, as marriage guidance, birth decline, etc., are treated in both works, the lack of which would indicate a deficiency both in the treatment of Social Hygiene as in Pastoral Hygiene. Even these subjects are presented in the *Compendium* in the most concise manner.

These contributions to Social and Pastoral Hygiene should also become a basis for the universal Psycho-Hygiene—in the meaning of the Roman adage: *"Orandum est, ut sit mens sana in corpore sano!"*

—THE AUTHOR

Contents

Compendium of Pastoral Hygiene

1 Basic Concepts[1]

I. CONCEPT AND NATURE OF PASTORAL HYGIENE

A. Universal Approach

Pastoral Hygiene can be understood in a twofold sense:

1. In the wider sense the logical application of the universal approach is manifested in the entire field of hygiene: if till now empirical hygiene was based solely on a physical, chemical and biological basis, so, in Social Hygiene, the purely empirical aspect was already extended in scope by the social—more accurately, sociological—that is, predominantly rational viewpoint. And if this were elevated still more by an ethico-metaphysical element and brought to a conclusion, there would result, as in Pastoral Medicine, a well-founded concept of Pastoral Hygiene. The universal manner of treating the subject matter, which widens the scope by including the social viewpoint and which surpasses and

---

[1] It should not annoy the reader to find under the heading "Basic Concepts" almost a verbatim repetition of paragraphs which are familiar to him since they are found in the *Compendium of Pastoral Medicine*. Any attempt to spare the reader, who is already acquainted with the *Compendium of Pastoral Medicine,* this repetition, would be for the reader not acquainted with the other compendium a serious obstacle toward the formation of fundamental ideas.

The fundamental concepts common to both compendiums certainly represent the basis for both works. A lack of clarity concerning basic ideas will definitely impede the acquisition of true knowledge.

1

settles by its inclusion of the ethico-metaphysical element, is in direct opposition to the former and predominant positivistic approach, not in an absolutely definitive (contradictory) antithesis, but rather in a completing and widening relationship.

Positivism, as a scientific method and approach, considered as the object of science only positive confirmed facts that were exactly demonstrable through number, measurement and weight. This is too narrow a view if one understands science as an acknowledgment of truth; it is false if Positivism becomes a *Weltanschauung* for which nothing else exists beyond the positively demonstrable factual world; therein, it identifies itself with Materialism.

Positivism, as a *Weltanschauung* (philosophy of life), is to be rejected; as a method of exact scientific research, it is to be acknowledged within its limitations. There is no need to do away with it but rather to extend beyond it.

Universalism acknowledges the need and right of the positivistic science within its limits, but also recognizes the need to extend beyond it and thus avoid stagnancy, the need also of including the associations and deeper background in scientific research; otherwise, science would remain at the point where problems begin to become essential. Science would thus have long ago given up all claim to a knowledge of reality.

Therefore, Universalism does not exclude Positivism but includes it: solid positivistic research of definite facts must remain the foundation, and without it Universalism will lapse into the realm of nebulous speculation.

Positivism acknowledges as "research" only the sphere of pure data research; in natural science only laboratory research is still considered as such. Research of fundamentals represents the substructure of data research. This has already succeeded in being recognized as "research."

Universalism demands of both research spheres, as a crowning conclusion, an association research of higher value, the recognition of which, as "research," has yet to be attained.

2. In a more limited sense, we can designate pastoral hygiene as the sum of all hygienic questions which are of importance and interest in spiritual direction, i.e., the practical pastoral activity.

B. Definition

We feel the necessity of defining pastoral hygiene as hitherto:

1. *In a wider sense,* by pastoral hygiene we understand the extensive field of hygiene which progressively arises from the extension of the biological to the ethico-metaphysical and, from there, concludes with a complete view, which considers man not only as a member of a natural but also of a supernatural society. Understood in this manner, pastoral hygiene includes all of social hygiene. Accordingly, the present compendium in unison with the *Outline of Social Hygiene* would then comprise what we understand under the wider concept of pastoral hygiene.[2]

2. *In a more limited sense,* pastoral hygiene has as its object all the hygienic problems related to spiritual direction, i.e., practical pastoral work, no matter whether it deals with questions of a purely scientific nature or with elements of social hygiene. It therefore treats in part of problems of a varied nature, as, for example: the part of the spiritual director in the protection of his health against contagious diseases (protection against infection in hearing confessions, etc.) and during the time of an epidemic, especially in regard to the gathering of great crowds (missions, pilgrimages, processions); hygienic questions in regard to religious services (church area, holy water; administration of the sacraments to the sick); and, finally, the special questions concerning the personal hygiene of the spiritual director and the religious state in general.

The present work will treat of pastoral hygiene only in the more limited sense. This *Compendium* and the *Outline of Social Hygiene* correspond to pastoral hygiene in the wider sense.

C. Medicine and Hygiene

By medicine (the art of healing) the branch of practical clinical medicine is meant. Its object is sick mankind, and its task is the healing of the same.

By hygiene (the science of health) we mean the science of human health and its preservation, especially the preventing of avoidable injuries (prophylaxis—prevention). Its object is, above all, the healthy person; its task is to preserve his health.

Hygiene can, as medicine, be considered from the viewpoint of

[2] *Grundriss der Sozial Hygiene* (cited: GSH), W. Maudrich, Vienna, 1956.

the individual or of society. According to this classification, we have the distinction of individual and social medicine and individual and social hygiene.

D. Social Medicine and Social Hygiene—Social Pathology

The basic difference between social medicine and social hygiene is, even in scientific circles, not yet clear. Both fields are often confused, although their objects are completely different. The only element common to both is that of the social approach of their object.

By social medicine we mean the entire practical clinical branches under the social aspect of human community life. The consideration of the clinical branches from the standpoint of "social insurance" is only one of many other such viewpoints and in no way the only viewpoint; it is true, however, that it is at the present time practically the most important since it is in the foreground. It is, therefore, erroneous to limit the concept of social medicine exclusively to an "insurance medicine" or to the idea of "labor protection" (so-called "Labor Medicine"). These aspects are important, but are only a part of the entire social medicine.

As pathology is the basis of all clinical medicine, so social pathology is the basis of social medicine.

By social pathology we mean the theory concerning the causes of disease through social causal factors and, at the same time, of the effect of disease on the social position of man. We accordingly distinguish social conditionality of diseases and social meaning of diseases.

Social conditionality and social meaning of diseases present the principal aspect in the judgment of conditions or circumstances of disease in social medicine. They are primarily the object of the social medical expert opinion in a social legal claim (for example, of a pension claim or sickness-benefit claim in the case of incapability of working, etc.). That is why social medicine is suitably taught together with social pathology; just as it cannot be taught separately (in contrast to social hygiene). Social medicine can rather be taught only by representatives of the individual clinical special branches who are masters of the social problems of their branch.

In practice, it is useful to attach social ambulances to branch clinics and large hospital departments. In theory, the social medical academies have proven this in the most efficient manner.

E. Social Hygiene

Matters are basically different in social hygiene. This is the social aspect of all hygiene.

If an individual, up to the present time, was able to teach the entire field of hygiene, even including bacteriology and serology (immunity biology), then one can and must be able to review and teach even the wide field of social hygiene as long as he relies on the universal approach. This task can become less strenuous for the hygienist if he is relieved of the subjects of bacteriology and serology which, included in experimental pathology, should be taught through another department.

There is still no full agreement among authors concerning the concept and definition of social hygiene. Some authors (especially between 1918 and 1933) wanted under social hygiene to indicate exclusively the milieu conditions (milieu hygiene), and the health-injurious effects of pauperism were primarily considered. The state of distress, the "social question," remained in the foreground.

Opposed to the milieu hygiene with its limited fixation on exogenous factors of the social environment, a trend arose (especially between 1933 and 1945) which concentrated exclusively on the endogenous predispositional factors, above all, on hereditary predisposition and race (hereditary health theory, eugenics). It sought to substitute race hygiene for social hygiene.

For a universal social hygiene there is, regarding the question of exogenous or endogenous causal factors, no "either-or," but only an "as well as also": it contains the milieu hygiene as well as the hygiene of hereditary predisposition (eugenics). It does not exclude but includes race hygiene, only, of course, insofar as its theories are correct and its requirements morally justified. Hence, we comprehend the concept of social hygiene in its universal meaning: as the hygiene of human society.

F. Moral Hygiene—Cultural Hygiene

Alfons Fischer was the first to demand, in 1920, that social hygiene, understood in his time as hygiene of the social environmental factors, should, through the inclusion of moral factors (moral hygiene), be extended to a comprehensive general cultural hygiene. We strive to meet this justified demand through the universal comprehension of social hygiene, that is, through a complete view of its biological and social elements, including its ethico-metaphysical background. Thus we have succeeded especially by including the requirements of mental hygiene in attaining again a definition of pastoral hygiene in its wider sense.

G. Mental Hygiene (Psycho-Hygiene)

If hygiene has as its object human health, it is evident that this task must not limit itself merely to physical health, but must also extend to mental health. That which is the purpose of psychosomatic medicine in the realm of clinical medicine, namely, of showing the manifold correlation between bodily and mental factors in the genesis of disease, is likewise the purpose of mental hygiene.

H. Concept of Health

A correct concept of the nature and purpose of hygiene stands and falls with the correct definition of the concept "health." Up to a short time ago, the concept of health was stated merely in a negative manner: namely, health as the absence of any disease. Positivism adopted this negative definition. When Alfons Fischer demanded that a life "worthy of a human being" be made a characteristic of health, the anatomical pathologist, Aschoff, countered with a purely positivistic view that it is not feasible to introduce into science a concept which, like that of human dignity, implies social and moral values.

In the meantime, progress favored a more extensive concept of health.[3] The World Health Organization declared in its statute of 1947 that "health is not merely the absence of disease, but a state of complete physical, social and moral well-being." From this concept also arose the need of a revision in the direction of a universal meaning of the terms "normality" and "abnormality."

"Normal" is, accordingly, neither to be likened to the "ideal image," somewhat of an absolute freedom for every conceivable morbid predisposition, nor to the "construction image" of a purely statistically calculated "average value." "Normal," in the universal connotation of the health concept, implies, first of all, a physical

---

[3] Cf. *Grundriss der Sozial Hygiene* (1956).

state of fitness in the entire organism so as to meet the demands of biological life preservation under regular conditions essential to life, with sufficient adaptation to the regular and extraordinary conditions of life and its demands; further, a mental state of well-being and adaptation to the regular and extraordinary conditions of life; finally, social and moral ability to arrange and adapt to the necessary demands of human society and of the community life. Whatever does not correspond to this concept of "normal" is to be considered abnormal, and accordingly, morbid.

A concept of health which was fixated on the physical capability element defined "disease" as "life on the border of life adaptability" (F. Lenz). This definition is unsatisfactory. Under the manifest influence of Existentialism (the philosophy of the *"hic et nunc et sic"*) in more recent times, the "ontological disease concept," which saw in disease a separate *"ens,"* was rejected, and it was held that "There is no such thing as 'disease,' but only sick people." That disease is not a separate *"ens"* we can agree; but the nominalistic view, which denies universality to the concept of disease, is to be rejected.

Without abstraction from the individual case; without a comprehension of similarity in difference; without the logical process of forming a general concept under which the concrete individual case is subsumed, there is no possibility of diagnosis, and, without diagnosis, no therapy. Medicine as a science would be impossible if it did not acknowledge the process of abstraction from the individual case and the concept of "disease" as a universal and, because of this, a logical entity.

Disease is by no means a separate ontological *"ens,"* but only a privation: a divesting of completeness and fullness of healthy, integral nature. In the final analysis, the concept of disease can only be understood in the light of *natura vulnerata*.

Although disease can at times result from individual personal guilt, so is the generalization of Christian Science decidedly to be rejected which holds that every disease is a result of personal sin and inadmissibly identifies the concept of "disease" and "sin." This interpretation is not universal but, on the contrary, one-sidedly "supernaturalistic."

Universalism also affirms nature in its totality; supernaturalism, on the contrary, affirms the supernatural exclusively and thus denies in part a substantial knowledge of truth. (Wegname = $\alpha\check{\iota}\rho\epsilon\sigma\iota\varsigma$, pronounced "hairesis"; compare with "heresy.")

In the sphere of mental health we have to distinguish carefully between that anomaly which is devoid of guilt and, hence, morbid, and the infraction of the norm or rule, which is wrong or immoral. There are borderline cases in which this distinction can be made only through extensive expert knowledge, placing the highest demands upon the one judging; for example, in the case of sexual anomalies. It cannot be simply indicated that all cases are schematically morbid and thus free of guilt, no more than that all cases are guilty and hence punishable.

J. Hygiene as a Descriptive and Normative Science

Hygiene is a science which not only describes conditions, establishes facts, demonstrates and proves causes and associations. It seeks much more to establish general laws, indicating the causes of harm to the health of the individual and society and how these are to be avoided.

One aspect of hygiene has a predominantly biological scientific element; the other has more of a sociological ethical character and, hence, a philosophical or rational element. Accordingly, it is not sufficient merely to establish what hygiene is (descriptive hygiene); we must also know what it should be, and what it should not be (normative hygiene, *Grotjahn*).

The norms of normative hygiene contain a positive and a negative characteristic insofar as they regulate what should be and what should not be. The same goes for the resulting practical measures.

The positive (furthering) measures seek to bring to a realization what is desired (should be); the negative (restrictive) measures seek to supress what is not desired (should not be). To this also belongs the prevention of injury to health (preventive hygiene, prophylaxis), for example, legislation concerning epidemic diseases. The tasks that are to be fulfilled in the fields of public health, medical policy, health guidance, health care, social care, social charities and public and private welfare work, their limitations and the medico-pastoral view and treatment of them are reserved in a special manner to social hygiene.

K. Hygiene as a Natural Science. Its Place in Relation to the Philosophical or Rational Sciences

There is not the slightest doubt that hygiene is, above all, a science and makes use of natural scientific methods of research. After the concept of health had received a wider and more universal meaning, it was definitely established that hygiene is not only a descriptive, but also a normative science which also has a sociological ethical nature. What is more, there are important phases of hygiene, especially of mental hygiene, that border on philosophical or rational sciences. Under this viewpoint, natural sciences and rational sciences no longer exclude one another, but complement each other and thus lead to the knowledge of truth.

L. Hygiene and Ethics

The relationship of hygiene and ethics arises from the normative aspect of hygiene. Ethics, as a science, is the study and justification of moral law on the basis of the natural knowledge of reason. Moral theology, as a science, is the study and justification of moral law on the basis of the supernatural knowledge of Revelation. The realization or application of this knowledge is designated as practical, or moral, ethics. It is essential that practical moral behavior agree with whatever has been theoretically acknowledged as proper. From the agreement between natural and supernatural knowledge it follows that there can never be insurmountable opposition between science and doctrinal theology. The same is to be said as between hygiene and moral philosophy.

M. Basic Law of Pastoral Hygiene

From this knowledge arises the basic law of pastoral medicine which is likewise the basic law of pastoral hygiene. *At no time can anything be hygienically correct if it is morally wrong.* Apparent exceptions to this basic law can be found only in cases of passing and momentary success arising from measures which contradict moral law. But, in time, such momentary success is transformed into failure: it manifests itself at most as an apparent success.[4]

---

[4] The following are some of the examples: the propaganda, in general, concerning places that are designated for the selling of "contraceptives" in order to avoid venereal infection; the momentary success of infection-pre-

Every neglect of this basic law brings with it an inexorable perversion of the nature and task of hygiene. If we are permitted to push standard hygiene to the extreme in small matters, we shall be pushed for it into serious catastrophic antihygiene. We shall find these special basic principles repeatedly confirmed in social hygiene.

II. A REVIEW OF THE SUBJECT-MATTER

Pastoral hygiene, in the meaning of this compendium, includes two principal groups of problems:

1. Points of hygiene in spiritual direction.
2. Points of hygiene in the spiritual director and the religious life.

Ad 1) The "hygiene in spiritual direction" can be taken as "objective" pastoral hygiene inasmuch as it deals with the objects. It includes, as such, all matters of practical pastoral activity which manifest a hygienic element. To it belong many problems of a varied nature. They are mentioned as hygienic points in religious worship, as, for example, ventilation and heating of the church; pews; wash and toilet arrangement in church proximity; cleanliness of church linens; avoidance of hygienic deficiency in sacramentals (especially baptismal water) and administration of the sacraments; avoidance of infectious diseases, especially comportment during epidemics (avoidance of mass gatherings); hygienic problems associated with pilgrimages, etc.; points concerning care of the sick.

Psychohygienic meaning of religious education: school instruction; spiritual direction of the youth; premarital instruction; marriage guidance; sex pedagogy; psychopathology and spiritual direction; alcoholism; addiction. Physical exercise, sport; influx of travellers on the parish. Free time, relaxation, theater, cinema, radio, television; points concerning hygienic instruction for the people.

---

vention is more than outweighed by the complete number of cases of infection arising from the removal of restraints.

Eugenic sterilization can be a momentary success in the individual case; perceived in its totality, it does not produce a true eugenic effect but a dysgenic effect as do all contraceptive measures: in time they promote only racial degeneration.

Hygienic consideration regarding questions of modern spiritual direction: activism, pragmatism, activity, life tempo. Thanatological questions, the nature of the burial process. Hygienic problems in the liturgy. The ecclesiastical year.

Ad 2) The hygiene of the spiritual director and the religious life is concerned with subjects ("subjective hygiene"). It comprises: healthy adaptation, fitness, examination; celibacy, religious life; mission activity; lack of priests; spiritual direction in the large city and in the country; personal hygiene of the priest; day and work division; breviary; asceticism; fasting; nourishment; clothing; lodging; work and recreation; old-age pension; premature exhaustion and diseases arising from exhaustion.

Many of the problems indicated above are common to both pastoral hygiene and social hygiene and are treated in these works. However, it cannot be overlooked that they are also to be discussed or at least mentioned in pastoral hygiene.

2 Hygiene in Spiritual Direction

Objective pastoral hygiene, which deals with the material problems of spiritual direction, cannot be completely separate from the consideration of subjective pastoral hygiene which treats of the personal hygiene of the spiritual director. It is evident, for example, that the question of church heating does not belong only to the objective hygiene of the building, but also to the personal hygiene of the priest. Since, in the division of the subject-matter, we begin with objects, we, therefore, treat also of these problems in objective hygiene.

I. OBJECTS OF RELIGIOUS WORSHIP

A. Buildings

In regard to the building structures which are used for religious worship, essentially the same hygienic requirements are to be indicated as those for secular buildings which accommodate a great number of people.

It must be immediately made clear that, regarding buildings designated for religious purposes, the hygienic element is not primary and, therefore, should not remain in the foreground as is the case with schools, theaters, concert halls, civic halls, etc. In the exposition of this matter, we must never lose sight of the fact that the primary purpose of these structures is religious: that is, that they serve *religio,* the reuniting of men to God, of nature with the supernatural. Just as we have resolved to reject any biased supernaturalism, so must we definitely reject all restrictive naturalism.

The requirements, even hygienically, for a structure intended for edification and recollection should definitely be different from those specified, for example, for an aseptic operating room. In the latter case hygiene is primary and emphatically in the foreground, while in the former it is in the background (and purposely so), and only then does it intervene when, through defects, health is threatened.

When circumstances increase the danger to health, as is evident, for example, in the gathering of many people during an epidemic, hygiene must lose its reserve and intervene. It is then that the spiritual director is to be as acquainted with its possibilities as the doctor is to respect its limits.

The following will be considered in our treatment of structures: church; parish courtyard; cloister; place of pilgrimage; etc; also, especially in villages, cemeteries on church grounds; and, finally, the burial process which will be treated separately.

1. Churches

a) STRUCTURAL DAMAGE

The principal danger to health on the part of the building arises from the structural deterioration of the church. In this respect, not only falling stones, decorations, bricks and heavy stucco, which can cause fatal accidents and perhaps involve serious inconvenience and annoyance (as, for example, in liability lawsuits), are to be considered, but also the fact that, through rising moisture in the masonry and the attack of dry rot *(merulius lacrymans),* the damp coldness of the church can cause or aggravate rheumatic diseases. Through this progressive deterioration the air will become spoiled, musty and mouldy. This condition is often the cause of the typical "church fainting spell" in predisposed neuropathic persons.

b) THE CHURCH AIR

(1) *Hygienic Requirements*

The hygienic requirements regarding air, especially in places used for large gatherings, concern air quantity and air quality.

In regard to the air quantity in churches, there is hardly any problem. Since the naves are usually considerably high, the air cubature, i.e., the number of cubic meters (cbm) at the disposal of every person in a completely filled church is always suitably great. If we, for example, calculate the complete air space of a medium-sized cathedral of 100m in length and of 25:40m in height and width, it would amount to 100,000 cbm. If the church contains 2,000 people, each person will share 50 cbm of air. Such an air cubature is never completely consumed especially when the church is filled for only a short time.[1]

Hygienically the most important elements to be considered in judging air quality are: temperature; degree of humidity; dust content.

The temperature of air in the church undergoes, in general, less variation than the air outside the church. It is warmer in the winter and mostly cooler in the summer than the air outside the church. Since the thick stone walls are heat conductors, so that the summer heat is retained in them for a long time, yet, since they are slowly heated after a winter frost, coldness is felt most in church not at Christmas, but usually at Easter.

The air humidity in the church is usually higher than that outside the church. Hygiene distinguishes among absolute, relative and maximum humidity.

The actual amount of humidity in the air, that is, the relation of water vapor to air in percentage, is the *absolute humidity*. The actual possible saturation degree of air with water vapor at a given temperature is the *maximum humidity*. The relationship of absolute moisture to maximum humidity is the *relative humidity*. The difference between absolute and maximum humidity is the saturation deficit. The warmer the air is, the more water vapor the air can contain, that is, the greater the maximum humidity will be. If the air is saturated with water vapor, then only a slight lowering of the temperature suffices to permit that which is above the diminished

---

[1] An air cubature of 20 cbm is sufficient for a school room; for hospital wards 30 cbm is suitable, so that a carbon dioxide content of air from 1-1.5% is not exceeded.

An air cubature of at least 3 cbm was prescribed for air-raid shelters. There the CO_2 content of air often exceeded the permissible maximal limit of 4%. This could be endured if a person remained for a short time. A high air-corrupting humidity was added to the carbon dioxide content.

saturation point to result in precipitation. This temperature is called "dew point."

Air that is warm and saturated with humidity easily leads to heat expansion. The body cannot give off any more heat through evaporation: it is "overheated," and this easily leads to sudden collapse ("heat stroke"). This is to be distinguished from the ordinary "church fainting spell."

In a heat stroke the face is blue-red, the entire body is covered with perspiration, the breathing is of a rattling nature, the pulse is feeble and frequent; there is serious danger to life. The ordinary fainting spell is characterized by an unchanged or pale face without the cited symptoms.

The dust content of church air is often greatly above the average. The architectural ornaments in gothic and baroque churches are difficult to clean (dust catchers); the dust is whirled by currents of air. Much of the dust will be carried on the feet of those coming to church. Church dust is, in general, relatively devoid of pathogenic germs. Yet the frequent removal of dust with a vacuum cleaner is a rule of hygiene.

(2) Church Fainting Spell

These fainting spells that occur in church are seldom due to the church air as indicated by those affected by the same—usually women. It is definite that the church air is not always agreeable to certain sensitive people: the air is stale since it is too seldom and too little circulated. This circulation of air is very necessary especially after a great number of people have been in church. The evaporations from the people remain in the area; the stagnant air is permeated with incense vapor which, of itself, does not cause any hygienic harmful effect, but rather impedes the "betterment" or clearing of air as unpleasant odors are stretched over the area.

It is interesting to note that among the church attenders who state that they cannot bear the "church air," practically all are women; those who regularly succumb to the fainting spell in church usually belong to a definite type: the type of hysteroidal woman who readily "makes herself interesting" and attracts the attention of others so that she usually becomes sick when this would astonish those present and disturb the environment.

The author has been able to establish in a number of cases that these women usually select the moment of elevation, the time of the benediction with the Blessed Sacrament and similar circumstances in which the sensational effects of their "attacks" or falls would be the greatest. Confirmations of this sort should not be generalized. Not all conditions of that nature are "church fainting spells" of the type just described. With persons of a vegetative-dystonic nature or heart and vascular injury one encounters similar external conditions which, however, indicate a true vegetative shock or vascular spasms which can possibly be due to stenocardiac attacks.

In regard to cases of this kind, the priest is advised to instruct the sacristan, the sexton and other male helpers to remove the patient immediately from the disturbing surroundings and to bring him or her into the sacristy. In the sacristy there should be on hand, at all times, a bottle of *tinctura valerianae* (tincture of valerian) from which a teaspoonfull with a sip of water should be given to the patient. This process should, however, be avoided if the patient is unconscious.

Patients affected by a simple fainting spell recover quickly when allowed to rest on their back and with their head raised. If this is not the case, then a doctor would have to decide whether it is a case of a cardiac or vascular attack and to fulfill what is necessary in the given circumstances.

In most cases the conditions already described are absolutely harmless and pass over very quickly; so much quicker the sooner the patient is removed from the scene of attack and the less is made of the situation. They, for the most part, are less harmful the more dramatic and theatrical the behavior of the patient and the more disturbed the patient appears to be. In cases of serious heart attack the patient is usually pallid and silent, more apathetic than excited.

c) VENTILATION

The question of sufficient ventilation is of greater hygienic importance, especially in the case of greater church attendance and, above all, during the warm summer days. The church windows are usually only partly opened, difficult to open and not correctly opened: ventilation coming only from the opened church doors is usually insufficient for the ventilation of the entire place and in the removal of stagnant and stale air.

The difficulty in church ventilation is due mostly to the great height of the naves. The heated air and that arising from human evaporation rises to the top of the church. By opening the doors, the cool air pushes in below without the warm and stale air receiving a sufficient outlet. This latter would be possible by inserting an electromotor ventilation system which would draw in the air on top so that the incoming pure air from below could be equally distributed in the given space. An opening in the dome (as, for example, in the Pantheon), is suitable for the spontaneous outlet of stale air if, from below, fresh cool air flowed through the doors.

The opening of a very large window could be dangerous and costly, especially if it is a glass painting of great artistic value, the opening of which would endanger every part of the window. Sufficient ventilation in the confessional is also of great importance. The use of electrically controlled ventilation removes all difficulties and, at the present time, no longer presents a problem. Even the cost remains within average means.*

d) HEATING

The heating of the church presents a more difficult problem than the ventilation. The difficulty lies, even here, in the height of the church. The installing of a heater is useless if its heat radiation in relation to the vast air cubature is minimal, thus unused, and lost in the area. Moreover, the warm air immediately rises above while the people stand or sit below, and the cold air rises from below. In a short time the feet of the people are cold, the capillary blood vessels are contracted to the maximum, and this easily leads to diseases that arise from catching cold, especially if an influenza epidemic rages (the so-called "cold" creates a special disposition for "catarrh infection").

The problem of heating a high place would be easily solved if there existed heating whereby the weight of air increases with the

---

* *Translator's note.* Modern air-conditioning methods eliminate many of the difficulties here presented. However, even in the United States there are many areas in which the hygienic suggestions here offered apply with great fruit.

rising temperature. Such a "temperature conversion" is, unfortunately, contrary to the known laws of nature.

The installation of steam and air heating and air conditioning, which has been very extensive in the new world, presents a difficulty in European countries because of the ever high cost.

From the hygienic standpoint, heating is a pressing necessity in winter for the church-goer, but much more for the priest, sexton and sacristan. The church-goer seldom spends more than an hour in the cold, but the priest must often spend many hours, especially when he sits in an unheated confessional. The priest cannot protect his hands against the cold during the celebration of holy Mass and, because of this, the effects of freezing and circulatory disturbances arise more frequently.

e) LIGHTING

We distinguish natural lighting and that which is produced artificially.

Natural lighting is a problem insofar as, in old, historical and artistic churches, the stained glass mosaic windows are of great aesthetic value, but absorb the greater part of the daylight. In this regard, we recall places like Notre Dame of Paris, Sainte Chapelle and Chartres as well as the medieval windows of St. Stephan in Vienna, etc. It is a case here of such skilled handicraft of unique charm that it would be unjustifiable perhaps to complain under the appeal of hygiene that "they take away too much light." To the old Gothic cathedrals belong the mystical half-darkness of the old mosaics with their glowing color magnificence. The modern person of our day has little taste for this. His demand for much light and sun is hygienically justified when it pertains to the arrangement of his living room or work room; but it is exceedingly unjustifiable when he permits the removal of trees from his shady garden because they "take away too much light." One should be awed by old churches and their artistry. Mental hygiene demands this more than physical hygiene. Man, in the midst of constant activity, needs an island of perfect repose. He who has never experienced the effects of this holy silence found in the half-darkness of an old cathedral has no right to appeal to "modern hygiene" against it.

It is the artificial lighting of churches that gives occasion for hygienic considerations.

Since the triumph of electrical lighting over gaslight, which has been almost supplanted, the strong corruption of air through the great multi-flamed gas candelabrum requires no added words. The development of electrical lighting is evidenced by the fact that the strong, clear, electric bulbs, which are unpleasant to the eyes, have been substituted by frosted glass and, recently, by fluorescent tubes.

Indirect lighting, taking everything into consideration, is well distributed and brings out the architectural and artistic beauty of the church edifice. The eye perceives many such beautiful elements, which were formerly overlooked, and that, from the standpoint of mental and cultural hygiene, is a great contribution.

The candle light has definitely not been subdued. On the altar on which the holy Sacrifice of the Mass is offered, at least two candles must burn; before the Blessed Sacrament in exposition at least three candles on each side are to be lighted. It would be absurd to oppose this regulation on the basis of hygienic consideration ("air corruption"). It suffices, when the regulation is being followed, that all open flames are so contained that every danger of fire is eliminated.

It is a rule that a perpetual light burn before every tabernacle in which the Blessed Sacrament is preserved. This was always an open oil lamp. Since wartime it has been permissible to use an electrical and economical incandescent lamp. This custom has been retained even when oil is easily obtainable. Its retention has nothing to do with hygienic motivation, not even from the standpoint of fire prevention.

f) FIRE PROTECTION. PANIC PREVENTION

Wherever great crowds of people assemble, whether in churches, theaters or concert halls, there exist police regulations concerning fire protection.

In churches built of stone the danger of fire is generally diminished, but it is a serious problem with wooden churches and chapels.

The outbreak of fire is practically always associated with panic, and panic means extreme danger to the lives of many people. The danger provoked by panic is usually greater than that of fire.

It is very important that the church doors be so constructed that, when both wings or parts are opened, a quick and unhindered emptying of the church is possible. But it is exactly in this regard that in most churches, even those having large doors, there is at present much to be desired. Rarely enough can the wings of the door be opened from the outside.

Even when church-goers are well disciplined and keep to the right in entering and leaving the church (in places where it is a rule to walk or ride on the right side), there is always a disturbing blocking of the entrance when certain individuals go contrary to the regulations. It would be helpful if the clergy would insist on the observation of this regulation.

When there is a great rush, the exit is then pressed by a crowd, and only two or three persons can pass through the narrow exit. The emptying of the church follows much too slowly. It is inconceivable, considering what can happen in case of panic, that so little thought is given to the matter. It must further be considered that a large church should have not only a main exit, but other exits as well.

In order to fight any small outbreak of fire promptly, there should be one or two extinguishers in every sacristy.

g) WATER SUPPLY. SANITARY FACILITIES

An unconditional hygienic requirement that should, as a minimum, be fulfilled in every greatly frequented church is that there be a properly functioning supply of running water. Fire hydrants with connected fire hoses should definitely be on hand. The old "wash buckets," still to be found in some old sacristies as well as in some school rooms, are hygienically forbidden.

The priest washes his hands before and after offering the sacrifice of the Mass. Water used at the altar is necessary at the Offertory, Lavabo, and for the ablution of the chalice. It is, therefore, evident that water used for this purpose be clean and easy to obtain.

Hygienically desired but fulfilled only in large and in some modern city churches is the presence of sanitary facilities (toilet rooms), at least in the vicinity of the church building. It can very easily happen, especially in great crowds, that someone will become sick, and it can be disastrous if there is no provision for such cases. Of course, there cannot be any hygienic objection that the sanitary supplies are not found within the church building, but they should be had in the vicinity of the church. This is to be taken into consideration in planning the building of the church.

h) SUBSIDIARY PLACES. SACRISTY

The sacristy is one of the most important subsidiary places of the church. From the hygienic standpoint, it must be considered, as Stoehr has stated, as a principal place. With justification Stoehr complained that the sacristy is often "treated as a stepmother." The sacristy is truly an "indication" of the care and cleanliness of the church and also of the understanding by the pastor and church directors of hygienic problems.

The manner of storing and caring for church linens and vestments permits the drawing of important conclusions in this matter. Stoehr has strikingly remarked that the sacristy should not, as formerly, be the *"partie honteuse"* of the church. She should be able "to let herself be seen"; and, above all, she should cease, through damp, musty, foul air, being an obstacle to the health of the priest and sexton.

In this regard Stoehr states: "In badly ventilated, dusty sacristies, we have repeatedly experienced a lower temperature than that in the church itself. This disagreeable circumstance cannot fail to affect the priest who comes from the church heated and damp with perspiration." [2]

j) SUBTERRANEAN VAULTS (CRYPTS)

The subterranean vaults (crypts) serve the purpose, even in our time, of providing burial places for bishops, abbots, illustrious pastors and priests of the church, as well as laymen who are thus honored in a special manner. Stoehr has spoken very definitely against such a practice and has posited most serious hygienic reasons. He is of the opinion that in the preservation of corpses beneath the church, where numerous people gather, serious dangers

---

[2] Stoehr-Kannamueller, *Pastoralmedizin*, Herder, Freiburg.

can arise. We cannot agree, in this regard, with the opinion of the old master of pastoral hygiene. It is a matter of deciding whether the air in the crypt is dry. That this is the case, according to the experience of the author regarding practically all the crypts with which he is acquainted, indicates that the preoccupation of Stoehr in this matter is unjustifiable. Corpses buried in crypts, even if they are not embalmed, do not succumb to putrefaction, but to mummification and dry decomposition.

The Capuchin vault in Vienna is one of the most frequented crypts in the world; its presence has not yet affected the health of any of the numerous faithful who have participated in the religious services in the church above it. The same can be said for the large crypt of St. Stephen. If the air is moist, then the development of mycelium of fungus can easily arise, but this is also harmless to health.

2. Parish Rectory

To every parish church there belongs a parish rectory with a dwelling place for the pastor, one or two chaplains (assistants) and a housekeeper. In rural parishes there is, also for the most part, a garden (fruit, vegetable and flower), as well as some acres of arable land. The rural rectory, especially in larger communities, are usually spacious and have a representation room which is used as the "bishop's room" for episcopal visitations. In general, the rural parish rectories, because of their gardens, are definitely more hygienic than the city rectories, especially if the latter are in the poorer sections.

The kitchen is, from the hygienic standpoint, one of the most important places in the home. When the water line and electrical current are at hand, the kitchen can be supplied with all the modern conveniences: electric range; hot-water supply; hot-air dryer; refrigerator; washing machine; a vacuum cleaner for the living room, etc. These facilities will essentially lighten the work of the housekeeper who undergoes all the burdens of a housewife without enjoying the same security.

The sleeping quarters must receive more attention than that allotted by modern home builders. These are no longer real "sleeping rooms," but only sitting and work rooms with couches or "camouflaged furniture" which conceal the beds. Individual comfortable rooms with beds must be set aside for the pastor and his curates. Man normally spends 35 to 40 per cent of his entire life in bed. His health demands an adequate bedroom.

A separate dining room should be an absolute hygienic requirement for every large rectory housing a pastor and his curates. Even when the pastor is alone, it is not advisable to take his meals in the kitchen. This would lead to a neglect of external forms which are not only of a purely social value, but also of an hygienic as well as of a physical culture value.

3. Cloister

A cloister *(claustrum, monasterium)* is basically different from a larger parish house because of its greater number of residents. The cloister is distinguished by its enclosure, i.e., the more or less severe separation from the outside world. The severity of this enclosure depends upon the severity of the rule of the Order. In the very strict Orders (Carthusians, Camaldolese-hermits, Trappists, Carmelites) the enclosure is a very strict one and is, at times, associated with a more or less strict silence. With the Carthusians, every monk has his own little house with workshop and small garden, whereby the idea of a *Coenobium* in a common cloister building seems to be lost, yet all the individual houses together form a large *Coenobium*.

The monastic life is proper to the cloister; hence, all structural elements and rooms should be arranged according to this way of life. Here we deal only with construction and space and not with the way of life, which will be treated in another place.

Ordinarily the following are associated with a cloister: the cloister church with the corresponding large priest choir *(presbyterium);* with choir stalls for the individual conventuals; with a Cathedral seat in Abbey churches corresponding to the episcopal seat in Cathedral churches; with a separate choir in case the liturgical choir prayers are not held in the church.

The cloister itself has a portal room as well as one or more consulting rooms or parlors outside the enclosure. Inside the enclosure the members of the community have either individual cells,

³ V.i., p. 133 ff.

which are also bedrooms, or, circumstances permitting, a community bedroom (dormitory) in which individual beds are separated by curtains.

The community dining room is the refectory, which usually adjoins the kitchen. From here the food is passed into the refectory through a sliding window.

In the cloister of women there will be a larger wash house, and in larger houses of the Order, especially when adjoined to hospitals, there will be a central laundry. For smaller houses the modern electrical washing machine will suffice.

The monastic life implies that the demands of asceticism take precedence over the requirements of hygiene. It is required only that serious and slight hygienic violations, which are avoidable, be prevented.

By slight violations that are avoidable we mean all improprieties which can be removed without causing any conflict with the rule of the Order. Since order and cleanliness are usually strongly insisted upon in the cloister, it is therefore not difficult to fulfill every hygienic law which has cleanliness as its primary object.

Without considering the personal hygiene of the religious, it can be said that, in regard to cleanliness, it is easier to fulfill the objective requirements of hygiene than to fulfill those of personal hygiene, especially of physical culture. It is always revealing news that it is completely in agreement with the requirements of asceticism to have a wash-sink with flowing water in every cell; that the old wash-stand with lavoir and dirty wash-bucket be removed. They are not only objectionable from the hygienic standpoint, but cause much unnecessary work.

Within the area of the cloister another community room is to be mentioned which should be designated as a relaxation room: the recreation room. The winter recreation room is usually a larger room which is somewhat better arranged; the summer recreation room is usually a large porch in the garden.

Recreation should really be a time of leisure. Its proper use pertains to the mental hygiene of the cloister.

Participation in meals is, according to the monastic sense, not a recreation but a religious exercise. Hence, for the most part, silence is kept in the refectory, and during meal times reading and meditation take place. The reading stand has a place in the standard arrangement of the refectory. Many large cloisters still have a separate winter and summer refectory.

4. Special Ecclesiastical Buildings

The following are to be mentioned as special ecclesiastical buildings: the episcopal seat (episcopal palace) with the curia of cathedral canons, ecclesiastical administration buildings with libraries and archives, etc. These structures do not present any special hygienic problems for pastoral hygiene, but their hygienic problems are none other than those pertaining to secular buildings.

B. Furnishings within the Church

The following furnishings within the church are considered under the hygienic viewpoint: the altar; pulpit; pews; confessionals; baptismal font.

1. The Altar

In the Catholic Church it is the table of sacrifice. On it the priest fulfills the mystery of the consecration of the offering—the transubstantiation. Hygiene is silent concerning this mystery; its requirement concerns itself solely with cleanliness, and that is required also by the dignity of the sacrifice.

Just a passing word concerning the following which are of secondary meaning: the Canon card which, besides the very Canon of the Mass, contains the words of the *Gloria, Credo* and the psalm *Lavabo,* should provide letters of such a size that even a myopic celebrant can read it without his glasses and without effort; the tabernacle should be clean and dry. Humid heat fosters the settlement of microorganisms on the consecrated hosts which are reserved in the ciborium for the distribution of Communion to the faithful and on the host in the lunula. This is especially the case with the *bacillus prodigiosus* which, flourishing in red colored cultures, can easily simulate the phenomenon of bleeding hosts; it can develop only in humid heat, and this condition is only seldom found in the tabernacle. Even other microorganisms can arise which can lead to a premature corruption of the sacred species (minute fungi causing mould, bacillus aureus, even pathogenic bacteria).

Cleanliness and dryness as well as relatively low temperature are the best protection against such effects. There is no need of a special prophylactic disinfectant. Once there is an attack of microbes, then a simple process of disinfection with formalin is to be carried out.

At the lower end of the altar or any other place that would serve the purpose the sacrarium is found. It serves the purpose of becomingly storing decaying sacred objects which undergo corruption; for example, the remains of baptismal water or blessed ashes and of already corrupting hosts. The sacrarium, a sort of small sink, should protect such objects of religious worship from all profanity and secure the same to their complete corruption.

An inner enameled box of metal that can be removed and whose contents, if occasion arises, can be burned with an overflow of alcohol is to be recommended for the sacrarium. The present prescript reads: the sacrarium must be inspected from time to time and cleaned; its solid contents can be mixed with lycopodium powder *(Stuppa, semen lycopodii)* and burned.

2. The Pulpit

The hygienic requirement for the pulpit is none other than that of the best possible acoustics. Good acoustics of the kind that the voice of the preacher can be heard throughout the church is of service to the preservation of the voice, the lungs, as well as the heart of the preacher.

Today there is less consideration of good acoustics since there is greater dependence on the loudspeaker. But that is not right; the loudspeaker should be used only when the voice or the acoustics do not suffice. The loudspeaker causes a distortion of the sound waves, so that the voice is disfigured.

Trusting in the working of the loudspeaker, one has occasionally removed the sound board from the pulpit without realizing that, through the reflection of the sound waves pressing upward and reflecting back from the high arch, very strong interferences arise which can cause the words to become almost unintelligible; at times, too, there are certain fading effects, so that the voice sounds very loud at one time and, at another, is completely inaudible.

The same interference and fading effect arise when the priest preaches from the altar instead of the pulpit. This is done especially at times when, out of liturgical consideration, a short sermon is preached by the celebrant himself between the Gospel and the Credo. In this case the greater part of the sound waves travel directly to the nave of the church and can be heard easily only by those near at hand. A smaller part travels first toward the ceiling and to the rear and is reflected by the arch. These reflected sound waves reach the direct sound waves to form an interference and travel in a modulated manner toward intensification and diminution and finally, to complete extinction. The result is that the people in the third row cannot understand a word of the sermon.

In Protestant churches, since they do not have the Sacrifice of the Mass, the pulpit and not the altar is the principal element in the church arrangement; it serves the purpose of preaching the Gospel, the word of God. For this reason, special emphasis is placed on the maximal use of the acoustics.

In many churches, especially in rotund structured churches, the pulpit is literally the center of the church, and the pews are arranged around the pulpit. In such cases the use of the loudspeaker is, for the most part, superfluous.

3. Pews

In the old-school hygiene, the construction of the school benches played a definitely remarkable role. But no attempt has been made to apply the viewpoint developed in that sphere to the construction of church pews. This seems very necessary since defectively constructed pews can become instruments of torture, especially since the pews are used both in sitting and in kneeling.

In Protestant churches the bench is used only for sitting, outside of the short time in standing during the reading of the Gospel. A defective structure will, in this case, be less felt than when the bench is used also for kneeling. Only a too narrow seat can cause a disturbance in sitting.

In regard to the pew we distinguish the front with the desk board, the back with the seat board (which is, at the same time, the front of the next bench), and the footboard.

The vertical distance of the seat board edge from the edge of the desk board is designated as the difference; the horizontal distance between the front edge of the seat board and the back edge of the desk board, projected on the horizontal of the seat board, is designated as the distance.

We speak of zero distances when a vertical plummet exactly joins the back edge of the desk board with the front edge of the seat board; of a plus distance, when the back part of the vertical plummet of the desk board edge is to the back; of a minus distance, when the front edge of the seat board under the back edge of the desk board is pushed toward the front. A minus distance in pews is to be avoided; a sufficient plus distance is to be desired.

We propose to designate the horizontal distance of the front from the back as the primary distance. This offers a measure for the comfort and spaciousness of the pew. If the primary distance is too short, then all the other structural defects will arise from this fact. This is usually the case when there is an attempt to place the greatest number of pews in a relatively limited space. Then the pews are too narrow and very uncomfortable for the corpulent person. In that case, the seat boards are also too small and again uncomfortable; or in the case of wider seat boards, there is a minus distance which causes discomfort when kneeling and standing; and kneeling in an upright position is not possible. From this arises the difficulty of a too small footboard which, in kneeling, causes painful alterations of the knee joints, especially for older persons with *arthrosis deformans*.

It is further important that the desk and footboard have a certain incline. When this is no greater than the maximal 10-15 degrees, it is favorable for the reading of a prayerbook or hymnal; even a completely slight incline of the footboard can be comfortable since it corresponds to the natural support of the foot while sitting. But when this incline is too high—especially when the footboard is small—then both sitting and kneeling in such pews will cause torment and bodily pain which, in turn, affect devotion. The footboards should be removable for the purpose of easy and thorough cleaning.

The desk board, especially when the incline is greater, should be enclosed by a strip which will prevent the sliding of inclining books. To be recommended is the installing of hat clasps on the front part of the pew under the desk board for the hanging of hats or handbags, so that they will not be in the way.

The seats should be numbered, and, when possible, this should be done on the front part at the lower end of the desk board, so that each person has enough room at his disposal.

We have omitted indicating the definite measurements of the primary distance, seat width, desk width and foot width, since the measurements must be arranged according to church space at hand and its best possible use. The consideration of the basic thoughts here developed will help in finding the correct measurement for the concrete individual case.[3]

4. Confessionals

The following hygienic considerations are related to the confessional:

1. Protection of the priest hearing confessions from droplet infection arising from minute particles expelled by talking, coughing or sneezing on the part of the penitent, and vice versa; sufficient ventilation.

2. Protection of the penitent from overhearing by others waiting to go to confession, especially because of the deafness of the confessor or the penitent.

3. Avoidance of uncomfortable body position by observing the basic rules in the construction of kneeling benches.

Ad 1) The danger of infection by breathing and coughing in the confessional should not be underestimated. It is droplet infection which plays an important role in the spreading of influenza and acute diseases of the respiratory organs (catarrh infection); and in

---

[3] We indicate, as an example, a church in Vienna whose pews are especially spacious and comfortable. We indicate the horizontal distance (distances) by the Latin letters (D, d), the vertical distance (differences) by the Greek letters (Δ, δ), the maximal distance by capital letters (D, Δ), the separate distance by small letters (d1, d2—δ1, δ2), the desk width by the letter "p," the seat width by the letter "s," the foot width by the letter "f," and establish the following measurements:

1) Primary Distance $D = 100$ cm
2) Distance between the Seat Board and Desk Board $d1 = +50$ cm
3) Primary Difference $\Delta = 85$ cm
4) Desk-Seat Difference $\delta1 = 35$ cm
5) Seat-Foot Difference $\delta2 = 35$ cm
6) $P = 18$; $s = 35$; $f = 40$ cm

In the first and exceptionally spacious bench the primary distance $D = 125$ cm. It is a matter here not of standard measurements, but of especially favorable optimal measurements, which are elsewhere difficult to attain.

angina, dyphtheria, scarlet fever and measles; even tuberculosis can be transferred through contactual infection.

The danger of infection is reciprocal; from the penitent to the confessor, and vice versa; but the former is definitely the more frequent since the priest cannot so easily avoid the coughing by the penitent as he can prevent the same toward the penitent. Coughing should be seriously avoided. This danger can be greatly eliminated by covering the confessional screen with a cellulose membrane which does not affect the sound waves.

In order to avoid harm to health and nausea, a sufficient air supply is a requisite for the confessional. The stagnant air in an enclosed confessional is seldom renewed; this can become intolerable for both the confessor and the penitent. The installation of a small electrical fan will present no technical or financial difficulty; for the rest, it is the task of the sacristan to see to it that there is sufficient ventilation.

Ad 2) When the confessional is open toward the sides, i.e., only the priest sits in an enclosed compartment, then only whispering prevents overhearing by those waiting to go to confession, especially when there is a great number of people. This can be disastrous when either the priest or the penitent is hard of hearing. The deaf person cannot easily modify the volume of his voice; he speaks louder than is necessary; on the other hand, the confessor must speak louder than usual in order to be understood by the deaf person.

It is advisable to construct additional compartments on the open sides of the confessional and to enclose the same with doors. Still better would be the designation of separate confessionals for the deaf or to install hearing aids in the confessional.

Ad 3) The same goes for confessional kneelers as for the church kneelers, with corresponding modifications. It is important, above all, that the footboard be not so small and so hard that the penitent is disturbed by the feeling that he is going to slip off.

5. Baptismal Fonts

The public reservation of holy water in the holy water fonts at the church entrance is often (especially in small village churches) such that it offends not only against hygiene, but also against the dignity of sacramentals. The condition has improved in the last decade, but there still remains much to be desired.

It does not suffice to state that, because of the salt content of holy water, nothing serious can happen and that the holy water will not become corrupt. Corruption as such would, hygienically, not be the worst thing; it is already extremely nauseating because of the odor and discoloration. But definitely more serious than the decomposition is the infection by morbific agents. As such, the following come into consideration: *bacterium coli,* the provoking group of banal wound infections *(staphylococcus, streptococcus),* especially with injuries to the dipping finger; *bacterium coli* can with other intestinal bacteria of enteritis, of typhoid, and of paratyphoid groups more or less cause severe intestinal infections when the infected water manages to get on the lips.

Apart from this, it is extremely disgusting and shameful when the holy water, usually in a metallic container which is difficult to clean, is turbid and dirty. It is useless and usually only a "symbolical treatment" (also definitely against ecclesiastical regulation) to add a few drops of a disinfectant solution (chloramine, lysoform) or a small amount of chlorinated lime to holy water. Much more important is the keeping of the holy water fonts clean. The customary metallic fonts with the shell-shaped "ornaments" are, as has been stated, hard to keep clean.

It has been suggested by established firms to cover the inside with a catalyzer (for example, of colloidal silver); the oxidizer takes effect and through it the anoerobic carrier is prevented from growing.

Basically better would be the stone receptacles with an entirely smooth surface, possibly of marble, in which the water is changed as often as possible.

It is advisable not to put into the font more holy water than is used, at most, in three days.

In a flat font the surface can better be seen and no dirt will escape the eye.

It is the duty of the pastor to instruct the sacristan in this matter and to make regular inspections to see that the instructions are being carried out.

These few examples indicate the number of hygienic problems that are to be considered in the construction and provision of places of worship. The examples given here should merely serve as a stimulus and motivation to give to religious worship at least the hygienic consideration that is justly due. Pastoral hygiene need not and should not require more than is necessary and authorized. Pastoral hygiene should be aware of its limitations and should never forget that it is her task to serve—to serve, above all, by freeing external worship from certain defects which can easily offend not only the outsider, but others.

C. Objects for Ceremonial Use and Holy Objects

1. Objects for the Sacrifice of the Mass

a) BREAD FOR THE SACRIFICE (HOSTS)

The bread used in the Sacrifice of the Mass is pure unleavened bread made of wheat. Church regulations concerning the matter of the sacrament of the altar define that *"Solus panis triticeus et solum vinum de vite sunt materia valida Sacramenti Eucharistiae."* [4]

By *panis triticeus* is meant a bread made solely of wheat flour. The different cultivated forms of wheat of the triticum family are the following: *triticum vulgare, triticum durum, triticum turgidum* and *polonicum.* The different varieties of wheat indicated as spelt *(triticum spelta, bicoccum* and *monococcum)* also consist of a pure white flour, but are generally not considered as *materia certe valida,* but often as *materia dubia.* [5]

Adulterations arise primarily through the addition of potato flour. The microscopic proof of the presence of potato-starch corn is relatively easy: the easiest way to ascertain whether there is any adulteration is to send the suspected matter to the food-testing station which is usually associated with state hygiene institutes. Mineral adulterations through gypsum (calcium sulphate) and heavy spar (barium sulphate) are easily detected through simple chemical analysis.

Definite rules are specified for the baking of bread. In former times, the baking, as well as the selection and grinding of the wheat grain, was usually performed as a religious act by the monks.

[4] Cf. Olfers, *Pastoral-Medizin,* p. 196.
[5] Cf. Alf. de Liguori; cf. Olgers, *l.c.,* p. 196.

We read that St. King Wenceslaus of Bohemia did all these things as well as selecting the grapes and pressing the same into wine for the holy sacrifice.

All these acts were accompanied by festive prayers, psalms, and hymns. The grain was prepared with pure cold water into the form of dough, which was then rolled flat and baked on a thin plate of metal; *"ex sola farina triticea et aqua naturali."* The vessel used for the forming of the dough must be absolutely clean and is not to be used for any other purpose.[6]

Because of the danger of hosts becoming easily corrupted, the reservation of the same in a dry place is strictly prescribed. The slightest visible sign of mould is already a proof that the entire host had been overtaken by fungus. It is then no longer pure wheat bread, but *materia invalida,* at least *illicita.* The consecration of the same is, at least, doubtful.

In general, hosts to be used for consecration should not be more than a month old. Hosts that are already consecrated should not be reserved for too long a time, but should be renewed in good time, and the reserved hosts should be consumed by the priest. The *Roman Ritual* prescribes: *Parochus . . . Sanctissimae Eucharistiae particulas frequenter renovabit."* How often this renewal should take place depends upon whether the place of reservation (tabernacle) is dry. The general rule indicates *"saltem semel in hebdomada."* A period of ten days should ordinarily suffice.

We have already mentioned that humid heat is very favorable in the development of mould *(penicillium glaucum; mucor mucedo, stolonifer; aspergillus niger, fumigatus)* and of blood fungus *(bacillus prodigiosus).* If red spots are seen on the host it should not immediately be proclaimed a "blood miracle"; rather, an investigation, according to canonical requirements, should be made by a doctor versed in hygienic methods of investigation. It can be easily established by means of the microscope whether it is a case of *bacillus prodigiosus* or of a genuine blood corpuscle *(erythrocyte).*[7]

---

[6] *"Vas, in quo conspersio continetur, mundum omnino sit, nec in alios usus convertatur, ut totum opus magna cum reverentia perficiatur."* Cf. Olfers, *l.c.*

[7] The definite proof of blood marks, even of old marks, is not difficult to obtain. With the help of spectroscopic investigation, it can be definitely established whether it is a case of blood; with the aid of microscopic and

The most important hygienic requirement which we deduce from this section is that the tabernacle must be kept absolutely clean, cool and dry.

b) WINE FOR THE SACRIFICE OF THE MASS

The Mass wine must be pure unadulterated wine—*vinum de vite*—that is, it must be taken from ripe wine grapes, the fruit of the *vinis vinifera*. It is not permissible to use any of the beverages that are merely similar to wine, whether they are made from fruit (fruit wine, must, cider), or from wild fruits (the ripened fruit of a rosebush, elder, currant), or whose fermented juice has a strong alcoholic content and tastes like wine. A "wine" which is not from wine grapes *(vinum de vite)* is likewise not a wine and, hence, *materia invalida* and *illicita* for the Eucharistic consecration.

Since wine put on the market is very often adulterated, at least "cut," i.e., mixed with other fermented pressed juices, it is of great concern that one buy one's wine from a selected firm. Even the specific rules concerning the place of wine supply should be followed. The supply firms should be willing to bind themselves in accurately following out the rules prescribed for the Mass wine.

Wine is fermented grape juice. The fresh pressed juice, the sweet must, undergoes a natural process of fermentation which is brought on by yeast fungi. In this cycle the grape sugar is fermented into alcohol and carbonic acid; the turbulent must develops a great number of fermentation gases (especially carbon dioxide, CO_2), which, being heavier than air, gather at the bottom of the wine cellar.

Pure wine contains, according to the primary sugar content and the "excellence of the year's crop" (which again depends on the consideration of the vine in late summer), on the average of 8-12 per cent alcohol (ethyl alcohol, ethanol).

Many southern wines (port wine, Jerez-sherry, *lacrimae Christi,*

---

serological investigation, it can be proven whether or not it is a case of human blood.

The distinction between true blood and an artificial product is made evident by means of ultraviolet light; moreover, the confirmation of radio-activity permits judgment concerning the age of the object under investigation. In the case of the still disputed shroud from Turin (S. Sindone), this made it easy to form a judgment concerning the authenticity.

Samos), containing 18-20 per cent alcohol, come, in this point, close to liqueurs.

White wine and red wine are distinguished not by their extraction from white or black grapes, but primarily by their treatment when pressed. If the grape peels are strongly pressed and fermented for a long time before they are separated from the mash and used as swine fodder or for the distillation of schnapps, then it is a red wine which, through this treatment, is richer in sharp tannic acid matter.

Strong southern wines (Madeira, Malaga and Grecian wines) as well as Hungarian wines are distinguished by their golden brown tinge.

In our locality (Austria) the white wine is used almost exclusively for the Sacrifice of the Mass. This wine can be identified by its cloudiness. There is no rule which forbids the use of red wine.

The adulterations of wine are, at times, so refined that they are often very difficult to detect because they manifest an excellent product. It is impossible to detect the adulteration in all cases. This shows how truly a confidential matter is the reference of a wine that is not objectionable.

Through the refinement of methods, it has become very difficult to define where the adulteration begins and how far the legal (unfortunately) methods of "embellishing" and "refining" extend. The process of "embellishing" merely serves to make the external view more conspicuous and more appetizing whereby the fashionable taste plays a definite role. At one time, fashion demands a completely light wine, at another time a deep golden yellow wine, and, at still another time, a green wine. At the present time cleverly suggestive fashion favors an "effervescent" wine, i.e., a wine in which (in distinction to the natural effervescent Moselle wine) the fermentation process has not completely subsided and which is prematurely taken out of the containers, artificially made "fit for bottling," so as to be sold sooner.

In the process of "embellishing" the wine to a golden yellow color, the addition of potassium plays an important part.[8]

Very extensive is the former strongly forbidden "sugaring" of

---

[8] Yellow potassium (potassium ferrocyanide): $K_4 Fe Cy6$
Red potassium (potassium ferrocyanide): $K_3 Fe Cy6$
(Cy = Cyanogen group: CN)

wine in order to effect a quicker and stronger fermentation. According to the present unfortunately too elastic opinion of wine producers, it is no longer an adulteration. Whether a "sugared" wine can be considered a *materia valida* for the Eucharistic consecration or whether it is at least a *materia illicita* if not *invalida* depends on whether it can be confirmed that it retains the nature of wine *("ut naturam vini retineat").* It is—already *exempli causa* —strictly advised that ecclesiastical authorities demand of the Mass wine suppliers an attestation of the unconditional naturalness of the Mass wine and to explain all the different sugaring methods.

The only means to be used for "embellishing" the wine is the traditional method of clearing the wine through the use of isinglass. Light cloudiness of wine is easily and completely removed by this method. Wine cloudiness is unobjectionable so long as it is insignificant and does not change the nature of the wine.

When a pure wine is bottled too soon, fermentation again takes place in the bottle: the wine "works." When this fermentation subsides, the wine is unobjectionable. If to the fermentation microorganisms a "mixture infection" arises from a stopper that closes badly or is possibly infected, then the wine "breaks itself," i.e., it becomes corrupted. The same goes for the transition into vinegar fermentation by the *fungus mycoderma aceti,* which first forms a "mucuous membrane" *(mycoderma)* and then changes the alcohol into acetic acid.

Wine just about beginning to go sour is not invalid but illicit matter: the consecration is therefore valid, but sinful: *"conficitur sacramentum, sed conficiens graviter peccat."* If no other wine is available, wine in the very first stage of going sour is permissible.

Dry wine should not be mistaken for sour wine.

Wine partly changes through freezing *(congelatio).* The water changes to ice; it contains a part of the extractive element which forms the "bouquet" of wine. The remaining liquid part contains the entire alcoholic content, the tinge, or color element, and the elements that are soluble in alcohol. The "frozen" fluid part contains more alcohol than the unfrozen wine. The same process takes place in the freezing of stout.

Wine freezes at 5-7 degrees centigrade (lowering of the freezing point). When the thawing process takes place, the elements separated by the process of freezing are united again: only the distinctive aroma and the tinge of the wine are disturbed. Be that as it may, it can be stated that the frozen and afterwards thawed wine *"naturam vini retineat"* and is, therefore, valid matter.

Wine as *materia sacramenti Ss Eucharistiae* is to be considered not only from the hygienic, but also from the pastoral standpoint. Problems arise in this sphere, the knowledge of which is very important for every priest and especially for every pastor.

c) WATER

Water is used more than once in regard to the Sacrifice of the Mass: it is first used at the *preparatio ad missam* and after the *gratiarum actio post missam* for the ordinary washing of the hands of the priest. This handwashing also has a hygienic meaning. Its true meaning, however, is that the priest should approach the altar with clean hands (i.e., *pars pro toto:* purity of body and soul).

The use of water during the Sacrifice of the Mass has already been briefly mentioned. At the Offertory, in the mixing of wine with water, water has a definite secondary meaning: it symbolizes the human nature which is taken up in the divine nature; only a few drops of water are poured into the chalice.

The handwashing at the Lavabo is a symbolically indicated washing: that before the Consecration the last remnants of adhering earthly dust must be removed.

After the priest's Communion the chalice is first rinsed with a little wine *(purificatio);* after the priest has consumed the purification, wine and water are poured over his fingers into the chalice *(ablutio),* and the ablution is then consumed. Pure drinking water is required for all of the above-mentioned purposes.

Water is not the *materia,* as wine is, for the Consecration, yet it must be pure natural water. But for the blessing of baptismal water in relation to the sacrament of Baptism, water is the *materia sacramenti.*

In the blessing of the baptismal water, natural water, the *creatura aquae,* is exorcised, i.e., it is freed from the diabolical power connected with fallen human nature. The water, through the imposition of hands, is taken in possession for God and is blessed; it is divided according to the four cardinal points; then the priest breathes over the water three times in the form of the Greek *Psi* (*psyche* = soul); then the Paschal candle, as a symbol of Christ, is dipped into the water three times, and each time deeper—a deep symbol of spiritual fertility; finally, the oil of Catechumens and the Chrism are mixed with the water. Some salt and blessed ashes have already been added to the water. Thus the baptismal water symbolically represents a microcosmos which unites all the elements of mortal, transitory human nature together with the elements of the spiritual and divine life.

It is clear that, for the blessing of baptismal water, only pure natural water *(creatura aquae)* is to be used. Distilled water is pure, but it is not natural water so much as an artificial product, and, hence, not *materia valida*—at least according to the opinion of St. Thomas, while St. Alphonsus de Liguori considers *aqua destillata* and even rain water as *materia valida: "destillatione ab elementis tantum extraneis depurgata"* (Lehmkuhl).

Valid matter (besides spring, well and drain water, river and sea water) is water from melted ice, snow or hail, condensed water from steam and mineral water. Natural mineral waters are valid matter provided they not contain too many foreign ingredients. If they contain more than 20 per cent salt, they cannot be considered "pure water." On the high seas and in case of necessity (shipwreck), emergency baptism with sea water would be valid.

Holy water is only a sacramental and not *materia sacramenti*. Rules are always prescribed for its formation. Instead of an addition of oil, one of salt is prescribed. St. Alphonsus states: *"Peccat graviter qui sacramentalibus falsam materiam supponit."* [9]

d) OIL

Only pure olive oil is to be used as the *materia sacramentorum* as well as *sacramentale*. Olive oil is the pressed juice of the fruit from the olive tree *(olea europea)*. Because of its high cost, it is often adulterated. Adulteration is primarily effected by the addition or substitution of an inferior element (peanut oil, *oleum arachidis,* from the *Arachis hypogaea;* sesame oil, *oleum sesami;* cottonseed oil; poppyseed oil, etc.), outside of vegetable oils (cocoa oil; palm oil); even mineral oils are used as an addition in adulteration.

The following attain liturgical use: the oil of Catechumens

[9] Cf. Olfers, *Pastoral-Medizin,* Herder, Freiburg, p. 194 ff.

(oleum catechumenorum seu oleum exorcizatum); the oil of the sick *(oleum infirmorum)* and Chrism, a mixture of oil and balm.

While the blessing of baptismal water takes place on Holy Saturday and on the vigil of Pentecost in the parish church, the blessing of the holy oils takes place on Holy Thursday in the cathedral church. The blessing of oil begins, as the blessing of water, with an exorcism.

The oil of the sick serves as the *materia* for the *sacramentum infirmorum,* the anointing of the sick (designated in colloquial usage as "extreme unction," *extrema unctio).*

Chrism is used in the sacrament of Confirmation. It is formed by the bishop from olive oil and balm or balsam. Balsam is an oily and resinous product from the bark of the Balsamodendron Gileadense (balm of Gilead or Mecca balsam). The Peruvian balsam *(Balsamum Peruvianum)* stemming from the *Myroxylon Pereirae,* a famous means for cleaning infected wounds, is likewise permitted. Moreover, there are different balsamic elements whose use in the preparation of Chrism is not permissible or is questionable: the Tolu balsam, the Benzoin Balsam (from the Styrax Benzoin); Myrrh *(Gummi Resina Myrrhae)* from the Balsamodendron Ehrenbergianum; the Styrax (Storax) from the Liquidambar orientals, etc.

e) FRANKINCENSE

Frankincense *(Thus, Olibanum)* is a fragrant gum resin. Genuine frankincense *(Olibanum arabicum)* is obtained from various trees of the genus Boswellia (Boswellia thurifera, Boswellia serrata) from India, in particular, of the Boswellia papyrifera and floribunda from Abyssinia.

The fragrance of genuine frankincense has a certain irritant effect on the respiratory organs and can, in restricted places and when it produces much smoke (the young incense-bearers are fond of it), become unpleasant. Hence it is advisable to add other fragrant matter to the incense which will modify the sharpness; but the amount of incense should by far exceed the other *("Quantitas thuris longe superet.").* In the admixture benzoin or storax may be used and, possibly, lavender blossoms.

Because of the high cost of genuine frankincense, adulteration is frequent: pine resin and spruce resin are used for this purpose; resin balls from ant hills are designated as "forest incense"; the resin of the stone pine is sold as "Russian incense."

f) CANDLES

The candles which are used for the celebration of Holy Mass should, according to ancient prescription, be of pure beeswax. A dispensation from the law can be received, as has been the case for a long time in poor lands. The Paschal candle must be of pure wax.[10]

In case beeswax for the altar candles can be procured only at great inconvenience, at least two beeswax candles must be procured for a private Mass and four for a chanted Mass or for a solemn high Mass, and for solemn exposition of the Blessed Sacrament, the deficiency to be supplied by other forms of light (S.R.C., Aug. 18, 1949).

The two candles used at Mass and the Paschal candle are to be of beeswax *in maxima parte* (67%); other candles placed on the altar are to be of beeswax *in maiore parte* (51%) (Cf. S.R.C., Dec. 14, 1904). For liturgical rites other than the Sacrifice of the Mass as, for example, in baptism, extreme unction, etc., the rule is less stringent.

Adulterations through substitute products are: stearin and tallow (obtained from the fat of animals, especially the fat of oxen); paraffin, ceresin (mineral wax), ozocerite (earth wax), etc. Even additions in the sense of a weight adulteration are used: meal, white lead, sulphur, etc. Powdered admixtures of this nature are easy to identify in the melting of the wax. The admixture of paraffin can be easily separated from the wax by means of a sulphuric acid test. Other adulterations require complicated chemical investigations.

[10] Cf. the formula for the blessing of the Paschal candle in the *"Exsultet"* of the liturgy for Holy Saturday: ". . . *Cerei huius laudem implere perficiat . . . quod in hac Cerei oblatione solemni . . . de operibus apum. . . Alitur enim liquantibus ceris, quas in substantiam pretiosae huius lampadis apis mater eduxit."* In former times, it was prescribed that only wax candles could be used for the Sacrifice of the Mass, and this rule was so strict that the Sacrifice of the Mass could not take place if wax candles could not be procured.

2. Liturgical Vestments

For the purpose of our treatment of the subject, we distinguish between vestments which are made of washable material and those which are made of non-washable material.

The washable vestments: amice (humeral), alb, corporal, purificator, together with the linen altar cloths and the linen cloths of the communion rail, comprise the "church linen." There is no need, on the part of pastoral hygiene, to indicate that the washable vestments should be kept clean with utmost care and concern. Reverence for the exalted liturgical purpose itself should be a sufficient motivation. Nothing is more depressing to a stranger and visiting priest than the uncleanliness of the church linens. Surely, poverty must be taken into consideration in many of these cases, but cleanliness is the least that can be required in the poorest of churches. When respect and reverence do not suffice in forming adequate motivation, then at least hygiene should be considered.

The non-washable vestments—stole, maniple, chalice veil and chasuble *(casula)* as well as the cope—are usually of material corresponding to the prescribed liturgical color. There is a complete variety ranging from costly brocade material with rich embroidery in gold to very simple material with plain edge trimming and middle stripes.

The Baroque period, with its love for pomp, from which arose the struggle to obtain the most expensive and most beautiful elements for divine worship, has given the Mass vestments the form which today is still customary especially in the Roman lands: the Baroque "Roman" chasuble. It has the hygienic advantage of a greater freedom of movement for the arms. This has been curtailed through the new "liturgical movement," especially in Germanic lands, by the acceptance of the older "Gothic" chasuble. This, instead of the heavy brocade material and the rigid form of the Roman chasuble, uses wide, soft "vestments" of very simple form but with preference for light fabric of genuine material. The preference for Gothic chasubles in Germanic lands can be partly associated with the symbolism of the "tree of life" and also with a certain opposition toward the spirit of the Baroque period and inclination toward puritanical simple forms. Insofar as poverty is also of importance, it is able to make "virtue out of necessity."

This opposition is found also with regard to the church music of the Baroque period, a tendency "to free the church life from Baroque influence."

One should not conclude from the discussion what degree of spiritual exaltation a festive high Mass can imply—in which united skills are used in effecting exalted divine praise. Insofar as the present form is motivated by want and poverty, hope can be expressed that a time of well-being and a deeper establishment of divine service are again made possible. The latter considerations are related to pastoral hygiene only insofar as they refer to mental hygiene.

The vestments and furnishings which require a blessing are: the chasuble, stole, maniple, alb, amice, and cincture; the pall, corporal, altar cloths and tabernacle should also be blessed.

The vestments and furnishings which do not require a blessing are: purificator, humeral veil, surplice, cope, dalmatics, burse, ciborium and lunula. It is, however, recommended that the ciborium and lunula be blessed.

Purificators, palls and corporals used in the Sacrifice of the Mass should not be given to lay persons, even religious, for the purpose of washing, until they have first been washed by a cleric in major orders; the water of the first washing is to be poured into the sacrarium, or, if there is no sacrarium, into the fire (Can. 1306 §2).

Lay brothers of the Order of Friars Minor, during the time that they are in charge of the sacristy, may, through papal privilege and if it seems expedient, handle the sacred vessels as well as fulfill the first washing of the corporals and purificators (Capobianco, Pacificus, *Privilegia et Facultates Ordinis Fratrum Minorum,* 2 ed., Salerno: ex conventu S.M. Angelorum, 1948). This papal privilege is usually granted to religious brothers and sisters of the Third Order Regular of St. Francis who serve as sacristans in their chapels. This privilege was renewed for five years (S.R.C., 7 July, 1956—*Acta Ordinis,* LXXV, 189).

Care must be taken that the chalice and the paten, and (previous to washing) purificators, palls and corporals used in the Sacrifice of the Mass shall not be touched except by clerics or those entrusted with the custody of these furnishings (Can. 1306 §1).

To sum up the essence of this theme, we may say that all matters associated with religious worship have also a hygienic element at least from the standpoint of mental hygiene. In the exaltation of the soul to God, its source and life, the soul makes use of power which originates in the supernatural, but which radiates within nature in a very intense manner. With such an approach, the universal treatment of pastoral hygiene attains its lofty and definitive outlook since it perceives man not only as a member of a natural society, as is done in social hygiene, but also as a member of the supernatural society, of the *Corpus Mysticum Christi*. This is exemplified, in a special manner, in man's connection with the Eucharistic celebration of the Sacrifice of the Mass. In this there is the culmination of the highest and final legacy bequeathed to man by the Redeemer.

II. HYGIENIC POINTS REGARDING THE SACRAMENTS AND THE SACRAMENTALS

A. Concept [11]

A sacrament is defined as an outward sign instituted by Christ for the purpose of producing grace. The essential elements *(partes essentiales)* of a sacrament are matter and form; to these are added the intention of the one who actually concurs in the confection of the sacrament *(minister)*. Hence, *materia, forma, minister.*[12]

Matter is an outward sensible object which is determined by a form.

The form (essential form) is that by which the matter is formed into a sacrament. It consists of the words *(formula)* spoken by the minister of the sacrament: *"forma est id quo materia determinatur*

---

[11] Since this book is primarily for spiritual directors, it would be superfluous to interject definitions which are known to every theologian. But in order not to overlook the need of those who are not theologians, especially of medical men, the more important basic concepts will be presented and explained in the form of footnotes which can be easily passed over by the theologian.

Explanations and citations will be according to the *Summa Theologiae Moralis* of Noldin-Schmitt; the canonical norms will be taken from the *Codex iuris canonici* (CIC).

[12] The concept of *materia* has already been considered in the chapter concerning bread, wine, water and oil; so also were the conditions by which one must consider *materia valida, dubia, invalida* and *illicita.*

ad sacramentum; forma ordinaria consistit in verbis a ministro prolatis."

A sacramental is an object or rite which is not instituted by Christ but by the Church. These are, to cite a few examples:

1) Sacred signs *(signa sacra),* as the sign of the cross.
2) Blessings *(benedictiones).*
3) Exorcisms *(exorcismi).*
4) Invocations *(invocationes).*
5) Blessing of objects (for example, rosary).
6) Use of holy water *(aqua benedicta).*

The above enumeration is exemplificative and not taxative, i.e., does not indicate all the various forms.

Even with sacramentals we can distinguish *materia, forma* and *minister.*

The Catholic faith teaches that there are seven sacraments: baptism, confirmation, Holy Eucharist, penance, extreme unction, holy orders and matrimony. The non-Catholic sects acknowledge only two sacraments: baptism and Communion.

The following matter will deal primarily with hygienic points and questions associated with the administration of the sacraments and the use of sacramentals, the knowledge of which is very important for the priest.

B. Baptism [13]

Baptism is defined as the sacrament by which, through the ablution of the body with water and the use of certain words, the grace of regeneration is obtained.

The matter of the sacrament is water. The required qualities have already been discussed. The form of the sacrament consists in the prescribed baptismal formula.[14] The minister of the sacrament is the priest *(minister ordinarius).* His intention is directed toward the incorporation of the one to be baptized as a member of the Mystical Body of Christ. The extraordinary minister *(minister extraordinarius)* can, in case of necessity, be any person hav-

---

[13] *"Renatus e fonte baptismatis,"* man as a *nova creatura* is recalled to the supernatural life and lifted from the state of original sin to that of sanctifying grace.

[14] *"N.N., ego te baptizo in nomine Patris et Filii et Spiritus Sancti."*

ing the use of reason.[15] This means that, in case of necessity, the doctor, even if unbelieving and not baptized, can validly administer emergency baptism provided that he has the intention through baptism of doing what the Church intends.

The Roman Ritual distinguishes between solemn baptism *(baptismus solemnis)* and private baptism *(baptismus privatus)*. Solemn baptism can, in certain extraordinary cases, also be administered in a private home (Canon 776). Baptism, in the form of *baptismus privatus,* can be administered anywhere (Canon 771).

In solemn baptism only baptismal water *(aqua consecrata)* is licit matter. In private baptism ordinary water *(aqua naturalis)* may be used. Some authors recommend, however, that baptismal, or at least holy, water be used. In emergency baptism *(baptismus necessitatis),* i.e., in danger of death, any *materia certo valida* may be used; if such cannot be had, then any *materia dubie valida* may be used as long as it is not *certo invalida;* in this case, baptism is to be administered *sub conditione.*[16] The water should be basically pure, i.e., without the admixture of any foreign matter.

If emergency baptism is to be administered to the child *in utero* or *in sinu matris,* it is permissible to add an antiseptic element to the water, e.g., a sublimate (mercury bichloride), oxycyanate, sagrotan and the like, provided that, without such an addition, there would be danger to the life of the mother. If there is no such danger, then the addition is not allowed. If the doctor recommends boiled water, it may be used. When the water is too cold, it may be heated.

A definite quantity of water is not required; it suffices that the water flow over the one being baptized. Baptism is doubtful and must be repeated conditionally if administered by the use of a damp cloth, sponge or wet hand when the water does not actually flow. The water must touch the person to be baptized. If the water merely comes in contact with the clothes, or the uterus of fetal membrane in case of uterine baptism, the baptism is invalid. If the hair alone and not the skin is touched, the baptism is doubtful.

Baptism is to be administered on the head.[17]

---

[15] *"Minister baptismi necessitatis est quilibet homo ratione utens."*

[16] *"Si haec materia valet."* If the person survives, then baptism is to be repeated *sub conditione:* "si non es baptizatus. . . ."

[17] *"Totus enim homo censetur ablutus, si caput abluitur"* (cf. Canons 738-748, 752, 754, 757, 758, 771).

Baptism is probably valid if one were to baptize on another more principal part, as the breast, neck or shoulder. It is probably invalid if one were to baptize on a less principal part, as the hand, arm or foot. But, in case of necessity, if it is possible to baptize only a less principal part, as the foot or hand, it is licit and necessary to baptize conditionally.[18] He who pronounces the words of baptism while the child falls into water, does not baptize validly.[19]

Definite rules *de baptizandis foetibus* regulate the baptism of fetus that are not mature *(foetus abortivi)*. An abortive fetus should always be baptized no matter when the abortion takes place;[20] the fetus should be baptized absolutely if it is alive; in case of doubt concerning life, it should then be baptized conditionally. It is considered a malformed fetus or a malformation provided that it is a human being.[21] If the fetus is enclosed in fetal membranes, the membranes are to be broken in water; then the fetus should be dipped in lukewarm water while the baptismal words are pronounced.

If it is a matter of a baptism during birth, and the birth does not go well, then it can be a question of baptism in utero.[22] If the mother dies during the birth of the child, a Caesarean section should be performed, so that, if the child is alive, he will be baptized absolutely; if he is apparently dead, he is to be baptized conditionally.

The strict canonical laws of the Church for the validity of baptism are to be understood in the sense that—baptism being indispensable for the salvation of the soul—they tend to demand greater possible guarantee for its validity.

C. Confirmation [23]

The matter of the sacrament of confirmation is the chrism blessed by the Bishop and made of oil and balsam *(materia re-*

18 *"Proinde hac ratione totum hominem esse ablutum."*
19 *"Quia infantem non ipse abluit qui baptizat."*
20 *". . . quovis tempore editi."*
21 *". . . si homo es."*
22 Cf. *Compendium of Pastoral Medicine*, English translation, Wagner, N. Y., 1960, p. 246.
23 Confirmation is defined as the sacrament in which, through the anointing with chrism and the imposition of hands accompanied by definite words, the Holy Spirit is received for the strengthening of baptismal grace.

mota); the *materia proxima* is the anointing of the forehead with chrism and the imposition of hands by the Bishop. The form consists of the formula used by the Bishop.[24]

Essential questions of a hygienic nature concerning confirmation were formerly not considered.

The norms concerning the age and capacity can be treated from the hygienic standpoint.[25] If the one to be baptized is an adult, then confirmation should follow baptism. According to the present custom, confirmation can be administered on the completion of the seventh year of age (at the end of infancy).

The general rule calls for sufficient instruction if the person has attained the use of reason.[26] In danger of death even a child may receive confirmation; the requirement of the use of reason prevails as a supposition for instruction; if the person to be confirmed has the use of reason, then he is to receive sufficient instruction.

The capacity of the mentally ill should not be absolutely denied even if the use of reason is hindered. The mentally ill are, according to Canon 88, §3, equivalent to a child under the age of seven. If, however, *in periculo mortis,* confirmation can be administered to children under seven years of age, then the same prevails for the mentally ill.

In regard to age, there seems to be a twofold tendency: some tend to lower the limit as much as possible, allowing children who are still infants to receive the sacrament; others would want to raise the age to that of puberty. The Code has not made any modifications, and hence an age higher than seven is not necessary for the reception of the sacrament. According to Canon 788, *"sacramenti confirmationis administratio . . . differtur ad septimum circiter aetatis annum . . . ,"* unless just and grave reasons establish otherwise.

When confirmation is received at a later age, its meaning is at times secularized and placed on the same level as that of a "youth initiation." In this regard, we often witness certain excesses on the part of the candidate for confirmation and the sponsor which are

[24] *"Signo te signo crucis et confirmo te chrismate salutis in nomine. . . ."*
[25] Cf. Canons 782, 786, 788.
[26] Can. 788: *"Si usu rationis polleat, sufficienter instructus."*

both hygienically and morally harmful, above all, the excess of alcohol and nicotine which often cause reactions detrimental to health and can culminate in alcoholic or nicotine poisoning. Besides these excesses, abuses arise which cause the confirmation celebration to be transformed at times into an "annual fair row." These things, discouraging both from the hygienic and moral standpoint and contrary to the dignity of the sacrament, are equivalent to the profanation of the sacrament.

D. Eucharist

1. General Concept

The sacrament of the Eucharist (sacrament of the altar [27] comprises more than the participation in the Lord's supper: the sacred banquet (Holy Communion) is only one part of the sacrament of the altar which, in the sacrifice of the Mass, culminates in the Consecration, the transubstantiation of the oblation.

The duration of the integrity of the consumed species can be presumed to be from one to twenty minutes. This can be proven experimentally by subjecting non-consecrated hosts to the chemical actions of pepsin.

The matter of the sacrament is white unleavened bread and wine *(panis triticeus; vinum de vite)*.[29] The form of the sacrament consists in the words of consecration spoken by the priest.[28] The minister of the sacrament is a validly ordained priest.

2. Hygienic Questions

The hygienic questions associated with the administration of the sacrament are the following: the distribution of Holy Communion to the sick (communion of the sick); the avoidance of defects

[27] The sacrament of the Eucharist is defined as the sacrament in which the Body and Blood of Christ are present under the species of bread and wine, and is partaken as spiritual food for the soul. It is essentially the doctrine of the Real Presence, i.e., the presence of Christ ("really, truly and substantially") which persists as long as the consecrated species are integrally preserved: *Christus in Eucharistia realiter prasens manet, quamdiu species sacrae manent integrae.*

[28] The words of consecration are:
   "Hoc est enim corpus meum."
   "Hic est enim calix sanguinis mei."

and carelessness through which the transmission of infectious diseases is possible.

a) COMMUNION OF THE SICK

Reverentia sacramento debita requires that the priest carrying the Blessed Sacrament to the sick do so with uncovered head *(detecto capite)*. If this entails a danger to the health of the priest, it would be permissible for him to wear a hat or biretta *(pileus* or *pileolus)*.

If the priest carries the Blessed Sacrament publicly *(publice)*, he should be accompanied by a server carrying a burning light (lantern); if he carries it privately *(occulte)*, no one accompanies him.

In the visitation of the sick, the priest can protect himself against infection merely by avoiding any direct breathing or coughing on his face by the patient. It is prudent to have the patient turn his head to the side and not directly toward the priest when speaking to him. This suffices for most of the cases and, above all, in diseases in which the transmission of "droplet infection" is possible. An absolute protection against this mode of infection does not exist since the air of the room is mostly saturated with microorganisms; but the danger of infection will be greatly increased by direct coughing. Hence, it suffices, for the most part, to have the patient turn his head in order so to lessen the danger that it is practically no greater than that present, for example, in a public conveyance during the time of an epidemic. The practical doctor who, during the time of an influenza epidemic makes many visits to the sick, can protect himself from the danger of infection in no other way than by having the patient turn his head to the side. But despite these numerous exposures on the part of the doctor, there are relatively few known cases of infection associated with visiting the sick.

We have selected influenza as an example since it is one of the most frequent infectious diseases and, during the time of an epidemic, is often associated with very serious complications, as pneumonia, but especially since influenza is the type of disease that is transmitted through droplet infection.

Things are different with regard to infectious diseases which are transmitted through contact. To this especially belong the infectious intestinal diseases (enteritis, typhus, cholera, paratyphus). Contact arises through the direct touching of patients (taking the patient by the hand, holding the patient). In this case, it is important to wash the hands after every contact, if possible, with the use of a disinfectant (sagrotan, lysoform, chloramine, oxycyanate; a sublimate should be avoided in case of sensitive skin) before one touches his face (nose, mouth) with the infected hand. These norms of prudence are to be followed by the priest both in the distribution of Holy Communion to the sick and in the administration of extreme unction, whenever he visits the sick.

The anxiety of infection is a terrible companion. He who professionally visits the sick often should not have an anxiety of infection. For when the danger of infection does exist and there is reason for fear, this attitude of anxiety can contribute to the actualization of the infection more easily. He who remains calm and prudent is less disposed by far to infection than the person who is fearful and excited even in the case of likely exposure to infections.

Very often the anxiety is objectively unfounded, especially in regard to cancer. We do not as yet know whether, in the origin of carcinoma, an "agitator" accompanies as a contributing factor; but this much is definite, that carcinoma is not transmissible through the free contact which occurs in visiting the sick. The cancer anxiety takes on the nature of panic. Even the anxiety concerning infantile paralysis is often greatly unfounded. In the phase of pronounced paralysis there is scarcely any danger of infection. The most dangerous phase is that of the uncharacterized first days of fever, which is merely equivalent to a common infection of influenza, a phase in which poliomyelitis can scarcely be diagnosed. It has a certain analagous relationship with encephalitis which, in that stage of manifest symptoms, is scarcely contagious. What is, in this case, transmissible is solely the uncharacterized general infection of the first phase. The cerebral localization of influenza is, as such, scarcely transmissible.

It would be natural to perceive in poliomyelitis also a spinal localization of the same virus infection which is etiologically responsible for both the poliomyelitis and encephalitis. While influenza is transmitted chiefly through droplet infection, in poliomyelitis transmission occurs mostly through contact. Therefore, the priest is warned to consider influenza seriously, but without anxiety; avoidance of anxiety, regarding cancer, infantile paralysis and encephalitis; avoidance of droplet infection and careful disinfection in contact infection.

b) DISTRIBUTION OF HOLY COMMUNION
AND DANGER OF INFECTION

The danger of infection in the distribution of Holy Communion in church is negligible. In the case of the most frequent of infections, that of influenza, the patients are, at the high point of the illness, bedridden and feverish and, therefore, the reception of Holy Communion in church is not a problem. But in the first stages which merely consist of the common cold, influenza is often characterized by an extraordinary contagiousness.[29] The patients sit in the pews and spray the entire congregation with infectious droplets.

The priest can, through carelessness and awkwardness in the distribution of Holy Communion, contribute to the spreading of infection. There are some priests, especially older priests, who cannot see very well and, in distributing Holy Communion, place their fingers too far into the patient's mouth. In this way, they easily spread infection from one patient to another. Under certain circumstances, this can become dangerous even for the priest himself. Where, for example, the foot and mouth disease is rampant (stomatitis infectiosa), contactual infections can arise in the specified manner. Even the transmission of syphilitic infections, primarily in the area of the mouth cavity, is not completely excluded; all the more so as the syphilitic character of a specific Angina luetica is not always immediately recognized.

It is to be desired that a pastor so influence his parishioners that all, who can possibly transmit sickness to others—for example, all who suffer with sneezes and colds of the upper air route—should accustom themselves to approach the Communion rail last.

---

[29] The onset of this illness with forcible sneezes makes the popular usage of the expression "God bless you," understandable. This practice originated in the middle ages during the time of the plague. When anyone began to sneeze, one was startled and exclaimed: "May God bless us." It is possible that, in former times, many an epidemic was designated as a "pestilence," which in reality was nothing more than a severe influenza.

It is a matter merely of following a few simple rules of prudence and, by the observance of the same, the transmission of disease will be limited to a minimum. But it is exactly because these rules are so simple that they are so seldom and unwillingly observed.

c) DISTRIBUTION OF HOLY COMMUNION IN THE CASE OF *Tussis* AND *Vomitus*

In cases of *tussis* and *vomitus* certain norms of caution are designated both for preserving the reverence due to the sacrament and for hygienic purposes.

Certain forms of coughing, especially convulsive coughing *(tussis convulsiva)* and whooping cough, are associated with sudden and violent coughing jerks, which sometimes turn into convulsive choking and vomiting. In this case, the limits between coughing and vomiting are not clear.

Vomiting appears in all possible feverish ailments, especially in the morbid conditions of the gastric and intestinal tracts. In *cholera nostras* (in contradistinction to the extremely dangerous *cholera asiatica*), which is an acute form of Enteritis, vomiting is accompanied by a profuse diarrhea.

There is also a purely nervous (hysterical) convulsive cough just as there is a *vomitus* of such a nature. Basically, the same prevails here as was indicated concerning the corresponding type of fainting spells that occur in church. In regard to these patients, an energetic reaction which exercises upon the patients an effect that is strongly suggestive is the most effective remedy. If the priest does not know whether he is dealing with such a case, he should then seek advice from the doctor. In such cases, the priest must be aware that the coughing attacks of the patient are easily followed by vomiting. In the cases in which the vomited gastric matter is itself infectious, as, for example, in Weil's Disease *(Icterus infectiosus)*, in gastroentiritis and diseases of the typhoid-cholera group, the priest can become exposed to the danger of infection.

From the standpoint of pastoral care and the duty of protecting the Blessed Sacrament from irreverence, the priest must observe certain norms of caution in the distribution of Holy Communion to patients affected by coughing and nausea. The text books on pastoral theology usually indicate practical points for the priest in regard to such cases. There should be at hand and near the sick bed a bowl or cup (kidney cup) which the nurse should place before the patient and so hold the head of the patient that the vomiting takes place in the bowl. The bowl or cup should preferably be of glass and, if possible, of enamel. Less hygienic are the cups made of black paper.

If the patient vomits the Sacred Species, they should then be removed (best done with pincers) and placed in a clean, flat vessel (saucer, petridish), washed off with clean water, and then reserved in the church in a suitable place until the species are completely dissolved and put, together with the fluid, into the sacrarium. If the Sacred Species can no longer be separated from the vomitus, then the whole matter should be mixed with lycopodium (stuppa) and burned, and the ashes are to be put in the sacrarium. If there is danger of irreverence to the Blessed Sacrament because of the nature of the sickness, then the priest should not give Holy Communion until the danger has passed. Since, however, the sacraments have been instituted for the spiritual welfare of mankind, it is not necessary that all, even the slightest, danger of irreverence be removed in order that Holy Communion be given to the sick, for it is the sick who need Holy Communion in a special way.[30]

Patients who suffer from coughing may receive Holy Communion and, at the hour of death, should receive Holy Communion provided that, between attacks of coughing, there is sufficient calmness to receive the Blessed Sacrament; danger of irreverence would be present only if, while receiving the Sacred Host, a coughing spell followed. If the Host has already been swallowed, then the danger is no longer present since the vomiting takes place through the esophagus, the coughing through the phlegm from the windpipe.[31]

---

[30] *"Cum tamen sacramenta sint propter homines, non est necesse, ut omne, etiam leve periculum irreverentiae sit exclusum, ut Sancta Communio praesertim infirmis dari possit"* (Noldin-Schmitt. *Summa theol. moral*, III, p. 137, n. 1934).

[31] *"Qui tussi laborant, eucharistiam suscipere possunt et in morte etiam debent, modo tantum quietis patiantur, ut s. Hostiam sumere possint; periculum enim irreverentiae solum adest, si tussis impetu afficiuntur, cum s. Hostiam sumunt; hostia autem semel sumpta periculum illud plerumque abest, quia alia via sputa, et alia e stomacho cibi eiiciuntur"* (*Ibid.*, p. 137, n. 135 a).

In the case of uncontrollable vomiting (e.g., even in *hyperemesis gravidarum*—the uncontrollable vomiting of pregnancy), the sick may receive Holy Communion and, in danger of death, should receive Holy Communion, if they have a short interval of calmness long enough for the Species to be consumed in the stomach (which is normally from 1 to 20 minutes); this time should not be computed scrupulously, especially when it is a matter of administering Viaticum.

In more difficult cases, a small particle may be given so that it can be consumed in a shorter time. If, however, there is a positive doubt whether the patient will vomit the small particle, then Communion should not be given. If it is not a case of Viaticum, a non-consecrated particle could be given beforehand for experimental purposes.[32]

d) OTHER TYPES OF SICKNESS

Holy Communion may be given to the mentally ill, the confused and delirious when they have a lucid interval and the danger of irreverence is removed. An experiment with a non-consecrated host may be made beforehand.

The unconscious, e.g., in the case of apoplexy *(apoplexia cerebri)*, of a coma (e.g., *coma diabeticum)*, and the state of agony, are not obliged to receive Holy Communion as Viaticum since they are not conscious of their duty nor are they capable of fulfilling the same. They may receive Holy Communion under the following conditions: 1) they must have the intention; this is presumed to be present when the patient has led a religious and upright life; 2) there is no danger of irreverence, as would be the case, for example, if, in the state of unconsciousness, the patient would behave indecently, repel or spit out the sacred species. In this case, it is not permissible to administer Holy Communion. These pa-

---

[32] *Qui iugi vomitu laborant, eucharistiam suscipere possunt, et in morte debent, si a breviore aliquo tempore, quod sufficiat ut species in stomacho corrumpantur, non evomuerint; quod tempus non est nimia anxietata dimitiendum, praesertim quoties de viatico agitur. Suadetur hoc in casu, ut parva tantum hostiae particula, quae brevi iam tempore corrumpatur porrigatur. In dubio positivo autem, num infirmus sit s. Hostiam evomiturus, ei danda non est. Si non agitur de viatico, etiam prius experimenti causa particula non consecrata dari potest"* (*Ibid.,* p. 137, n. 135,b).

tients can receive the means of grace in another manner, through absolution and extreme unction.

Mentally ill patients (insane, *amentes*) who, after a long use of reason, have fallen into mental illness, may receive Holy Communion if their intention can be reasonably presumed and there is no danger of irreverence. A test with a non-consecrated host could be made.

Great prudence and caution should be used in cases of hysteria. The author has known a female patient who received Holy Communion many times a day from different priests and who removed the same from her mouth and reserved the Sacred Species for the purpose of sacrilegious profanation.

Imbeciles (half imbeciles—*semifatui*) and those with *dementia senilis* may receive Holy Communion (just like children) as long as they are capable of distinguishing the spiritual food from ordinary food.[33] Even in these cases one should not proceed with excessive anxiety and scrupulosity, since Holy Communion is also useful to these patients.

e) THE COMMUNION OF CHILDREN

While formerly it was customary to receive first Holy Communion at the age of ten, the decrees of Pope Pius X on Holy Communion, contrary to Jansenistic rigorism, promulgated the frequent reception of Holy Communion and even permitted the early Communion of children as long as the children were able to distinguish between the spiritual and ordinary food.

The observations that can be made concerning this point pertain to mental hygiene: we should be grateful that children can be protected very early against spiritual danger through the reception of grace.

3. The Eucharistic Fast

The ecclesiastical law of fasting before the reception of Holy Communion *(ieiunium eucharisticum)* pertains to the proper bodily disposition for the reception of the sacrament. This disposition requires that one approach the table of the Lord *(Coena Dominica)*

---

[33] *"Ut inter cibum spiritualem et profanum discernere possint."*

not only with a clean soul *(dispositio animae)*, but also with a clean body *(dispositio corporis)*, and in becoming attire *(corpore mundo, habitu decenti)*.

We distinguish here between a *dispositio corporis essentialis* and *accidentalis*. Clothing belongs to the accidental disposition; fasting *(ieiunium naturale)* to the essential disposition. *Ieiunium eucharisticum* comprises the ecclesiastical prescription of absolute abstinence from food and alcoholic drinks three hours before the reception of Holy Communion, and from non-alcoholic drinks one hour before Communion. Water never breaks the fast. The sick may take medicine without any time limit. Respect for the sacrament is the reason for the Eucharistic fast.

E. Penance *(Poenitentia)*

1. General Concept [34]

The purpose of penance is to restore the lost state of grace. If baptism is the basis of the supernatural life, then penance restores the supernatural life.[35]

The essential elements of the sacrament of penance are: sorrow for sins; confession of sins; and absolution.

Sorrow is the painful regret of having sinned through one's own fault. If sorrow is based on natural motives, e.g., if one is sorry for one's sins because they have ruined one's health, this would be pure natural sorrow. This type of sorrow does not suffice, for it is required that the motive for sorrow be supernatural, since man, through sin, has offended God. If sorrow is based on the fear of God's punishment and judgment, then it is a matter of imperfect sorrow *(attritio cordis);* but if the sorrow is based on the fact that one through sin has betrayed the love of God, then it is complete or perfect sorrow *(contritio cordis)*.[36]

---

[34] Penance is defined as the sacrament through which the sins committed after baptism are repented, confessed and forgiven through the priestly absolution and in the name of God.

[35] Penance and baptism are called "sacraments of the dead" in distinction to the remaining sacraments, called "sacraments of the living," which presuppose the state of grace.

[36] For the validity of the sacrament, any sorrow based on a supernatural motive suffices; therefore, even *attritio*, since *contritio* represents the more perfect degree.

The *materia* of the sacrament consists of sorrow *(contritio seu attritio)*, the confession of sin *(confessio)*, and eventual satisfaction *(satisfactio)*. The *forma* of the sacrament consists of the words of absolution prescribed by the *Roman Ritual*.[37] The minister of the sacrament is the priest who sits in the tribunal of penance "in the place of God." [38]

2. Hygienic Questions

a) PHYSICAL HYGIENE

The question of the possibility of transmitting a disease in the confessional and the protection against the same has already been discussed in treating of the proper arrangement of church furnishings.

Concerning the confession of the dying *(absolutio moribundorum)*, there is essentially nothing more that can be added to that which has already been indicated when treating of the Communion of the sick and sacrament of extreme unction. The dying person is often physically incapable of making an integral confession, i.e., a complete confession of all his sins. As soon as the priest is assured of the disposition of the penitent, he may give him absolution, even after only part of the confession has been made. The disposition of the dying pentitent who is unconscious can be presumed, i.e., assumed as long as the contrary is not evident. The capacity dwindles with the disappearance of the last signs of life.

In articulo mortis general absolution is given when there is a common danger of death, e.g., to a group of soldiers before going into battle; it can also be given to the dying who are unconscious and can no longer receive the last sacraments—even to the criminal before execution. Moreover there is an *indulgentia in articulo mortis*, i.e., a complete remission. This cannot be applied to those already deceased.

---

[37] The essential words of the form of absolution are: *"Deinde ego te absolvo a peccatis tuis."*
[38] Cf. Canons 871, 878, 882, 884, 886, 888, 555, 590, 909, 910.

b) MENTAL HYGIENE

(1) *Sollicitatio*

An important problem not only of moral theology but also of pastoral hygiene is that of *sollicitatio in confessione*. It is the abuse of the confessional for the purpose of sexual advance or stimulation, whether the solicitation is on the part of the priest or on the part of the penitent (mostly women). The frequency of *sollicitatio* is usually exaggerated, in particular through scandal sheets which readily exaggerate relatively harmless occurrences.

The priest is, because of the seal of confession, defenseless against such defamation. It is rarely that the solicitation of which he is accused is not that of the penitent, who then "turns the tables"—a tactic which, since the Old Testament report concerning the defamation of Joseph, the Egyptian, by the woman of Potiphor, never fails.

However, when it is truly a case of *sollicitatio ex parte confessoris,* then it is definitely a matter of serious sacrilegious abuse of the sacrament—of a sacrament whose purpose is to raise up the consciously guilty and suffering soul and which is now abused so that the soul is thrown deeper into guilt and distress. That from such psychic trauma not only a shattering of faith but also severe neurotic reactions can arise is clearly evident. The priest cannot be too careful in the positing of questions and in the choice of words when dealing with *peccata contra VI praeceptum.* He must literally weigh every word before speaking and anticipate just what effect these will have upon an hysterical penitent and how they may be interpreted and distorted.

(2) *The Scrupulous*

The scrupulous is the exact opposite of the hysterical person. Even he is a particular cross to the priest in the confessional.

Scrupulosity is a form of neurotic deviation in the realm of religion, which, of its nature, falls under the concept of obsessive neurosis.[39] It is erroneous to consider scrupulosity as the expression of a particularly delicate or tender conscience; on the contrary, it

[39] Cf. HSPM. V. p. 81; *Compendium of Pastoral Medicine,* English translation, Wagner, N.Y., p. 341 ff.

is a qualitative deviation from normality, of an abnormal, neurotic and erroneous attitude of conscience.

The scrupulous person is not satisfied in delaying the priest in the confessional for a long time explaining insignificant details. No sooner has he made his confession when he begins to doubt the validity of the same, repeats the confession many times, and jumps from one priest to another, when he feels that his pathological "guilt feeling" has not been rightly understood. Confession becomes a source of constant self-torment instead of a source of spiritual freedom and elevation. The priest must know the nature of scrupulosity and recognize it as an obsessive neurosis. It follows from this that the scrupulous person is to be treated as a sick person and should be directed toward psychotherapy. In serious cases of scrupulosity the spiritual director must work with the psychotherapist in order to attain the complete effects of spiritual direction.

(3) *Confession and Psychoanalysis*

Both the defenders and the opponents of psychoanalysis have often presented the analogy between confession and psychoanalysis in a false and distorted manner so that they argue either against confession or psychoanalysis or, if possible, against both.

In order to understand the matter clearly, it is necessary to realize that it is a case of two different phenomena which have two different bases and are absolutely dissimilar despite certain external similarities, a certain external analogy which is no more than a pure analogy. In this matter, we prescind from every abusive application of psychoanalysis, especially, the intentional excavation from the subconscious and agitation of sexual matters as well as every abuse of the confessional through *sollicitatio;* only the unobjectionable forms can be compared and will be compared.

Psychoanalysis strives for a psychocatharsis by making conscious all unconscious disturbing psychic elements (complexes), and the "abreaction" of the same. It therefore deals with unconscious disturbances leading to mental illness. Confession, on the other hand, deals with sin, i.e., with conscious and therefore responsible offenses against God's moral law. Its essential form is sacramental absolution, i.e., the formal proclamation of the divine act of grace and the recovery of the state of grace. The effects of psychoanalysis are merely in the natural realm, whereas those of confession are in the supernatural sphere.

The restoration of the state of grace, i.e., the sanctifying grace acquired through baptism and lost through sin, constitutes the essence of the sacrament of penance. Hence, penance and baptism are designated as "sacraments of the dead" since they restore the supernatural life after spiritual death. So understood, even the psycho-hygienic effects of the sacrament of penance cannot be too highly estimated: it again imparts to the soul peace with God and, with it, peace with oneself.

(4) The Seal of Confession and Medical Professional Secrecy

We shall briefly consider the analogy between the priestly seal of confession (sigillum) and the medical professional secret (secretum).[40] The same prevails here as in the analogy between confession and psychoanalysis. It is merely an analogy and nothing more; it is only external, on the periphery; essentially both are absolutely different. The seal of confession to which the priest is held is on the supernatural plane, while the professional secret is on the natural plane. In the one case, it is a question of soul healing; in the other, that of bodily health and legitimate worldly interests of the patient. Hence the sacerdotal sigillum binds in an absolute manner, i.e., under all circumstances, but the professional secret binds only relatively, i.e., just so long as legal limits are not imposed. Within these limits it obligates absolutely; insofar as it is based on natural law, it can treat only of limits which are, in turn, based on natural law and not merely on positive law.

When certain presuppositions are verified, the penitent can release the priest from the seal of confession, for example, for the purpose of discussing the case with the doctor in the interest of the penitent both from the physical and spiritual health standpoints, or to direct the penitent to the care of a trustworthy doctor. Even these matters are of great psycho-hygienic as well as of somato-hygienic interest for the penitent and the patient. Its proper use can contribute much to his physical and spiritual health.

40 Cf. APM, II (Aerztliche Ethik), p. 244.

F. The Anointing of the Sick *(Sacramentum Olei)*

General Concept [41]

The designation "extreme unction," which was in use at one time, is now substituted by that of "anointing of the sick" *(unctio infirmorum)*. The older designation often brought to the mind of the sick the idea that all was over and that there was no longer any hope of recovery. Because of this, even today there are still too many who oppose the reception of the sacrament at the proper time and defer it until it is too late—too late at least to receive it consciously.

Among the effects of the sacrament and besides the spiritual effects (strengthening of the soul, removal of venial sin and the punishment due to sin, and forgiveness of mortal sin), even the recovery of the body is one of the effects of the sacrament. This occurs, according to the teaching of the Church, not only *per accidens,* i.e., as an indirect result of peace of soul, but also occasionally (not always) as a direct effect of the sacrament, when it is conducive to the health of the soul (hence, *conditionate*). Therefore it is to be held that even the recovery of the bodily health is one of the purposes of the sacrament.[42]

The *materia* of the sacrament is oil *(oleum infirmorum)* which is consecrated by the bishop with a special blessing. It is seriously prescribed that it be olive oil *(oleum olivarum)*. The form of the sacrament consists of the words spoken in the anointing of the eyes, ears, lips, hands and feet. The minister of the sacrament is the priest.[43]

a) HYGIENIC QUESTIONS

Regarding the avoidance of infectious diseases, the same prevails as has already been stated concerning the Communion of the

---

[41] Extreme unction is defined as a sacrament in which, through the anointing with olive oil and the prayer of the priest, to the seriously ill is conferred health of soul and, at times, even health of body: *"Extrema unctio est sacramentum, quo per unctionem olei olivae et orationem sacerdotis graviter aegroto confertur sanitas animae et quandoque etiam corporis"* (Noldin-Schmitt, *Summa th. mor.,* p. 445, n. 429).

[42] Epistle of St. James 5; 14, 15.

[43] Cf. Canons 938, 940, 941, 943, 947.

sick. The priest is obliged under strict obligation of conscience to administer the sacrament within his territory to anyone who requests it. He is obliged *cum gravi incommodo* and even with danger to his life, when the sacrament represents the only means of salvation for the soul of the sick person who is in the state of mortal sin.

During the time of an epidemic this duty can be diminished if the administration of the sacrament constitutes a serious danger and the sick persons are capable of going to confession. However, when the sick persons are not able to receive a definitely valid absolution and cannot provide for themselves, the priest is obliged to administer the sacrament even when the danger of infection is great.

During the time of serious danger of infection (e.g., plague)[44] the rubric of anointing with the thumb may be disregarded; it is permitted, by way of exception, to use a small paint brush or a little wand (cotton wand). In case of emergency, i.e., when death is imminent, the sole anointing of the forehead with the short form suffices.

In general, it is well to consider that the sick receive the sacrament at the proper time, i.e., before it becomes an emergency and while the sick person is still conscious. Here the doctor is bound in conscience to inform the relatives of the proper time so as to fulfill all that is necessary.

Only one who is seriously ill is a *subjectum capax* of the sacrament; it is also required that he *ex morbo de vita periclitetur.* By sickness is here meant a condition from which, according to experience, the death of the body will take place with a certain probability. Hence, a seriously wounded person (even if wounded in a duel) can receive the sacrament; so, also, one seriously ill who is to undergo an operation; the same can be said for a seriously dangerous delivery and of old-age cachexia. But the following are not considered sick and *subjectum capax:* the soldier before going into battle; the condemned before execution; the sick before an operation; the mother before a normal delivery.

To be seriously sick means, according to the above, that the

---

[44] The true Asiatic plague caused by the bacillus pestis (Kitasato, Yersin, 1894) appeared in two forms: as the Bubonic plague and Pneumonic plague. In Europe the plague has not appeared since 1839 (Odessa), prescinding from the isolated laboratory infections (Vienna, 1904).

sickness, of its nature, can cause death and is so advanced that, in all probability, death will result. As long as this danger of death can be assumed, the sacrament of extreme unction may be administered. It must be administered when it is morally certain that death is imminent.

It has been demonstrated from physiological experiments that the death of the bodily tissues (absolute death) does not take place at the same time as the cessation of breathing and the activity of the heart, but rather that a phase of relative death precedes these phenomena. It can therefore still be assumed that a definite phase of cellular life takes place. This is not to be confused with the latent life *(vita minima)* which is in apparent death. Relative death does not pertain to the concept of apparent death *(mors apparens),* but to the concept of real death *(mors realis).* It can be assumed that within the duration of two hours after the substantiation of death, i.e., after the cessation of breathing and heart activity, signs of cellular life are still present. The capacity to receive the sacrament expires only with the cessation of the last signs of life.

If a doubt exists concerning the danger of the illness, then the sacrament can be administered *sub conditione (si capax es).* The conditions are the following: *"si vivis," "si usum rationis habes" (vel aliquando habuisti); "si graviter aegrotas"; "si haec materia valet"; "si nondum unctus es"; "si sufficientem intentionem habes."* If the sacrament is administered conditionally, the condition should be *"si vivis,"* if one doubts whether the person is still alive. This condition should be expressed in the formula. If one administers the sacrament conditionally for any other reason, the condition *"si capax es"* or *"si sacramentum valet"* is used. These need not be mentioned in the formula, but it suffices that they be conceived mentally.

Extreme unction may be repeated as often as the patient falls into a new and serious illness. It is to be administered only once within the time of the same sickness. The sacrament may be repeated in the same sickness when the patient has improved and has then fallen again into the danger of death; as happens, for example, in the cases of tuberculosis of the lung or cancer as well as in the case of heart ailments, etc.

The dignified and hygienic arrangement of the sick room for the reception of the sacrament of extreme unction pertains to physical hygiene.

When feasible, both clean personal linens and bed linens should be supplied; the bed should be at least orderly arranged; the sick room should be aired before the sick call. For the use of the priest there should be a washbasin and soap, a hand towel and disinfectant solution, and the water which is to be added should, if possible, be warm. The table for the holy oils should have a crucifix and two candles, a water glass, containing some holy water, and a holy-water sprinkler. On a clean plate there should be five pieces of cotton for the removal of the oil from the priest's thumb, and, finally, some salt.

As a suitable effect of the sacrament for the physical health of the patient, we have, in agreement with the teaching of the Church, established according to experience that, after the reception of the sacrament, the condition of the patient's health has often improved and this, in relation to a "crisis," can result in a recovery and not to be ascribed to a purely "psychogenic" effect.

b) MENTAL HYGIENE

The mental effects of the sacrament are evident in practically all cases in which the patient receives the sacrament while in the conscious state. Anxiety, restlessness, excitement and doubt are removed from the patient and give place to peace of soul and often to a certain serenity.

The author recalls two relatives in whom this effect was experienced.

The first person died of an *apoplexia cerebri* at the age of 69. Before the reception of extreme unction he was very restless and excited. After the reception of the sacrament, he was very peaceful, well balanced and serene, and he clearly looked forward to his going home.

The other relative died at the age of 80 after she had lost complete contact with her surroundings in the last years following a *dementia senilis*. After the reception of the sacrament, these disturbances seemed to have completely vanished. She was completely clear and spoke with her children calmly, deliberately and lovingly as in her better days.

One cannot easily overlook such outstanding changes. They cannot be explained merely on a natural basis. Mental disturbances have been, as it were, "washed away" under the influence of the sacrament, and clarity and orientation have been immediately re-established. That such mental changes can have a deep influence upon the physical element needs no further proof. This psychogenic action is still in the natural sphere, but alone it cannot explain all the effects that follow.

G. Marriage (Matrimonium)

1. General Concept

Marriage is to be considered in a twofold sense: as a natural institution; as a sacrament.[45]

In the first sense, the legal quality as a contract is more manifest. In the second sense, matrimony is presented as a means of grace.

Canon Law specifies the basic conditions concerning marriage, its nature as a contract and as a sacrament.[46]

According to natural law, the basic characteristics of marriage are unity and indissolubility. In Christian marriage these natural qualities are anchored in the supernatural order.

In Christian marriage there is no distinction between marriage as a contract and marriage as a sacrament. The legally valid contract between two baptized persons *(inter baptizatos)* is *ipso iure* a sacrament. The sacramental nature cannot be separated from the contractual nature. The *consensus nuptialis* is confirmed by law *(constitutive)* and, in this case, confirms at one time the contract and the sacrament.

The *materia* of the sacrament is the *traditio mutua* of the *ius in corpus;* the form is the consent corresponding to the legal formula (the "yes" of the couple). Matter and form cannot be strongly separated here. The ministers of the sacrament are both the contracting parties.[47]

---

[45] Marriage *(matrimonium connubium),* as a sacrament, is defined as a permanent union between two baptized persons who are by law capable of entering this union on the basis of mutual free consent before God, whereby sacramental grace is bestowed upon them.

[46] Cf. Canons 1012, 1013, 1081.

[47] The priest is not the minister, but the *assistens.* His assistance and the cooperation of the witnesses is prescribed for the confirmation of validity

The formula *"ministri sacramenti sunt ipsi contrahentes"* is often repeated in German in the following manner: *"Die Eheleute spenden sich selbst das Sacrament"* ("the spouses themselves administer the sacrament"). The objection to this formula is that it is often misunderstood by the young married couple.

The author experienced a case in which a young psychopath, separated from his wife, wanted to remarry. When told by the pastor that sacramental marriage cannot be broken, he retorted with the following statement: "Oh, that makes no difference. You yourself have told us that the contracting parties themselves administer the sacrament."

In some cases the spouses think that the "mutual administration" of the sacrament consists in the consummation of the marriage, that is, in the marriage act. This idea indicates the sexual act of consummation instead of consent as the essential, constitutive element. If this idea were correct, then it would follow that a nonconsummated marriage *(matromonium non consummatum)* would be essentially neither a sacrament nor a natural marriage. It would therefore be null. But, in reality, only from a *matrimonium ratum,* i.e., a valid marriage which has not been consummated through the marital act, can a dissolution be given.

The dissolution basically presupposes the validity of the marriage *(matrimonium ratum).*

2. Marriage Impediments (Impedimenta matrimonii)

The matrimonial impediments are divided into impedient impediments *(impedimenta impedientia)* and diriment impediments *(impedimenta dirimentia)*. The diriment impediments render marriage invalid. There is a further distinction between minor and major degrees of impediments *(gradus maioris seu minoris)*[48]

—the Tridentine form: *"coram parocho proprio et duobus testibus"* (exception: *matrimonium necessitatis,* Can. 1098).

[48] Cf. Canon 1042. To the impediments *gradus minoris* belong, among others, consanguinity in the third degree of the collateral line and affinity in the second degree of the collateral line; spiritual relationship *(cognatio spiritualis)*. Only spiritual relationship arising from baptism invalidates marriage.

a) IMPEDIENT IMPEDIMENTS

To the impedient impediments belong:

a) The simple vows of virginity, of perfect chastity, of not marrying, of receiving sacred orders, and of embracing the religious state.

b) Legal relationship. In those countries in which legal relationship arising from adoption renders marriage illicit according to civil law, marriage is illicit also according to Canon Law.

c) Mixed religion. The Church most severely prohibits everywhere the contracting of marriage between two baptized persons, one of whom is a Catholic while the other is affiliated with a heretical or a schismatical sect. Moreover, if there is danger of perversion of the Catholic spouse and the offspring, the marriage is forbidden by the divine law itself.[49]

The *votum simplex* is distinguished from the *votum solemne;* the latter is associated with solemn profession.

By *mixta religio* Canon 1060 intends the difference of religion between two baptized persons. As a rule, one of the parties is a Catholic and the other party is non-Catholic. Before a dispensation is given, guarantee *(cautiones)* must be given that the children will be brought up Catholics (Canon 1061).

b) DIRIMENT IMPEDIMENTS

To the diriment impediments of hygienic importance belong age, impotence, and consanguinity.

Some of the other diriment impediments are: prior marriage, sacred orders, solemn vows, disparity of cult and affinity (all degrees in the direct line; in the collateral line, to the second degree inclusively).[50]

The impediment of *disparitas cultus* excludes matrimony between baptized and non-baptized persons.

The impediment of *affinitas* excludes marriage between those related by marriage in the direct line (e.g., father and step-daughter) and between those related in the collateral line up to the second degree inclusive (e.g., between husband and deceased wife's first

[49] Cf. Canons 1058-1066.
[50] Cf. Canons 1067-1080.

cousin. It is closely related to the impediment of *publica honestas* which impedes marriage in the first and second degrees of the direct line between the man and the blood relatives of the wives and *vice versa*. The case of *cognatio spiritualis* belongs to the diriment impediments, even if of *minoris gradus*.

The matrimonial impediments belonging to the first group also have a notable bio-hygienic importance; those of the second group have a predominantly religious importance regarding the sacrament of matrimony and its indissolubility as well as regarding the sacrament of sacred orders and the profession of solemn vows.

From the standpoint of pastoral hygiene we should consider particularly the impediments of age and impotence; and partly the impediments of consanguinity in the degrees calculated by Canon Law.

(1) Age

The matrimonial impediment of age as contained in Canon 1067, §1 is based on ecclesiastical law; natural law demands merely that age which makes it possible to give a valid consent. Persons who do not possess physical sexual maturity—apart from mental maturity, moral maturity and maturity of character required for marriage—cannot be considered *personae iure habiles*.

The Code of Canon Law prescribes, as the minimum age for the man, the completion of the sixteenth year; for the woman, the completion of the fourteenth year. That is the absolute minimum age, even for the Orient. In Europe, custom indicates a higher minimum age. Minors need the permission of those who hold the *patria potestas* and without this permission ordinarily cannot bind themselves contractually in a legally valid manner.

(2) Impotence

In regard to the impediment of impotence, reference can be made to a former and special presentation of the subject.[51]

Impotence in the sense of Canon 1068 *(impotentia coeundi)* is not only to be distinguished from sterility *(impotentia generandi)*, but also from the purely mechanistic concept of impotence as interpreted by most civil laws.

---

[51] Cf. HSPM, II, pp. 233-287. Cf. *Compendium of Pastoral Medicine,* English translation, Wagner, N. Y., 1960, pp. 121 ff.

According to the mechanistic concept, impotence consists purely in an inability regarding *immissio membri virilis in vagina.* It is no longer a matter of impotence, therefore, so long as *immissio* is possible. However, according to Canon Law, more than the mere mechanical *immissio* pertains to the *consummatio matrimonii,* to the *fieri unam carnem;* hence also the *penetratio debita vaginae* and the *effusio (veri) seminis intra eam.*

A man surgically sterilized is considered by most civil laws as having only *impotentia generandi (sterilitas),* but contrary to this and according to many canonists as having complete impotence *(impotentia coeundi),* since the requisites for the true *consummatio matrimonii* are lacking. Yet the Holy Office on Sept. 28, 1957, stated that in the case of double vasectomy, marriage according to the mind of Canon 1068, §2 must not be impeded.

A woman who has undergone a radical operation *(mulier excisa)* is considered a case of *sterilitas* according to Canon Law since she is capable of fulfilling what is required by natural law: *recipiendi membrum virile et retinendi semen.*

The reason for the different consideration of man and the woman is based on the fact that the man is the *principium generationis activum* and the woman is the *principium passivum.* Further, it is based on the difference between *actio humana* and *actio naturae* in the woman. It is required of the woman only that the *actio humana* be integral; the *actio naturae* intervenes in the *organa supravaginalia;* hence, their absence has, for the woman, no longer the significance of an essential defect in the consummation of marriage.

Against this idea, which corresponds with the jurisprudence of the Holy Roman Rota, it has been objected, on a biological basis, that in reproduction the woman contributes the same amount of chromosome substances *(hereditary mass)* as the man and even a greater contribution in nutritive substance; hence, her participation should yield to the same consideration (theory of parity). Against this, the theory of difference can base itself on the predominantly finer cytologic differences in the function of the sex cells, differences which confirm the active and activating role of the human germ cells. From the standpoint of social hygiene, the traditional idea of the jurisprudence of the Holy Roman Rota can be completely accepted.

From the standpoint of pastoral and social hygiene, the enormous increase of potency disturbances in both sexes, especially in the woman, should not be overlooked. In the woman, impotence manifests itself mostly in the form of vaginismus; but absolute and relative psychogenic impotence can appear without the defensive motor spasms associated with it. The increase of potency disturbances in both sexes is obviously associated with the extension of *abusus sexualis seu matrimonii* and with the habituation to inadequate sexual stimulation.

(3) Consanguinity

The impediment of consanguinity has also a deep biological justification. It is based not merely on a traditional "taboo" or on limits of respect "inculcated by education," but has deep psychological reasons. The so-called "incest barrier" and the "Oedipus problem" lie deep in human nature; the latter essentially deeper than Depth Psychology has formerly considered.[52]

The biological reasons for the impediment of consanguinity are found, on the one hand, in the "degradation of ancestors" and, on the other hand, in the strong confluence of recessive, hereditary, morbid predispositions.

From the standpoint of hereditary hygiene, the easy granting of a dispensation which will bring on a relaxation of the marriage impediment is to be greatly advised against. The sphere of the marriage impediment is more extensively fixed in Canon Law than in civil law.

According to Canon 1076, marriage is not permitted between blood relatives: a) in the direct line (between all in the ascending and descending line); b) in the collateral line to the third degree inclusively. The canonical computation of the degrees does not completely coincide with the customary computation found in civil-law books, but coincides with natural law.

The following schema will help one compute the definite degree of consanguinity:

[52] Cf. HSPM, V. p. 222. Cf. *Compendium of Pastoral Medicine*, English translation, Wagner, N. Y., 1960, p. 373 ff.

1. *Linea recta*

Probandus (p)

Descendentes	Ascendentes
1	1
Filius	*Pater*
2	2
Nepos	*Avus*
3	3
Pronepos	*Proavus*

2. *Linea collateralis*

a) *Descendentes:*

1st degree: brother, sister

2nd degree: cousins

patrueles: the two fathers are brothers;

consobrini: the two mothers are sisters.

3rd degree: great-nephews and great-nieces,

patrueles magni, amitini magni,

consobrini magni.

b) *Ascendentes:*

1st degree: *patruus* (brother of the father); *amita* (sister of the father); *avunculus* (brother of the mother); *matertera* (sister of the mother);

2nd degree: *patruus magnus* (great-uncle), *amita magna* (great-aunt), *avunculus magnus, matertera magna;*

3rd degree: *propartuus* (brother of the great-grandfather); *proamita* (sister of the great-grandfather); *proavunculus* (brother of the great-grandmother); *promatertera* (sister of the great-grandmother)

Besides these, degrees of consanguinity *(simplex),* double and multiple consanguinity *(consanguinitas multiplex)* can arise, i.e., if one or more ancestors (grandfather, great-grandfather; grandmother, great-grandmother) coincide.

In the Latin language, the relationship of relatives is definitely more exact than that of the German language, where, for example, the designation "male cousin, female cousin, uncle, aunt" are used without indicating whether the relationship is from the father's or mother's side.

The general rules for the canonical computation of degrees distinguish primarily between the *linea recta* and *linea collateralis;* in the latter they make a further distinction according as the two collateral lines are of the same length or not *(linea collateralis aequalis vel inaequalis).*

In the direct line there are as many degrees as there are generations or as there are persons, not counting the ancestor *("tot gradus quot generationes," seu "quot personae stipite dempto").* Cf. Canon 96, §2.

In the collateral line, if the distance of both relatives from the common ancestor is equal, that is, if both lines are of equal length, there are as many degress as there are generations in one line not counting the common ancestor. Thus brother and sister are related in the first degree.

If the lines are not equal, then there are as many degrees as there are generations in the longer line or as there are persons in the longer line not counting the common ancestor (cf. Canon 96 §3).

Considering the general biological and psychological considerations against the marriage of blood relatives, one cannot help but acknowledge the canonical regulation, even from the hygienic standpoint, as being very acceptable and accurate.[53]

3. Hygienic Questions

a) PHYSICAL HYGIENE

The hygiene of marriage holds a central place in both social and pastoral hygiene and must be grasped from many sides. The entire problem cannot be completely treated from the sacramental standpoint alone. The various questions require special treatment in separate chapters. In our time especially questions of marriage and sex life play a prominent role in spiritual direction. The health and social problems of marriage and the family are, at present, in the foreground.

In this chapter we shall consider questions regarding marital-

---

[53] Cf. Canons 1020, 1027, 1033, 1035, 1042, 1043, 1053, 1058, 1059, 1060, 1061, 1067, 1068, 1071, 1076, 1077, 1080, 1081, 1082, 1083, 1087, 1093, 1094, 1098, 1104, 1110, 1111, 1118, 1119, 1120, 1128, 1129, 1133, 1134, 1138, 1141.

health suitability (marriage fitness) which forms an integral part of the matter considered in premarital guidance. In this sphere, questions concerning physical and mental health unite, one with the other. Here even the question of sanitary (eugenic) marital impediments are to be discussed. It should be remarked beforehand that there is no need of "eugenic marriage impediments," especially since the present norms of Canon Law offer sufficient possibilities for the recognition of all the needs that are eugenically justified. "Eugenic marriage impediments," which would necessarily lead to the forbiddance of marriage, would be incompatible with the freedom of contracting marriage, which is based on natural law *("matrimonia libera esse debent").*

b) MENTAL HYGIENE

The questions treated in marriage counseling, in turn, form an integral part of mental hygiene. They can be treated in unison with this or in sexual hygiene—in particular, social hygiene.

Among the psycho-hygienic problems of marriage occupying a central position is the ever-increasing number of ruined marriages with their extensive consequences regarding the disturbance and ruination of health, especially the relationship between the percentage of divorces and that of suicide, of the increase of children difficult to educate and psychopathic and of the neurotic children that arise from such marriages. This emphasizes the conviction that psychopaths are not suitable for marriage and that, in many of these cases, marriage is to be discouraged even if the prohibitions are neither desirable nor effective. These elements of the problem are significant not only for the doctor and hygienist, but, above all, for the spiritual director.

H. Holy Orders (Ordo)

1. General Concept

Holy Orders *(ordo, ordinatio)* comprises seven grades.[54]

[54] Holy Orders may be defined as the sacrament by which spiritual power is conferred together with the grace to exercise properly the respective office.

For the priesthood the *materia* is the first imposition of the bishop's hands which is done in silence. The continuation of the same imposition through the extension of the right hand and the last imposition which is accompanied

The first four are called minor orders *(ordines minores)* and include porter, lector, exorcist, and acolyte. The importance of these preliminary orders was greater in the past than at the present time.

The major orders include the subdiaconate, diaconate, and priesthood. The priesthood, in turn, includes two degrees: the simple sacerdotal state *(sacerdotium minus, presbyteratus)* and the episcopal state *(sacerdotium maius, episcopatus)*. Those who have received the major orders are obliged to celibacy. The major orders are also called sacred orders *(ordines sacri)*. The major orders which are sacramental in character confer a character *indelebilis* (as baptism and confirmation). The subdiaconate and the minor orders are of ecclesiastical origin; the diaconate and the priesthood (both the simple priesthood and the episcopate) are sacraments.

2. Irregularities and Simple Impediments

An irregularity is a canonical impediment of a permanent nature which directly renders it unlawful to receive ordination and indirectly forbids the exercise of the orders received. A simple im-

---

by the words *"Accipe Spiritum: quorum remiseris peccata,"* etc., do not belong to the matter.

The form consists of the words of the Preface, of which the following are essential and, therefore, required for validity: *"Da quaesumus, omnipotens pater, in hunc famulum tuum presbyterii dignitatem; innova in visceribus ejus spiritum sanctitatis, ut acceptum a Te, Deus, secundi meriti munus obtineat censuramque morum exemplo suae conversationis insinuet."*

The ordinary minister of holy orders is a consecrated bishop. The extraordinary minister is a person who lacks the episcopal character, but has faculties to confer orders either by common law or by an indult of the Holy See.

For the episcopacy, the *materia* is the imposition of hands which is done by the consecrating bishop. The form consists of the words of the Preface, of which the following are essential and, therefore, required for validity: *"Comple in sacerdote tuo ministerii tui summam, et ornamentis totius glorificationis instructum coelestis unguenti rore sanctifica."*

Although for the validity of episcopal consecration only one bishop is required and sufficient, nevertheless the prescriptions of the Roman Pontifical must be observed. Therefore, all the co-consecrating bishops must employ both matter and form, i.e., each must impose hands, touching the head of the Bishop-elect with both hands, while saying the form, and having formed the intention of conferring episcopal consecration together with the bishop who is consecrator. (Apostolic Letter, Nov. 30, 1944, AAS 37-131) pediment, unlike an irregularity, is not of a permanent nature. An irregularity is removed only by a dispensation, whereas a simple impediment eventually may cease of itself.

Canon Law distinguishes two types of irregularities: 1) irregularitas *ex defectu;* 2) irregularitas *ex delicto;* [55]

An irregularity *ex defectu* is the lack of qualification required for ordination for which the candidate is not responsible; an irregularity *ex delicto* is an impediment based on a grave sin of the candidate.

Persons irregular *ex defectu* are illegitimates; bodily defectives; epileptics; the insane; the diabolically possessed (even after they have been cured); bigamists; the infamous who have incurred infamy of law; judges who have pronounced a death sentence; executioners and all voluntary and immediate assistants in the inflicting of the death penalty.

Persons irregular *ex delicto* are apostates; heretics; schismatics; whoever has allowed himself to be baptized by a non-Catholic, except in case of extreme necessity; those who attempt marriage or go through the civil ceremony while bound by a valid marriage bond, sacred orders, or simple or solemn religious profession; any man who attempts marriage with a woman who is bound by such a religious profession or marriage; voluntary murderers; those who have effectively procured abortion and also all accomplices; those who have mutilated themselves or others, or have attempted suicide; clerics who practice medicine or surgery without an apostolic indult, if the death of a patient has followed such practice; those who abuse sacred orders by performing acts of orders reserved to the clergy in major orders when they have not received the respective orders or, if they have received them, are forbidden to exercise them by reason of a canonical penalty.

The simple impediments to ordination are children of non-Catholics, as long as their parents remain in their error; married men, as long as the wives are living; those who occupy an office or administrative position forbidden by clerics; slaves, properly so-called, until they have been emancipated; men liable to ordinary military service until they have finished their terms of service; neophytes, until they have sufficiently proved themselves; the dis-

[55] Cf. Canons 948, 951, 968, 971, 974, 984, 985, 986, 987, 990, 991.

reputable or those who suffer from infamy until they have recovered their good name.

a) IRREGULARITAS EX DEFECTU

We shall consider only those irregularities which are associated
with pastoral hygiene.

From the standpoint of pastoral hygiene the following facts are
to be noticed. Bodily defectives are those who on account of debility cannot safely or, on account of deformity, becomingly minister at the altar. The *defectus* must be *gravior defectus*. If one
is already ordained, a greater defect is required to prevent him from
exercising his orders; those actions are not forbidden him which
can be properly performed despite the defect.

After two world wars, there were many seriously wounded men
who, as belated vocations, applied for the priesthood and through
the generous bestowal of dispensations attained their desire. For
the most part, these dispensations were granted on the basis of a
medical judgment concerning the type and extent of the bodily
defect; for example, the inability to kneel or to elevate the Sacred
Species, etc. The author knows of many cases of war injured and
crippled who have obtained a dispensation from their defect and
have proven themselves well as priests.

Blindness *(caecitas)* is generally considered a *defectus gravis;* in
individual cases even the *caecutientes* can be dispensed from the
irregularity *ex defectu* under definite circumstances in which again
the medical judgment is of importance.

Difficult to obtain is the dispensation from the bodily deformities
of serious degree; e.g., in the case of a serious humpback *(malum
Patti, gibbus)* or in the case of a serious crippling of the extremities
which make difficult the movements at the altar and the manipulations during the Sacrifice of the Mass. Even the paralysis of the
nervous system, both of a central or peripheral nature, can render
one irregular, although even in this case a dispensation is very
possible. The author has known priests who have been able to
celebrate Mass well despite their sclerosis multiplex. But the decision is made only from case to case and on the basis of the report
concerning the condition.

Epilepsy and insanity render one irregular, even after one has been cured. He who has suffered *("sunt vel fuerunt")* is never certain that a relapse will not take place. If such diseases befall one only after ordination and if one is definitely and completely cured, one may be permitted by the Ordinary to exercise the orders received. If one so afflicted has attacks only every two weeks or even less often, he may apply to the Holy See for dispensation. Epilepsy renders one irregular since one suffering from this disease can suddenly fall over and lose consciousness. If this happens to the priest during the celebration of Mass, especially at the time of the Consecration, the effects would be serious regarding *reverentia sacamenti.*

It is, however, very possible in cases of symptomatic epilepsy (which, for example, are caused by a brain tumor or meninx scars) that the epilepsy can be completely cured after an operation, so that the danger of relapse will be removed. In such cases, an appeal based on the medical judgment should be made for a dispensation.

In regard to insanity, even after a clinical cure (freedom from symptoms) a dispensation should not be sought. He who is or has been insane is and remains unsuitable for the sacerdotal state.

The author can recall a case of a clinically-healed schizophrenia after a lobotomy in which he had to express his opinion against suitability of health.

The judgment concerning diabolical possession is less a matter for the doctor as it is a matter of the Ordinariate. The doctor, as adviser, can do nothing more than establish whether psychopathy, hysteria or psychosis is at the base, and whether the symptoms can be explained through it. If a natural explanation cannot be given, then only the Ordinariate is competent to give a judgment of the case.

Bigamy as an irregularity is understood in the sense of *bigamia successiva,* i.e., those who have successively married at least twice. The meaning of this prescript may be that a man who cannot live without a woman is unsuitable for the priesthood. When it is a question of obtaining a dispensation from this irregularity, it can be stated that, in the case of a widower remarrying, it is often a case of pressing domestic and business reasons and has nothing whatsoever to do with sexual motivation.

The participation in a death sentence and execution confirm the *defectus plenae lenitatis.* The respect for life speaks out.

b) IRREGULARITAS EX DELICTO

This irregularity is primarily imposed on voluntary murderers and those who have effectively procured abortion, and also all accomplices. Since the killing of man in dueling already imposes irregularity through *infamia iuris,* there is no need to go into detail.

In the procuring of an abortion, an irregularity arises only *effectu secuto* and not by mere attempt, and it is also obtained by all the accomplices *(omnesque cooperantes).*

Clerics who practice medicine or surgery without an Apostolic indult, if the death of a patient has followed such practices, incur irregularity. In general, practice on the part of clerics or priests is forbidden. But in special cases, as in mission fields, for example, this may be permitted when there is a lack of doctors. Basically, it is not desirable that a priest practice medicine even if he possesses the necessary knowledge. It is a different matter when a doctor later desires to become a priest.

The question is asked whether he is irregular if, in the course of his practice, he is involved in cases of death. It can be assumed here that it is not a matter of deliberate homicide but, at most, of homicide through negligence; it is almost always a case of mishap concerning which the doctor cannot be held responsible.

3. Hygienic Questions

a) PHYSICAL HYGIENE

The sacerdotal ministry is one of the most strenuous professions. The health of the priest will be affected more seriously because of lack of priests and this fact seems more so at the present time. Hence, it is necessary that anyone wishing to embrace this life should possess strong health and should receive a medical confirmation of the same. (The health requirements will be discussed in more detail in the chapter concerning the hygiene of the priesthood and the religious life.)

The tasks and problems of spiritual direction, at the same time, especially in large cities, has become very complicated and difficult. This circumstance—and the scarcity of young candidates—affects the priest who is active in pastoral work by making his task almost unbearable. The consuming of energy is enormous, and premature death through consuming diseases, especially from heart exhaustion (myocardiac lesions, coronary circulatory disturbances, blocking of blood vessels and angina pectoris), strikes many priests around the age of fifty.

Even the priesthood is affected by the tempo of the times, so that numerous and burdensome sacrifices must be made by the priest. For a long time the priestly profession was considered one of the most peaceful and healthiest, as age statistics indicated. But today it has become one of the most strenuous and most difficult of professions. For this reason, the health requirements in determining suitability for the priestly vocation should be given serious consideration.

The doctor who has to give the health certificate therefore finds himself in a difficult situation. He realizes the urgent need of vocations and yet has to declare the greater part of the few who apply as unsuitable because of health. The task of the doctor is relatively easy when it is merely a matter of physical defects; in case of doubt he can always decide in favor of vocational fitness. But the situation is quite the opposite when it is a matter of mental defects.

b) MENTAL HYGIENE

Among the aspirants for the priesthood we find today, in ever-increasing proportion, certain individuals who, from the standpoint of mental health, do not comply with the necessary requirements. In case of doubt, the doctor is strictly bound in conscience to cast a negative vote, and it is preferable that this happen too often rather than too seldom.

The general difficulties of life cause some, who do not feel equal to the other professions, to try the priesthood. For a number of these the determining motivation is nothing else but a neurotic escape from the world and life. With this type one cannot be too cautious. The priesthood requires strong and sound personalities. At the present time, among those who are directed to the doctor for health examination there are, in ever-increasing number, not only neurotics, but also definite psychopaths. The doctor can never be too severe in the rejection of psychopaths and should therefore proceed with the greatest rigor. He will be of greater service to the Church when he refuses a health certificate to these persons than when, through softness and indulgence, he grants such a certificate. The giving of a certificate in such a case is a matter of going contrary to sound reason.

Psychopaths are persons who encounter at all times and everywhere difficulties of life, provoke discord, conflicts and clashes. They have played an unhealthy role in the history of the Church: they were always the initiators and leaders of all the subversive and revolutionary movements; they were always the *homines semper novarum rerum studiosi* who, often subjectively in good faith, have by their aggression and lack of moderation caused disastrous effects. The emotional instability and excessive sensitiveness of their nervous system affects them in such a manner that, even in their instinctual life, they are usually overpowered. This is especially so in the sexual realm where psychopaths seldom bring the instinct under control and often fall into all possible defective attitudes or behavior (perversions; *psychopathia sexualis*). They are the ones who hold that it is impossible to control the instinct. They generalize from their own case to all other cases.

While the normal person can control the instinct and realizes that abstinence is not only possible but necessary, the psychopath is not even able to overcome his "puberty masturbation." He is a failure and later blames celibacy by which the Church expects from men the impossible; finally, he deserts his vow and religion, marries, and even in marriage encounters deep unhappiness. Finally, he will not heed the warning of the doctor that he who, because of psychopathy, is not fit for the priesthood is usually also not suitable for marriage and that he will fail in marriage as in the priesthood. The doctor who knows these facts would act contrary to sound reason, contrary to duty and conviction, if he declares a psychopath qualified for the priesthood. Even the scarcity of candidates for the priesthood cannot alter this fact.

The tragedy lies in the fact that, in proportion as the number of healthy candidates decreases, the number of defectives increases. This is the same problem that confronts us in the dysgenic effect of birth decline.

MONITUM FROM THE HOLY OFFICE

NCWC New Service (Foreign)
Holy Office Warns against Practice of   7/17/61-S.
Psychoanalysis by Clerics, Religious

Vatican City, July 15 (Radio, NC)—The Sacred Congregation of Holy Office has issued an official warning against the practice of psychoanalysis by clerics or Religious and against its use for testing religious vocations.

The Holy Office document, called a "monitum" (warning), was issued July 15. It stated:

Since many dangerous opinions are being published and spread regarding the sins incurred by violation of the Sixth Commandment (Thou shalt not commit adultery) and regarding the imputability of human actions, the Sacred Congregation of the Holy Office established the following norms for public knowledge:

1. Bishops, presidents of faculties of theology, rectors of seminaries and schools for Religious must require that those whose duty it is to teach moral theology and similar disciplines comply exactly with the traditional teaching of the Church (Canon 129).

Canon 129 provides that clerics must not neglect the study of the sacred sciences and that in their studies they must always follow the sound doctrines handed down by the Fathers of the Church and commonly accepted by the Church. They must also avoid profane novelties of expression and what is wrongly called scientific.

The document continued:

2. Ecclesiastical censors must use great caution in censoring and passing judgment on books and publications which deal with the sixth precept of the Decalogue.

3. Clerics and Religious are forbidden to practice psychoanalysis according to the norms of Canon 139, paragraph two. Canon 139 provides that cler-

ics must avoid affairs which, although not unbecoming in themselves, are foreign to the clerical state. Without special permission they may not practice medicine or surgery or accept certain public offices.

The document concluded:

4. The opinion of those who consider that a prior psychoanalytical examination is definitely necessary before receiving Holy Orders must be disapproved. Likewise disapproved are the opinions of those who hold that the so-called psychoanalytical examination and relative investigations are necessary for candidates to the priesthood and for religious profession. This applies also if it is a matter of investigating the aptitude required for the priesthood or for religious profession. Likewise, priests and men or women Religious must not go to psychoanalysts except with the permission of the Ordinary and for grave reasons.

3 Hygiene and the Spiritual Director

The hygiene of the spiritual director includes the hygiene of the priesthood and the religious life in the sense of a community hygiene, as well as the personal hygiene of each member of the state. Further, certain hygienic timely questions pertaining to practical pastoral activity are included, which not only concentrate on the personal hygiene of the spiritual director, but whose influence extends also beyond this sphere. The matter will be divided in the following manner.

1) Hygiene of the priesthood.
2) Hygiene of the religious life.
3) Diseases of the spiritual director.
4) Modern hygienic questions pertaining to practical pastoral life.

I. HYGIENE OF THE PRIESTHOOD

A. Sanitary Presuppositions

The requirements concerning physical and mental health which are established before entering the seminary and, when possible to be examined, again before the bestowal of major orders have already been briefly discussed in the preceding chapter. It must be repeated that the doctor cannot take too seriously the duty he takes upon himself in giving a certificate of health. We have shown that under certain circumstances a physical defect can be taken less seriously than a mental defect. We have especially taken occasion to warn against the acceptance of psychopaths.

The danger of declaring a psychopath suitable is very great, first, because of the general increase of mental disturbances in our time; secondly, because of the lack of priests even the conscientious seminary rector and his medical adviser can be moved to overlook the situation, i.e., to declare an unsuitable candidate suitable; finally, because of this, that the incompetent psychopaths seek in the priesthood and religious life a so-called *refugium* from the world. It is in such cases that the motivation to dedicate oneself to the priesthood is not a genuine vocation, but a neurotic escape from the world.

Neurotics should not become priests. Psychotherapy should be recommended to them, and this by a trustworthy doctor. Only then are they to renew their application when the therapy has been successful. But even then the suitability is still problematic and requires attentive control for a longer time than is otherwise necessary.

The question of a vocation to the priesthood is something different from the suitability of health. The doctor passes judgment merely on the suitability. The judgment concerning the vocation is the duty of the proper ecclesiastical authorities. The vocation is a grace and, therefore, a sign of a supernatural calling; but suitability is based on rational dispositions.

If the words *"gratia supponit naturam"* are taken in the sense so often reproved by us as meaning that "grace presupposes nature," and if one holds by such that the integrity of health (hereditary health included) is the necessary presupposition for the workings of grace, then a true vocation can be present only in a person who is completely healthy. Then the establishment of health would be an absolute presupposition for the vocation. Such a concept would definitely lead to an error of naturalism which is to be rejected as much as the error of supernaturalism which holds that it can completely disregard nature.

The words *"gratia supponit naturam,"* correctly understood, mean that grace builds on nature as a basis; it surmounts nature and perfects it *(implet et perficit naturam)*. Neither nature nor grace alone do all. The former would be naturalism and the latter supernaturalism. Nature and grace work together, maintaining, of course, the primacy of the supernatural.

When there is present a true supernatural vocation and this is confirmed by definite signs, the health preoccupations are to cease, even if, without the extraordinary signs of a vocation, the health factors were serious enough to justify the refusal of the candidate.

Under normal circumstances one would, for example, declare a candidate afflicted with tuberculosis as unfit according to the sanitary standpoint. But this does not exclude the fact that an extraordinary vocation can be present in such an invalid. In that case hygienic considerations should be silent.

In questions regarding the hygiene of the spiritual director, it is decisively important to define the sphere of activity between the natural and the supernatural. Hygiene has a very important word to speak, but definitely not the last word since, in matters in which the supernatural has a definite part, the criteria of hygiene are too limited.

The basic considerations will be discussed often, for example, in the question of sacerdotal celibacy and religious vows, in all the questions of asceticism and mysticism insofar as these also present a medico-hygienic aspect.

As in the judgment of miraculous cures, so also in all cases of this nature, the task of the doctor consists, first of all, in exhausting all the possibilities of a judgment purely natural. He would render the Church the worse service if he would renounce too quickly the possibilities of a natural explanation and the natural criteria of judgment. It is not his task to express a supernatural judgment; this is the definite duty of the ecclesiastical authorities.

Only after having exhausted all the natural possibilities of explanation, in particular, of judgment, can the doctor conclude that a cure "is not explainable by natural means," and, in regard to the suitability of the candidate for the priesthood that, "considered simply from a purely natural standpoint, the candidate is not sanitarily suitable." Whether an extraordinary supernatural vocation indicates that the preoccupations of health are not to be considered is not a question that has to be decided by the doctor, but by the bishop.

If a priest, animated by an extraordinary ascetical spirit, leads an austere life of penance and, by taking upon himself the expiation of the sins of others, experiences extraordinary graces in the sense of authentic mysticism, considered simply from the hygienic standpoint, this would have to be considered "unhealthy" and, from the pure medical standpoint, serious.

If, for example, a mystic moved by grace absolutely abstains from food for a long time *(ieiunium absolutum),* this is, from the hygienic standpoint, erratic and absolutely "unhealthy." But if he rises to the supreme heights of spiritual elevation and, with this means, opens for others torrents of the life of grace, such a life of sacrifice can no longer be exclusively judged from the hygienic standpoint.

Finally, from the exclusive standpoint of hygiene, it is likewise "unhealthy" if the soldier, the fireman, or even the doctor expose their lives for the welfare of others.

Even in the sphere of purely natural life there are situations in which the hygienic viewpoint alone is not definitely decisive. For those who desire to become priests, for those who desire to dedicate themselves to the missions or desire to embrace the religious life, health cannot represent the ultimate and decisive standpoint. This consideration cannot and should not hinder the doctor in giving, with the greatest severity and utmost seriousness, his judgment concerning health suitability for the priesthood and religious life.

B. Daily Hygiene

The hygiene of daily life is of no less importance to the priest than to other men. The priest should give it the necessary attention. It would be an irresponsible mistake to take lightly the demands of hygiene without extraordinary and impelling reasons. Its negligence is far from being a sign of a particular *mortificatio corporis ascetica,* but more of general behavior of negligence.

1. Bodily Hygiene

Daily hygiene begins with bodily care. Its first and supreme commandment is cleanliness. The basic washing of the entire body, especially of those parts which have a greater need of cleanliness, should be absolutely evident. This is best accomplished by a shower. A cold or lukewarm shower bath fulfills the purpose of cleaning better than a cold bath. A short, cold washing at the end of the cleaning process will increase the resistance of the body against colds.

In order that the use of cold water be helpful, it should be applied for only a short time. After a short cold bath the skin becomes red, the cutaneous capillaries dilate, and this phenomenon is associated with an intensive pleasant feeling of warmth. But if the use of cold water is prolonged, a paradoxical reaction takes place: the cutaneous capillaries become contracted, the skin becomes pallid, and there arises an unpleasant feeling of coldness which persists for a long time with chills and chattering of teeth. This is always a sign that the cold influence has lasted too long and, at times, also of the fact that the organism, following a vascular disturbance, does not tolerate the cold water. In such cases the doctor should determine the cause of the disturbance and of the abnormal reactions.

The cleanliness of body should also be an expression of the purity of soul, of internal cleanliness.

The soiling of the body often provokes an unpleasant odor of sweat especially distressing to those around (the so-called "odor of the poor"). This is not to be confused with the so-called "body odor," which emanates even from the bodies of scrupulously clean persons and which constitutes a personal characteristic. The body odor is due to the action of the cutaneous glands of the armpit and to the secretions of the genital region. If maintaining oneself accurately clean is not of itself sufficient in eliminating a very acute body odor, this can be neutralized by the use of chlorophyl tablets. It would definitely be a mistake to use the tablets of chlorophyl as a substitute for cleanliness. First, cleanliness is necessary, and only when this is not sufficient should recourse to chlorophyl be had. The characteristic odor of the genital organs is almost always the result of insufficient cleanliness.

A patient experienced a certain repugnance in cleaning himself since he feared that such a process would provoke a sexual excitement. The greatest protection against such an effect is a calm objective and interiorly pure attitude and the realization that cleanliness is an hygienic necessity. If, then, cold water is used for the washing, the "cooling" effect that results cannot but cause a favorable reaction.

Among the unpleasant odors against which the priest can and should protect himself is that of halitosis, the *foetor ex ore*. This would be sufficient to keep some very sensitive penitents away from the confessional.

The causes of halitosis can be various. Often it is due to a mass of pus in the tonsils, to decaying teeth that need care, or to a purulent inflammation of the dental periosteum (*pyorrhea alveolaris,* abscesses, etc.); often it is due to gastric ailments. For the most part, the person afflicted with halitosis recognizes the fact less than those around him. It is well to remind him of this condition in order to induce him to undergo a medical examination or an examination of the teeth. A certain temporary alleviation can be obtained by the use of peppermint tablets, but these cannot affect a permanent remedy.

Many foods, as marinated herring, onions and garlic, are often the cause of bad breath. This bad odor can be eliminated for the most part by brushing the teeth and washing out the mouth. But in the case of onions and garlic not much can be done. These vegetables foodstuffs and spices—of themselves very healthful—penetrate the entire body (its therapeutic effect depends on this); and because of it their acute odor emanates from all the pores of the skin and not merely from the mouth. He who uses onions and garlic for therapeutic purposes should, during this period of cure, avoid contact with other persons.

Distention of the intestines (flatulence, *meteorismus*) can likewise be the cause of bad breath produced for the most part by unperceived escape of intestinal gas. He who suffers with this disturbance should have an intestinal washing several times a week (*clysma,* irrigation) with the infusion of chamomile and, in case of necessity, from time to time an intestinal bath which, together with the suppression of intestinal fermentation, eliminates the elevation of the diaphragm which in turn can be the cause of unpleasant cardiac disturbances (gastro-cardiac disturbances). Measures of this kind require in every case medical prescription and control.

The care of the feet has an important role in bodily hygiene. To maintain them healthy is a necessity for the priest who is often forced to remain on his feet for a long time, to walk much and to climb stairs.

The first and most important factor in the hygiene of the feet is still that of cleanliness. The value that is given to this in the Orient can be gathered from the numerous passages of Holy Scripture. To wash the feet regularly, and daily if possible, and drying accurately the interdigital spaces are most efficacious means of removing the remnants of sweat which can in turn lead to bad odor. This phenomenon is not to be confused with *pes sudorinus* in the strict sense. The latter consists of a hypersecretion of the sweat glands *(hyperhidrosis)* which, for the most part, is often of a constitutional origin. These forms, despite frequent treatment, require an especially accurate care of the feet and drying treatment, and often a general treatment. In any case it is absolutely necessary to change the socks frequently.

A completely different pathological process is that of the so-called "foot fungus," a dermatomycosis or epidermophytosis of the feet, which is particularly localized in the interdigital spaces and which becomes worse mostly in the summer months and often develops into a very unpleasant odor. This ailment is based on a purely parasitic skin infection which is predominantly transmitted in very crowded swimming pools. Its specific agent is a filamentary fungus of the hyphomycetes group. The use of penicillin in powder or ointment form has been of great therapeutic effect.

Of great importance for the hygiene of the spiritual director is the protection against foot lesions of a static nature, i.e., from harm arising more from unhygienic footwear and excessive weight on the feet than from functional overstrain. It is a matter, first of all, of the static modification of the foot arch: of the flat foot and the foot that is spread out. The former is due to the collapse of the longitudinal arch and the latter to the weakness of the transversal arch. The cause of both forms is to be sought in the weakness of the articular ligaments. That corpulence *(adipositas)* increases the static burden factor is definite. When one stands on one's feet for a long time, pains arise and travel to the lumbar musculature which are often mistaken for sciatica, lumbago or rheumatism of the dorsal muscles (static myalgin). The only remedy against such pains consists in the formation of a well-fitted arch support (model arch supports are recommended).

A flat foot caused by inflammation can render one incapable of working for a long time. The origin of such a condition can be prevented only by the proper care at the proper time. The specialist will decide when it is necessary to use orthopedic shoes.

Among the most unpleasant foot difficulties which can be avoided by means of appropriate treatment are the ingrowing toenail *(unguis incarnatus)* which becomes infected at times and requires surgical treatment, and the hooked, or incurved, state of the nails *(onychogryphosis)* which is a degenerative thickening, for the most part, of the toe nails. By means of adequate care of the feet (pedicure), one can avoid such ailments which hinder the performing of one's profession.

Cleanliness is the most important element in pedicure in order to prevent inflammation of the matrix of the nail *(paronychia)* which in certain circumstances can lead to dangerous septic infections.

2. Physical Exercise

Bodily exercise also belongs to proper body care, but this must be of a nature that is adequate to the age and state of health of the priest. There is no need of a sport that requires great performance; and even when the priest is director of a youth group, he has other duties besides participating in the sports of the youth.

The priest, however, is perfectly justified in keeping his body healthy and efficient, and the fact that he is a priest does not mean that he has to be a bookworm or that he should always stay indoors. He should participate in various physical exercises as walking, swimming, tennis, fishing, golfing, etc., in order to strengthen his body. But he is to avoid any exaggeration of physical exercise to the point of emphasizing too much the sport aspect, of concentrating on increasing the performance of the activity, and of attaining records. In so doing he loses sight of the limits of one's physical capacity. In such a case physical exercise ceases to be useful to health.

The "sports priest" is a figure which is not common in Europe, and it is good that it is so. It is not necessary to cultivate a type of priest who has the reputation of being able to participate in all the sports of the youth and even to surpass the youth in these sports. He must be able to impress the youth through qualities other than strength of muscles and agility.

Swimming is one of the healthiest physical exercises. It activates the entire musculature of the body and, at the same time, it is associated with an excellent respiratory gymnastic. It would be desirable, especially for young priests, if adequate opportunity would be presented to them so that they could easily participate in this effective exercise.

It may seem strange, but, despite the many swimming pools, there is everywhere lacking a truly adequate opportunity for clerics. *Decorum clericale* renders it almost impossible for the priest to frequent the public swimming pools, especially in small towns where the priest is known by all. We do not wish to speak against the public baths, especially if it is truly a family bathing place. It is useful that an opportunity be given to the family, i.e., father, mother and children, to enjoy bathing together as a family. But it must be admitted that the way things are managed in the community bathing places has nothing to do with "family bathing" and less to do with hygiene, because less clothing is worn by people. It is simply false to hold that the maximum denuding of the body is the result of hygienic considerations.

It would not be an infraction of hygienic norms if, in the public baths where fungi spring up from the ground, separate compartments for both men and women be established. But today this is completely lacking. Here we do not speak merely of the priest who would be grateful for the opportunity of enjoying the use of the bath without causing public astonishment; but we speak also of the great number of men and women, in need of rest, for whom the surroundings of the public bath are too noisy, or who for other reasons (for example, because of their adiposity or some bodily deformity) are ashamed to appear publicly in their bathing costumes before persons of the opposite sex.

In the large cities the opportunity for private bath for the priests and even open-air swimming places should be offered. In any case, from the hygienic standpoint, we cannot recommend a more healthful exercise than that of swimming. With systematic habituation swimming can take place up until late autumn. But one must consider that one's stay in cold water must be shorter, the colder the water is. With a temperature of 4°C, a few seconds suffice; a longer stay will provoke the "paradoxical vascular reaction" with consequent harm to health. But he who has learned to resist the 4°C can stay in ice water for seconds without injury to health.

Swimming represents, in general, the ideal type of gymnastics. Daily gymnastics can be recommended to the priest only occasionally. It need not unconditionally be morning exercise since the priest is busy in the morning with the celebration of Mass, meditation, reading of the breviary and many other activities which, without doubt, take precedence. But one can participate in gymnastics even in the evening.

The exercises to be used are to be selected according to one's personal choice. It is advantageous to adopt the exercise of the extremities with the exercise of the abdominal muscles. The exercise of the abdominal walls can really prevent the accumulation of fat which arises so easily in those who lead a sedentary life. In any case, every form of exercise should be associated with a respiratory exercise. In this regard it is to be noticed that, by inhaling, the abdomen protrudes since the diaphragm must sink in. In exhaling, the abdomen is so drawn in as if it wanted "to squeeze the liver as a sponge"; the diaphragm is pressed upward.

We have already noticed that a persistent elevation of the diaphragm which, in case of insufficient respiratory exercise, is for the most part accompanied by intestinal atonia (deficient muscular tonicity) and flatulence can easily lead to cardiac disturbances (gastro-cardiac disturbances). These arise from the transversal position of the heart pressed upward and from its inclination toward the base of the aorta. These can cause difficulties similar to an angina pectoris (stenocardiac disturbances) and can in time lead to genuine stenocardiac attacks and hence to genuine angina pectoris, to coronary insufficiency and blood disturbance of the heart. To these there is easily associated, because of the formation of blood clots, the so-called "myocardiac infarct," or coronary infarct, which in definite circumstances can easily lead to sudden death.

Persons who have a tendency toward adiposity and, at the same time, lead a turbulent life are more exposed to such complications than the slender and sinewy persons who preserve themselves physically efficient to old age.

At a time when the lack of priests is so great, the priest has the moral obligation of conserving himself in health and in efficiency as long as possible. But if one already has an organic lesion of the heart—above all, a myocardiac lesion, then one should be extremely prudent in regard to physical strain. A little excess can cause more harm than the enjoyment one can obtain from any exercise.

The proper norm for judging the wholesome aspect of physical exercise is the physical well-being after the exercise. If after the exercise one does not feel fresh, but tired, this indicates that it has been abused. If after even a light exercise one always feels strained and exhausted, this is a sign that the physical exercises are badly endured. One should, therefore, consult a doctor for the cause of this phenomenon. In any case, the priest should, insofar as possible, participate in healthful movement. A form of life which is constantly sedentary forms and leads to a heavy accumulation of fat, even in a person who is very active and enthusiastic in spiritual activities. Adiposity is, therefore, nearly always detrimental to health.

As a form of movement, long walks are especially recommended. Walking, in our day of sports, is too little appreciated for its sanitary value. But through its mild action, it constitutes a form of bodily activation which includes all the muscles of the body. With those convalescing from cardiac affections, they can, by a gradual and progressive increase, be transformed into a systematic "terrain cure."

3. Means of Transportation *

The priest who is stationed in a large country section, especially in the "diaspora" (i.e., dispersion of parishioners over a large radius), must often cover extensive territory. A diaspora pastor often has more territory to cover than a bishop in an enclosed territory. Hence, in the long run, it is scarcely possible to get along without some form of mechanical transportation or conveyance. The bicycle has the advantage of being simple and not expensive. Its maintenance does not require any extensive technical knowl-

* Here, as in other places throughout this volume, the translator has not edited the original to apply more realistically to the general U.S.A. scene. As the original stands, it may be literally applied both to home and foreign missions.

edge; its use does not require much ability or physical power, at least on level terrain. But in mountainous sections the use of an ordinary pedal bicycle requires strong legs and heart; the heart and respiratory organs are subjected to an excessive strain. In case of a cardiac lesion, even a slight lesion, one should give up riding a bicycle even though its moderate use can be healthful.

The ordinary pedal bicycle can be transformed into a light motor bicycle through the application of an auxiliary motor which can be turned off at will when riding on even terrain. Thus the advantages of a bicycle and a light motor bicycle can be united.

The motor scooter is simply a motor vehicle. This has the advantage of a very low seat so that, in cases of necessity, the feet can very quickly and easily touch the ground. The "Vespa" form of this vehicle prevents the serious lesion of the legs in an accident.

In order to control the heavy motorcycle, it is necessary to have the complete knowledge and technique of a motor driver; the high-powered machines develop such a high velocity that accidents result in serious damage. A crash helmet is a protection against skull fracture, but not against fractures of the extremities.

The automobile offers greater safety than the motor bicycle, but, because of high cost and expense in maintenance, it is still inaccessible to the majority of our country pastors. But in America it is practically part of the pastor's inventory.

Besides these modern means of locomotion, to which in missionary regions the aeroplane is added, we should not forget the oldest helpers of man: the horse, the donkey and the mule. The last is still used as a means of transportation almost exclusively in the southern sections of Europe, as also in the elevated plains of South America.

Riding is without doubt one of the most pleasant forms of transportation, especially in mountainous sections; besides, riding is one of the most beautiful and healthful of physical exercises. The use of a horse with saddle can be recommended to a priest who lives in a hilly section. For mountainous sections the mule or donkey is recommended. A horse and wagon can be of great help to the country priest.

When time permits and there is no hurry, one should consider the old and apostolic means of locomotion (*"per pedes apostolorum"*). Affected by the full motorization of the time, people have almost completely forgotten that they can also move on foot, a form of locomotion which is accompanied by a form of healthful physical exercise.

No matter what means the priest uses, he should have as the basic principle: *"festina lente."* The speed compulsion of the times has also caused hygienic harm: on the one hand, the ever-increasing number of victims of highway accidents, and, on the other hand, the restless haste which calms the wild driver and which causes the wear and tear of nerve resistance and of health.

The diseases arising from wear and tear, the phenomena of premature breakdown, is a typical symptom of our times.

4. Nourishment

The principle that nutrition serves only for the needs of the organism and is not an end in itself is a principle that prevails for the priest more than the laity.

No strict asceticism is required of the parish priest, but he will be justly suspected if he exaggerates a good table and tends toward intemperance. Nothing forbids him from giving importance to good cooking in his parish house; the old saying, *"bona culina—bona disciplina,"* contains within certain limits his justification. No one will find fault with the parish priests who will celebrate with a festive meal the special feast days which also entail greater work for them.

That which interests us here is the standpoint of hygiene. We have already indicated that the sedentary life provokes the accumulation of fat and tends toward adiposity. This at times occurs in a degree that is injurious to health and can even constitute a serious danger to health. As we have indicated, adiposity is one of the causes of foot weakness. A vicious circle arises: when one becomes heavy, the feet are not adapted to the weight; since flat feet cause inconveniences, walking becomes difficult; since walking becomes difficult, one prefers to sit; and since one sits much and walks little, more fat will accumulate, etc.

Adiposity is also a cause of cardiac diseases. The heart itself stores fat within its muscular strata (*obesitas cordis*); the musculature of the heart becomes affected in its activity, but the cardiac

[1] Cf. GSH (1952).

muscles must work more intensely in order to furnish blood for the heavier body. Peripheral vascular disturbances arise especially in the capillary circulation; in time disturbances of hemorrhage in the coronary circulation are added; finally follow the already described conditions of the elevated diaphragm, the gastro-cardiac symptoms of stenocardia angiospastic states which finally degenerate into genuine stenocardia and, in the attack of angina pectoris, constitute a true menace to life.

To these dangers, conditioned exclusively by adiposity, there are added the damages which arise from too intensive work and living tempo of our times; finally the damages to the cardiac and vascular systems provoked by the effects of pleasure poisons of all kinds, especially through nicotine abuse. We shall discuss this later in more detail.

If the priest, besides tending toward sumptuous nourishments, also tends toward the enjoyment of alcohol, then his health is threatened by other vascular diseases, among which the first to be mentioned is that of blood pressure disease, the (essential) hypertonia. At one time one spoke of the calcification of the arteries (arteriosclerosis) and assumed that the primary vascular lesion consisted in the depositing of calcium on the vascular walls; these became fragile and tended toward local rupture with extravasation of blood (apoplexy). Such ruptures in the realm of cerebral arteries are to be especially feared (*apoplexia cerebi,* cerebral stroke). These can lead to sudden death if the hemorrhages are extensive and severe or are centered on vital centers.

Slight apoplexies, for the most part, absorb themselves; they leave more or less quickly passing paralysis of the arm, leg or speech musculature according to their seat, following the rule ("crossed") : if the seat of the hemorrhage is on the right side, the left extremities are paralyzed, and vice versa. He who has been once struck with apoplexy must always take into consideration the possibility of falling back into this at another time (*"semel apoplecticus, semper apoplecticus"*).

When there is a tendency toward apoplectic seizures, especially in the case of high blood pressure with attacks of vertigo, one has to avoid in nutrition whatever leads to congestion of the blood toward the head (congestions); above all, alcohol, coffee, excessive use of meat and strongly spiced foods. In case of subsisting fixed high blood pressure (essential hypertonia) it is necessary to have a diet which is as salt-free as possible. This is to be imposed especially when the essential hypertonia is accompanied by renal insufficiency (Bright's disease).

Kitchen salt provokes the retention of water and favors the gathering of abnormally large amounts of fluid in the intercellular tissue spaces of the body (edema). The danger of food with salt is mostly in the ions of sodium. One can follow a salt-free diet by preparing food without salt and then by giving the patient 2 grams of kitchen salt a day, which he must divide throughout the day. Since food with absolutely no salt cannot be tolerated for a long time and will be refused, one can make the food more tasty by using, in the place of mineral kitchen salt, vegetable products which have the same taste as celery salt and garlic salt.

Garlic and onion have been used from ancient times as an efficacious means against vascular infections and against diseases of the digestive organs, especially against flatulence and intestinal infections. From the hygienic standpoint, their use, if served in a fresh, natural state (thinly chopped with tomatoes or other salad produce), is to be recommended. A garlic cure is possible only if one is not constrained to meet people.

In modern dietetics there is attributed—contrary to the opinion of the past—greater importance to vitamins of vegetal origin than to nourishment rich in calories, especially that of animal origin.

The vitamins analogous to hormones—the products of glands with internal secretion—are enzymes, which in small quantities (practically immeasurable) exercise an intensive action upon the entire organism and are indispensable for the economy of the body. Their deficiency provokes the so-called deficiency diseases (for example, scurvy, rickets, beriberi, xerophthalmia, etc.).

Among the vitamins of animal origin, the most famous is that contained in cod liver oil. Besides fat of high value it contains predominantly Vitamin D (antirachitic vitamin).

Vitamin A is found above all in the green parts of plants (anti-xerophthalmic vitamin; antiscorbutic vitamin, i.e., Vitamin C); Vitamin B (antineuritic vitamin) is found in the shell of rice and grain. Vitamin C (important for its power of defense against infectious diseases—influenza, etc.) is found in the beet root, the ripened fruit of a rosebush, tomato, lemon, etc. Here we cannot go into the subdivision of every species of vitamin.

Calories represent the norm for the establishment of the combustion value in the various kinds of food. Since digestion is essentially a process of combustion (process of oxidation), heat is produced and this is measured in calories. A small "gram calorie" is the amount of heat required to raise one gram of water 1 degree C, i.e., from 15° C to 16° C. The (large) "kilogram calorie" is the amount of heat required to raise one kilogram of water from 15° to 16° C.

In regard to the production of calories, the proteins (meat, eggs, vegetables) and the hydrocarbons (flour, sugar, potatoes, etc.) have the same value (isodynamic); the fats have about double the caloric value. It is important to know that, when there is a tendency of accumulating fat, even the hydrocarbons should be limited as much as possible since they, too, in excessive quantity, produce a strong accumulation; especially to be avoided are white bread, sugar, potato and paste. On the other hand, meat in a moderate quantity is permitted, as also fish, greens, fruits and lettuce. The diet indicated for adiposity is very similar to that of diabetes *(diabetes mellitus),* in which the exchange of carbohydrates is disturbed.

Meats and proteins should be limited in renal diseases especially if there is an increase of residual nitrogen in the blood; that is, in case of insufficient elimination of products of the decomposition of protein on the part of the kidneys. That is especially so in the case of the so-called nephrosclerosis, of the so-called Bright's disease which for the most part begins with essential hypertonia and then leads to the maximum values of blood pressure (over 220 RR, that is, according to Riva-Rocci = mm of mercury).

The generalizing dietetic theories which, for example, recommend for all and indiscriminately "raw food"—theories which are unilaterally orientated toward vitamin content—are to be rejected; as is to be rejected any excess of the consumption of sumptuous foods which introduce an excess of calories in the organism, which, lacking a sufficiently physical elaboration, is not able to master it. In such cases "slags" are formed in the organism, that is, a residue of insufficient combustion which is not eliminated and cause disturbances in the economy of the body.

It must be mentioned, however, that the expressions "slags" and "reduction to slag" are abused since they constitute a useful means of facilitating the diagnosis and of giving the public the impression of deep knowledge on the part of the doctor in matters of modern dietetics.

In regard to scientific dietetics, one cannot remain silent to the fact that in no other branch of medical research has there been such change of opinions in the last decade as in this branch. If around fifty years ago extreme importance was attributed to "substantial" nutrition, i.e., nutrition predominantly rich in proteins, today the undoubtedly precious knowledge of the vitamin theory is generalized and exaggerated. As often happens, even in this matter, popularization signifies the degeneration of a theory that is *in se* correct.

In the incessant change of opinions of nutrition theorists only one principle remains valid for all time and which constitutes the true and proper nucleus of every hygiene of nourishment: moderation in food and drink. The entire hygiene of nutrition rests on this principle. One has to be able, especially when faced with a sumptuous table, to stop eating when it tastes best. This goes not only for eating but also for drinking, especially the drinking of wine. Wine, like every other nourishment, is a gift of God when used reasonably and in moderation; but it is a curse when one becomes a slave to it and cannot live without abusing it.

It is typical of every mania that people who have followed it to excess can no longer leave it, and it constantly increases so that one loses sight of the norm and falls into excesses. If all men could keep the norm, the hygiene of nourishment could be reduced to a few simple fundamental rules, among which moderation would hold first place.

5. Luxuries

A univocal definition of luxury cannot be given. The authors are, however, in agreement concerning this point, that luxuries are not used for the satisfaction of a bodily need (as food in general), but rather because they have a certain pleasant taste or because they effect a "stimulating" reaction.

a) GENERAL CONCEPT

It is not easy to indicate in what the "stimulating" effect consists, for example, in coffee, tea, alcohol, etc. It is predominantly the feeling of euphoria which especially arises after the taking of coffee and a glass of wine: an elevated feeling of life; also a feeling of well-being which is, for the most part, accompanied by the dilatation of the peripheral capillary blood vessels (as, for example, in the dilatation of the cutaneous vessels following a brief cold bath). Hence, in view of this physiological process, we may call auththentically euphoric those stimulants which have a vasodilatory effect; and as "unauthentic" those substances which have a vasoconstrictive effect, as nicotine: in an organism that is not yet acclimated it produces a reaction of severe shock (grave shock of the sympathetic nervous system). Only when it is accustomed to the nicotine does the organism demand it: if the poison is refused, unpleasant feelings arise, and these are eliminated only when it is taken again.

"Authentic" stimulants, i.e., euphorically active in a primary manner, are coffee and alcohol. If an excessive quantity is taken, a state of excitation takes the place of the euphoria, which finally (speaking of alcohol) gives way to a paralytic condition of the cerebral cortex (somnolence, sopor, coma). This is the order in which the various stages of alcoholic intoxication follow. It begins with euphoria and this it is that induces one to drink more, thus opening the way for the mania: the necessity of continuously seeking the stimulant without which one cannot live.

In stimulants which lead to intoxication the mania is increased by a further factor: when one awakens from the sleep of intoxication one experiences unpleasant feelings which can lead to the deepest depression (the so-called "lament of the cat"). The bad feature is that these unpleasant feelings are very quickly removed through a new intake of an intoxicating drink. In this manner is the fatal vicious circle closed and the fate of the one who has fallen prey to the mania seized.

This phenomenon attains the maximum intensity when it is a case of poisons belonging to the group of true narcotics: morphine, opium, cocaine, heroin. The same occurs with hashish (marijuana), etc. Here we are dealing with manias of stupefacients in the strict sense (narcomania). The demoralizing effects of the dope addiction and cocainism are well known.

Somewhat less innocuous—at least under the external aspect— is the addiction to alcohol. This addiction often begins with the tendency toward sociability, and facile and common distraction.

We have already emphasized the fact that moderation constitutes the essence of the hygiene of nourishment; the same must be said, and for greater reasons, when it is a case of stimulants. It is not necessary to have recourse to these in order to live; and in order to live it is necessary to renounce them absolutely; one should be able to live without them; one should never arrive at the point where he cannot live without them.

b) ALCOHOL

This applies principally to alcohol which in our society is the means of addiction par excellence. There are important differences according to the form in which the alcohol is imbibed: beer, wine, schnapps or mixed drinks (so-called "cocktails"). Every one of these forms represent a species of the "alcohol-culture," a "culture area" of alcoholism, insofar as one can speak of "culture"; in reality it is a matter of the decadence of the personality and its culture.

Beer-drinking is considered incorrectly as the most harmless form of alcoholism. Beer presents the advantage of quenching the thirst well; the disadvantage—especially during warm days—of making one very tired. One should, therefore, avoid beer-drinking during the day and reserve the same for the evening.

The chronically addicted beer-drinker tends to consume great quantities of beer and distinguishes himself by a strong tendency toward adiposity (beer belly), by an affability apparently "jovial," more exactly, by a dulling of the mind and spirit which leads to brutalization and diminishing of the higher spiritual power. Hand in hand with this there is often a very deep ethical decadence.

Symptoms of the organic deterioration found in the chronic beer-drinker are: hypertrophy of the heart (beer heart) and of the liver with parenchymetous damage ("drunkard's liver"), often resulting in shrunken liver (cirrhosis of the liver).

Wine, in general, does not quench the thirst but increases it. It can only eliminate thirst when mixed with ample mineral water. Wine-drinking seldom leads to the enormous consumption of the chronic beer-drinker. In cases of definite addiction it also leads to a rapid degeneration of the personality. The face of the beer-drinker becomes coarse and bloated while that of the wine-drinker presents a localized reddening (cheeks, nose); the eyes are floating (wine eyes).

The moderate wine-drinker gives greater importance to the quality rather than the quantity of wine. He prefers not to drink wine rather than drink a low-grade wine; he is not compelled to drink wine, but, when he does drink, it must be pure and natural wine. He would rather drink seldom and little than drink wine of low quality which causes disturbances of the stomach (heart burn, gastric acid).

Schnapps-drinking leads the most quickly to the decadence of the personality. The women generally show preference for sweet liqueurs—at times in the non-offending form of liquor bonbons; the men prefer unsweetened distilled schnapps among which cognac also belongs.

Addiction to schnapps is characterized by the fact that it demolishes very rapidly all moral inhibitions. The schnapps-drinker very often falls into the typical alcohol psychosis (delirium tremens, hallucinosis, Korsokoff's psychosis).

Extremely deleterious is the addiction to mixed drinks, imported to us from the new world. It assumes unlimited dimensions even in the feminine world; it is often accompanied by an uninhibited addiction to cigarettes. Even the schnapps-drinker very often succumbs to the deleterious effects of cirrhosis of the liver.

In the realm of the sexual life, alcohol exercises a stimulating effect on the libido and a paralyzing effect on the potency. This leads to the removal of inhibitions concerning prostitutes of the street and, as a result of protracted coitus, very often leads to venereal infections. Alcoholism, prostitution and venereal diseases are united by a close reciprocal causal nexus.

The effects of alcoholism from the social, economical and ethical standpoint are so devastating that the spiritual director cannot neglect the question of his stand toward this mania that has become quite prevalent.

It would be a rigorism not imposed by an objective norm to

require absolute abstinence of all priests without exception. That which is required as a minimum for every priest is a prudent moderation. He should at least be able to give the example that he can abstain from alcohol and that, when he takes wine, he is able to do so with prudent moderation, that he will never drink more than he can hold in maintaining complete control of all his faculties. Every priest should be able to do this, and he who feels that he cannot do this should not become a priest.

If the misfortune has already taken place and if a person who has not been able to control drinking has already become a priest, he will soon find his circle, which will praise the reverend father for his "joviality," which considers him a person who "knows how to live in the world," and with whom one can "speak so easily" —until he is discovered seriously drunk one or more times. From then on the priest loses the respect of the community. If the priest has become a compulsive drinker, there no longer is any restraint. Then there is only one thing to do: *principiis obsta.*

He who recognizes his weakness and knows that he cannot resist alcohol or cannot hold it because of an abnormal intolerance and who reacts pathologically (so-called "pathological intoxication"); he who has a tendency toward periodic attacks of dipsomania—for such as these there is only one way: absolute abstinence. Absolute abstinence is required for anyone who takes upon himself the task of combating alcoholism. He who wishes to champion a cause must himself give good example.

In no other manner can the priest engender more serious scandal and have others lose confidence in his message than by behaving in such a manner that it can be said of him: "He preaches water, but he himself drinks wine." Hence for any priest participating in the movement against alcoholism, definite and total abstinence is required. He must give the example that one can live—and live better—without taking alcohol in any form; that he can control himself and not take another drop so that he can be justified by a good conscience. Moderation and total abstinence are not antithetical, but they should complement each other.

c) NICOTINE

Contrary to alcohol and coffee, which we have designated as truly euphoric, nicotine is pseudo-euphoric. The reasons for this distinction have already been explained. To the circumstance, however, that nicotine acts only as pseudo-euphoric is to be imputed the fact that its use degenerates into a mania of such great intensity. It is for this reason that the feeling of nausea that it provokes in one smoking for the first time ceases only with one's habituation to the poison.

Nicotine causes, especially on the vegetative nervous system and blood vessels, such an enormous toxic effect that it can justly be considered as one of the most powerful poisons there is. A very small quantity—a fraction of a milligram of pure nicotine—can have a definite deadly effect.

The symptoms of acute nicotine poisoning are extremely dangerous: deadly pallor of the face, cold sweat on the forehead and face, slight, extremely frequent pulse, feeling of being close to death; in certain circumstances, vomiting and profuse watery diarrhea pertain to the first stages of the illness, typical of the young man who smokes for the first time in order to prove his "virility." If this first shock is overcome, the second time the vegetative nervous system will no longer react to the action of the poison because "habituation" has intervened—no reason for feeling proud since one has seriously disturbed the normal manner of reaction on the part of the vegetative system, and this disturbance of reaction persists as long as the habit of smoking continues.

Acute nicotine poisoning in adults only rarely becomes the object of medical observation; hence many doctors do not realize the severe and dangerous features of the disease and often do not believe that it can be so serious. Similar poisonings present themselves particularly after a long period of abstinence from nicotine; that is, when the vegetative nervous system has recovered from the habituation to nicotine; or, occasionally, in pipe smokers, when a drop of tobacco juice is swallowed. This tobacco juice is extremely concentrated and rich with nicotine: this is rapidly absorbed by the stomach and reaches the blood path. The deadly cases of nicotine poisoning which occasionally present themselves usually come through this unforeseen manner.

The moderately acute and chronic poisoning is found, above all, in cigarette smokers, who excessively surpass their daily quantity, or in occasional smokers of very strong cigars to which they are not accustomed. These poisonings through overdose manifest themselves in heart disturbances and restlessness, tremors, excitement and insomnia. The heart disturbances are associated with strong feelings of anxiety.

It is impossible to indicate in general the number of cigarettes that can be tolerated without damage and the point at which the danger of a poisonous effect begins. The tolerance differs from person to person, just as the disposition in the same person. Today the cigarette has extensively displaced the other forms of smoking (pipe, cigar) as well as the taking of snuff. The "triumph of the cigarette" has led to the present mass consumption.

The Austrian tobacco monopoly registered, in the latter half of 1953, a native consumption of 3,795 million cigarettes. The greater part of this mass consumption is attributed to women. The cigarette had first made women mass consumers. More than fifty per cent of the consumers are women smokers.

If one considers the price of a cigarette on the average as 0.50 schilling, then he will arrive at the complete figure of almost 2 thousand schillings for a half-year; 4 thousand schillings for a year —alone on cigarettes. This is an enormous sum for a poor land. Tobacco has become an important factor in the national economy, on an equal basis with alcohol. If, on the one hand, the many millions that are spent for smoking and the resulting economical gain from alcohol is disturbed—since so many people live because of the tobacco industry and the production of alcohol—the struggle against these elements would cause serious difficulty and strong resistance on the part of economy. A general prohibition of these products would lead to the unemployment of thousands of workers. One speaks correctly when speaking of a capital of alcohol; for the same reason one must speak of a capital of nicotine; in this sphere, the State, through monopoly, has reserved to itself the profit from these sources; it thus favors the addiction and does not combat it.

We have experienced that in a State without a tobacco monopoly statistical research was published from which it was gathered that lung cancer arose more frequently in smokers than in non-smokers. A short time later, in a State where a monopoly exists, experimental investigations appeared which tried to prove the contrary, but whose force of scientific proof was very scarce; these were based on laboratory experiments in which nicotine was injected in mice and rats. In the animals subjected to experimentation lung cancer was not found. On this basis it was proclaimed in great headlines: "Lung cancer is not caused by smoking." Evidently, in that section, because of the fear of pulmonary cancer, the consumption of tobacco had undergone a regression. Hence, it is clear that before experiments were made, the conditions were so formed that it was not possible to demonstrate a causal connection between pulmonary cancer and nicotine. Proceedings of this kind do not speak in favor of the independence of scientific research from the capitalistic interests of the State.

The nicotine mania produces more disastrous effects upon the complete organisms of the woman than that of the man. In women, the generative functions are specifically affected. And during pregnancy and lactation the child is seriously harmed. From the standpoint of a responsible social hygiene these ideas should become a common heritage of all women. Once the woman is addicted to nicotine it becomes more difficult for her than for a man to overcome this tendency.

How seriously this mania alters even the moral sense of responsibility is demonstrated by forest fires started every year by smokers who cannot do without smoking while in the woods and who throw a lighted cigarette away in a careless manner. This is also demonstrated by the explosions in garages and filling stations started by a cigarette carelessly thrown away. This type of behavior is justified by stating that there is a need for smoking "in order to calm the nerves." Nothing is more self-deceptive than the argument of the person addicted to nicotine that the cigarette "calms the nerves," for this overlooks the fact that the nerves are already shattered since the desire has become so irresistible that one can no longer live without cigarettes.

The spiritual director who takes to heart the *curia animarum* should, within his territory and by word and instruction, rise at least against smoking by women. He will put his "popularity" at stake much more today since the woman is an important factor in public opinion.

The spiritual director should not overlook the fact that the compulsive smoking of women, as a mass phenomenon, goes hand in hand with the problems of sex life. The effect of nicotine on the feminine sexual functions is negative; without doubt this is predominantly in regard to the normal sexual functions which serve the generative functions of reproduction. The *libido sexualis* which has been intensified through mania will be the less altered the more it deviates from the norm. A perverted sexual desire is increased more rapidly.

If the spiritual director is resolved to undertake the struggle against this addiction, just as in the struggle against alcoholism he is not to spare himself and should completely abstain from smoking. Only the way of absolute abstinence remains for him. We do not wish to generalize this requirement for all priests without extreme necessity. Even though it is so discouraging to see a priest smoke one cigarette after another, yet we do not want to fall into narrow-minded rigorism.

As in the past the pastor enjoyed smoking his pipe in his study, there is no objection against the peaceful enjoyment of a good cigar after an enjoyable meal and of a cigarette after coffee, when it increases the joy of work. But, if one smokes cigarettes, one should avoid the serious sanitary defect of "inhaling" the smoke. The cigarette-smoker claims that smoking without inhaling gives him no satisfaction, but this is a matter of auto-suggestion. The gustatory nerves are exclusively in the region of the mouth cavity. The epithelium of the windpipe and of the bronchial tubes, with their fine and finest ramifications, is absolutely devoid of all sensorial cells for the sensation of taste. Instead it presents to the action of nicotine an enormous enlargement of the surface of absorption; contrary to the pure "mouth smoking," the intake of nicotine is increased in many ways. Thus the poisonous effect is increased in an incalculable manner.

In regard to men, the struggle should be against the inhaling of smoke (and thus indirectly against cigarettes); for the women, against smoking in general. If women knew the seriousness of the damage that their reproductive organs undergo as a result of smoking, they might perhaps give up smoking. Against the powerful dictate of fashion any instruction manifests itself as powerless.

In the exposition of the problem concerning stimulating substances we have limited ourselves to two which today are practically considered the two most important: alcohol and nicotine. The corresponding consequence regarding the other luxuries arise *per se:* if a mania is not to be feared, there is no objection against the moderate use of euphoric stimulants as coffee, tea and chocolate.

Coffee and tea should be avoided in late afternoon and evening hours because they disturb sleep. The limit for coffee is 4 P.M.; and for tea, 5 P.M. Alcohol in moderate quantity can be harmless. In regard to stupifacients (narcotics) even the first attempt should be scrupulously avoided, for "with the first we are free, with the second we are slaves."

6. Clothing

For secular priests the hygiene of clothing presents no special problems; it is distinguished from the general hygiene of clothing only in a few points. On the other hand, the monastic habit presents hygienic problems of great importance.

The secular clergy wear a gown for official church occasions and solemnities. This gown is a long black outer garment, which reaches to the ankles *(tali)*. In Latin countries it is customary that the priest wear his gown on the street; and, as a head-covering, the flat round Roman hat is ordinarily used. In German and Anglo-American lands the priest wears, as a non-official piece of clothing, the soutane, which is not essentially different from the black frock coat. In such cases he is distinguished as a priest only through the collar: a white shirt collar, buttoned in the back and fastened to a bib, or rabat. A collar made of celluloid is hygienically undesirable; collars of material that can easily be washed are more practical. In the cold season the priest wears a dark winter mantle; in case of rain or damp weather, a mantle with a wide cape or a cloak. As a head-covering for winter some wear a black fur-lined cap; and for the summer, the so-called basque cap or beret or a straw hat of a dark color.

From the hygienic standpoint, there is little to say concerning the winter apparel. During winter everyone should keep the feet and lower part of the body warm. The wearing of woolen underwear (the so-called hunter's shirts) is less recommended than the wearing of porous underwear which, because they hold a great quantity of air, keep the body warm and at the same time airy. For the feet, cork-sock in-sole is to be preferred to the rubber.

Woolen gloves are a necessary part of the winter apparel: in greater cold weather woolen gloves without fingers are advisable. A priest who has to travel during very cold weather through the country by carriage should bring with him a foot sack and warm blankets. A travel fur also belongs to the winter outfit of the country pastor. A fur muff is very helpful in avoiding the freezing of the hands.

In the United States all the above cautions concerning the clothing of the priest are quite different. Since the chief means of transportation is the automobile, the above prescriptions concerning apparel are superfluous, since the auto, with heater, will eliminate all the winter weather difficulties.

From the hygienic standpoint the summer apparel presents problems. In many places it is customary for the priest to wear the same woolen soutane both for the winter and for the summer. This is justifiable from the economical standpoint, but, when this need not be so, frugality is out of place.

Whenever possible the priest should during the summer wear a light soutane of black color or dark grey. Even the black color on very warm and sunny summer days is burdensome enough since it absorbs the solar rays and does not reflect them. A black woolen soutane is an accumulator of heat in summer, and, if the air contains great humidity, there arises a dangerous accumulation of heat: the face turns from red to blue (cyanotic look), sweat covers the entire body—especially the face and head—and, in such circumstances, can very easily lead to heat apoplexy. This is encouraged by a very tight collar. Heat apoplexy and sunstroke are not to be confused with each other.

Heat apoplexy is based on the accumulation of heat which is verified when the humidity of the air impedes the evaporation of sweat which serves as the regulation of the body temperature. Heat apoplexy arises mostly from cloudy skies and humid sultriness.

Sunstroke, on the other hand, is caused by direct insulation through intense solar irradiation of the uncovered head. This produces a hyperemia in the region of the meninges, a meningeal irritation which manifests itself in numbness and headache.

One can protect oneself from sunstroke by covering the head, preferably with a large-rimmed straw hat. When there is danger of sunstroke, it is not advisable to remove one's hat. But against heat apoplexy one can protect oneself by taking off the head-covering at the proper time, by loosening any constraining clothing, by opening or removing the collar, and by avoiding any unnecessary movement. One can also protect oneself against sunstroke by placing a damp cloth on one's head which, through evaporation, produces a cooling effect. With heat apoplexy this is of little value since air saturated with humidity impedes evaporation.

If, when the air is humid, one feels dizzy and experiences black spots before his eyes, it is advisable to refrain from any movement and to lie down in the shade, with head resting high, and as soon as possible seek out a cool room. It is better not to wear linen clothing, certainly not to wear such close to the skin, i.e., without undergarment, since linen clothing, not being porous, does not absorb the sweat. This can easily lead to an accumulation of heat or to a severe cold.

In the summer time the socks should be as light as possible, but even these should be of very absorbing porous material. Material which does not absorb well, such as modern artificial material, can easily cause sweating feet.

The basic norm for summer apparel should be: the lightest and most porous material, comfortable shoes, a collar that is sufficiently large, soft and easy to open: a light and broad-brimmed straw hat, absorbent underwear that is easily washable (not woolen material). If the priest has to perform long and strenuous liturgical functions during sultry summer heat (e.g., Corpus Christi procession), the apparel under the heavy cope should be as light as possible.

If these directives regarding the garb of the secular clergy are observed—and they are not difficult to follow—then the assertion, that the clerical garb "is a mockery to hygiene" has no basis. We must consider this assertion more in regard to the religious habit.

7. The Daily Work

We refer here only to the work that the priest does every day and not to his true priestly functions. These elevate him above the banality of daily life even if, as in the case in the celebration of the Holy Mass and the recitation of the breviary, these take place daily. The divine service *in sacris* does not pertain to the daily work, even if celebrated daily. It is and always remains a solemn celebration.

a) THE DIVISION OF THE DAY

But the priest must daily do a certain amount of work which is tiring and which requires an enormous use of physical and mental energy—an amount of work which can be fulfilled only when one divides the day according to a definite *horarium*, the observance of which becomes a habit.

Although it is wise not to follow rigidly a definite program and thus to allow a certain elasticity, it is, however, important to bind oneself as much as possible to a definite order, once and for all, in regard to the more important daily tasks.

The priest is accustomed, because of the daily celebration of Mass, to begin his daily work early. Moreover, he has, since seminary days, been accustomed to an "early daily rhythm." This ordinarily requires that one retire early in the evening, but this is not always possible: study, correspondence, lectures and spiritual reading often occupy the priest until late in the night, so that his nightly repose is often reduced to a minimum.

Five hours sleep are to be considered as the absolute minimum which can be sufficient for quite a long time. One can certainly also do with three hours sleep for a few consecutive days—but only for a few days. Older men require less sleep than the younger men; younger men under forty years of age should normally have no less than seven hours sleep; men under thirty years will for the most part require eight hours sleep, and those under twenty years of age will require at least nine hours sleep.

The sleep of the older person is, in general, a lighter sleep; he awakens quite early in the morning, often around four o'clock, but is then tired before mid-day; toward evening time he is usually very tired and has need of going to bed early (the so-called "sleep of the old").

There are two basically distinct types of sleep, namely, the "morning sleep" and the "night sleep." There are, therefore, two types of sleepers: the "night sleeper" and the "morning sleeper."

The "morning" type is usually a "night sleeper": he is tired in the evening; he falls asleep very easily and attains the deepest sleep a short time after falling asleep. After midnight the depth of sleep diminishes greatly and toward morning the sleep is so light that spontaneous awakening occurs early. If one is awakened from such a sleep before midnight, it occurs with great difficulty, and the awakening reacts like a shock; and it takes a long time before consciousness is attained.

The "night" type is usually a "morning sleeper." He is very active only at evening time; he goes to bed very late, often after midnight; he falls asleep with difficulty; his sleep is superficial and restless in the early hours and reaches its maximum intensity toward morning. If he is awakened at this time, it is a long time before he overcomes the shock and, for the most part, he remains tired and beaten for the entire day.

The "morning" person attains the highest intensity of work in the morning hours; the "night" person often only in the late evening and night hours.

The "morning" type corresponds without doubt more to the normal "rhythm of life"; that of the "night" person is a type of the rhythm of life modified by the "influence of civilization." For the "morning" type, the sleep preceding midnight is not only "the better," but also absolutely necessary. It is less damaging for him to sacrifice one or more hours of sleep prior to midnight: it is just the opposite for the "night" type of "morning sleeper."

It is not only more hygienic, but simply necessary, that the priest belong to the "morning" type. The "rhythm of life" depends only partly upon the congenital and difficult modifiable constitutional characteristics; it is, for the most part, formed by habit and can be modified in the early years of life. The education imparted in the seminary can greatly contribute to the formation of life rhythm for the future priest. In later years the habit is so rooted that a change seems quite difficult.

The first two hours after awakening are, for the priest, a time of meditation, prayer, spiritual reading and divine service. The normal daily work begins after breakfast.

Breakfast, which is taken after the Holy Sacrifice of the Mass and Holy Office, should be substantial and plentiful. A good rule, recommended (but little followed) in America, is the following: breakfast for a prince, lunch for a common citizen, and supper for a beggar.

It is definitely not hygienic to go to bed after having had a plentiful supper, for this encourages an accumulation of fats. It is, therefore, advisable to have supper as early as possible.

In regard to the division of the day, their arises the question of the noon-day siesta and the best way of bringing to term the bodily functions of digestion. When it is possible, it is best to habituate oneself to bring to term the functions of digestion regularly in the morning immediately after arising. Whoever is able to habituate himself in controlling the vegetative functions can register an important hygienic success. The emptying of the intestine pertains to the morning toilet. When this is not possible, it is due in part to the lack of habituation and partly to the functional disturbances which become more fastidious with increasing age. We merely mention how disturbed the priest can become in the celebration of morning Mass if he has not beforehand fulfilled his bodily functions.

The question of noon-day siesta can only be resolved on an individual basis. For the majority of persons, especially for those advanced in age, it is almost an irrefutable necessity to repose a little after lunch time. This need of rest after lunch time is physiologically based on the fact that, after the taking of food, there is a greater flow of blood in the region of the digestive organs (the so-called region of the Splanchnicus nerve). The diffusion of blood from the cerebral vessels to the region of the Splanchnicus nerve produces an anemia of the brain which manifests itself in great tiredness and which calls for rest.

We have mentioned above that resting after meal time encourages the accumulation of fat; hence, we do not wish to recommend the mid-day siesta in general. Though it constitutes a beneficial break in the daily routine, above all, we do not recommend this to younger persons; and in no case should it be too prolonged. If it lasts more than a half hour, it is more harmful than beneficial, especially for those who tend toward adiposity, and it is these very persons who feel the desire of a long siesta. But even here one has to avoid the *circulus vitiosus*.

It is not possible to establish a general norm equally valid for all types of constitutions. An ancient rule states: *"Post coenam stabis—seu passus mille meabis."* It is a question that each individual has to resolve according to one's own individual disposition whether to rest after meal time or "take a thousand paces." A short and not too long a walk will certainly invigorate the young man of leptosome body structure just as the noon-day snooze is indispensable for the older person of pyknic body structure so as to restore the vigor for his postmeridian work.

Professor Hoff has recommended the mid-day sleep as a prevention against the damages of the disturbing and restless mode of life.

b) DIVISION OF WORK

To the rhythm of the morning life belongs the division of work in such a manner that the more important works take place in the morning hours, corresponding to the apex of the curve accomplishment. This does not mean that these must be the most strenuous works—by no means the most strenuous physical works. It is better to dispose of the work which requires greater capacity of concentration at the moment of the maximum of productive capacity.

Works that are physically more strenuous, for example, the care of souls in the high mountain sections, often constitute a relaxation for the intellectual worker. We therefore counsel the distribution of the more important work of the administration of the parish in the morning hours and reserve the external service for the afternoon hours.

For true and basic spiritual activity—reading of books and reviews, literary work, the editing of a parish bulletin or diocesan paper—there remain only the evening hours when the "morning" type person is tired out and no longer at the highest point of productive capacity. Then there exists the danger of protracting the work into the late evening hours and thus inverting the rhythm of the day and, consequently, the type of sleep.

He who goes to bed late after difficult intellectual work will find it hard to fall asleep; the curve of sleep levels in the first half and deepens in the second half and begins to become like that of the "morning sleeper." If the danger of the *circulus vitiosus* is present, it must be concluded that evening work, tolerable as an exception, cannot absolutely become the rule.

Intellectual work also represents an expenditure of intensive physical force. Exact measurement of the loss of weight associated with the various works has been undertaken; and it has been concluded that in intensive intellectual work the loss of weight is not less than that verified in physical strenuous work.

The greatest mistake that the intellectual worker can make is that of remaining stimulated by coffee or tea toward evening time when a great tiredness overcomes him. The result is that he is unable to sleep, and then seeks refuge in a soporific. Thus the curve of sleep deepens only in the morning when it is time to arise. And so one remains tired during the morning hours; the curve of performance reaches such a deep point by evening time that one cannot do without a stimulant. So coffee is again taken toward evening time, and after midnight a soporific is again taken and, from day to day, the *circulus vitiosus* increases until one day there is a complete nervous breakdown.

This complex of circumstances presents for the priest grave dangers which are increased further through overwork brought on by the present lack of vocations. The dangers to health presented by overwork cannot be eliminated completely but can be reduced to a bearable measure by an efficient distribution of work. In regard to the distribution of work the same prevails as in the case of the division of the day: it should not be pursued with rigid pedantry, but should possess a certain elasticity and should allow a certain margin; otherwise every unforeseen change, even the slightest, can disturb the whole program of the day. The lack of priests and the overburden of work are at present the chief causes of the enormous consumption of strength. Even here a vicious circle develops: one evil produces another, and both reciprocally aggravate their effects.

The enormous consumption of work strength exposes the organism to sickness never before exposed. Moreover, the ever-new tasks which the priest has to fulfill do not give him either time or tranquility for the interior life and meditation, of which the priest has greater need than anything else and which represents the fructifying source of the inner life of the soul. He suffers in ever-increasing measure from aridity and lack of elevation and, at the same time, he barely has the strength to contribute to the elevation of others in helping them bear their manifold miseries and of being an enlightening guide of souls.

Many methods of the modern care of souls are more apt to

increase deficiency as to diminish it: they effect more a vast dispersion rather than a necessary coordination of strength, and, hence, nothing more than an increase of external activity.

The activity dedicated to the care of souls in the parish has been transformed into an "operation." A certain success in the care of souls was intended in subdividing the parishioners into various groups and by having their own particular "spiritual conferences." So there are conferences for the school children (for whom religious instruction should suffice) : for boys, for girls, for men, for women, etc., and each of these groups is entrusted to one individual priest. The author once experienced in a large parish the announcement of twenty-four different groups of spiritual conferences.

The ravishing of energy associated with such an "operation" on the part of the spiritual director would be tolerable if such a method of systematic division were justified through success. But the results at the present time seem scarce.

At least at a time of scarcity of priests we cannot approve such a dispersion of energy, especially in consideration of the health of priests and of the conservation of energy for their work. Sickness associated with the inability to work is more frequent today than in the past even among the younger priests.

c) LARGE CITY AND COUNTRY

As great as is the difference between the work of the doctor in a large city and that of the doctor in the country, so great are the differences that arise between the activity of the spiritual director of a large city and that of the country pastor.

There is a tendency to hold that the activity of the large city spiritual director is more intensive than that of the country priest. This could have been the case a few decades ago. The incessant process of urbanization even in regard to the spiritual director has not stopped. The country priest is confronted by the same problems that have made life difficult for his city confrere.

The eradication of religion from the masses of people is at present also a phenomenon of the country; here the antireligious orientation is often stronger—at least more noticeable—than in the large city. On the contrary, in the city—at least in the circles of ancient culture—one can already notice a strong movement toward the return to religion, especially in academic circles. It was from these circles that the movement of defection started, which today, after a decade, has also affected the country folk. These circles are today the first to find their way back; from them the example should be drawn which will influence the less cultured to come back, just as their example led to the defection.

The general movement of defection has removed a contact between the priest and his community. This loss of contact has placed the pastor in a state of isolation which, in the case of psychic liability, can act as "neuroticizing trauma." This can occasion a feeling of inferiority and insufficiency and can lead to depressive states or ideas of persecution.

From this point of view the spiritual director of the large city has an advantage over the majority of country pastors. That which renders spiritual care in the city difficult is the tension of the life tempo and the many obligations which is a burden to the priest: he has to hold conferences in all possible circles and at times be present for the same; he has to take part in the cultural management of Catholic spiritual life.

The university town with the theological faculty, the seminary, work in Catholic formation or a Catholic academy, Catholic charities and Catholic Action, diocesan film office—all have need of his counsel and cooperation. The result is very often a dispersion of precious energy, which is prematurely brought to exhaustion.

We have not yet mentioned the very laborious task of preaching. Once the priest has attained fame as a preacher, he no longer has peace until he has given his all.

The country priest, on the other hand, has to cover long and hard roads; he lacks the means of communication found in the large cities; often at night he has to climb on foot the roads of high mountains, and this with great danger in order to assist his parishioners. In order to accomplish this difficult task he has to possess robust health. The author recalls a pastor from the mountain section of Vorarlberg whom he accompanied one Monday of Pentecost during a snowstorm to a mission church in the mountain section. During the Mass of Pentecost the pastor was assailed by a shivering fit; with difficulty he was transported to his rectory suffering from inflammation of the lungs. Later he succumbed to the effect of this forced march. Nine months of winter and three months which are by no means summer months—this was the climate described by the pastor. The avalanches often precipitated down to the vicinity of the rectory, and because of this he was called the "avalanche pastor" by his confreres. He was one of the noblest priests the author has known.

From the hygienic standpoint it is difficult to say who has it more difficult—the big city priest or the country pastor. This depends exclusively on circumstances. The author has had the opportunity of knowing country pastors who led an idyllic life of a better time and could lead a truly meditative and tranquil existence; but even this oasis of peace has become rare in our time.

Today both have it difficult in their own mode of life: the large city priest and the country pastor. Both ways of life require great energy and solid health which will not succumb under the pressure of daily work.

C. Free Time and Recreation

From what has already been said, it seems clear that the concept of "free time," which was regulated by the legislation of labor as a right guaranteed by law to all manual laborers, in reality does not exist for the priest. For him even Sunday, a day of freedom for the workman, does not exist. Prescinding from the fact that the meaning of Sunday represents sanctification and demands upon the priest and can certainly mean for him also a more intense supernatural source of strength, we must evaluate primarily from the purely natural and hygienic viewpoint the inestimable hygienic-social importance of free Sunday. Alfred Fischer [1] stated with reason that, if we knew nothing else about Moses but that he was the first to announce the commandment of God regarding the sanctification of the Sabbath, this fact would suffice to consider him *as one of the greatest social hygienists.*

Modern man has almost forsaken the due solemnization of Sunday. We can really say that we do not have Sunday any more! Instead of recollection one seeks "distractions," often of a questionable nature. Sunday is transformed into a day of excesses— excesses in traffic accidents, excesses of an alcoholic and sexual nature. The work week begins on Monday not with rested strength,

---

[1] *Grundriss der Sozial-Hygiene,* Karlzruhe, 1928.

but with exhausted energy particularly after the double festive days. The efficiency curve of Monday is the lowest; the accident curve is the highest of the entire week.

If rightly applied, the Sunday rest would be the most complete recreation for all; it cannot be replaced by the "week of five days," especially when alternate changes are made, in which case there is no longer a true day of rest. The absolute Sunday of rest in England, against which many objections of an "economical" nature have been made, has in itself, with its deep silence, something extraordinarily restful.

It is definite that the priest never has "free time," never a "free evening," in the sense understood by the manual laborer.

He can concede himself—generally seldom enough—a short vacation. If he can do so every three weeks, that is really much, but in his working circle he does not have a free day. On the vigil of a great feast there is an increase of penitents for confession; the festive day itself requires more liturgical functions, greater demand of celebration (bination, etc.) and preaching activity, so that the priest, when it is possible, takes a short vacation immediately after the great solemnities.

From the hygienic standpoint we shall welcome the day when the present burden of priests will be relieved by an increase of the number of priests. If only the priest could have at least an hour of rest from his daily activities in order to restore his physical and psychic energy.

A short vacation can never compensate the harm to health that arises from the rush and ceaseless work of every day, so much more so since immediately after vacation the tempo is increased in order to make up for the arrest in work.

The duration of vacation time should be regulated according to the following norm:

Age	Weeks
20 - 30	2
30 - 40	3
40 - 50	4
50 - 60	5
Above 60	6

For the most part, the priest can take his vacation only during school vacation, at least when he also gives religious instructions at school. This constitutes a difficulty inasmuch as during the "high season" all tourists' places are crowded, quarters are difficult to obtain, and are, besides, more expensive, especially in the large health resorts.

It would be wonderful if certain health resorts would reserve a spa hotel for priests in which first-rate treatment is given, so that all means of care could be offered within the place, and this at a reasonable price. Institutions of this kind, very beneficial, should be established in all the large spa hotels.

Since vacation time is for the benefit of health, it should be designated according to age and condition of health. The younger priest is less inclined to spend his vacation at a health resort. If he lives in the lowlands, he will go to the mountains; he will go to the sea when he lives in a mountain section or in the city. He might accept the hospitality of a fellow priest and show his gratitude by celebrating Mass and preaching or betake himself to a cloistered vacation home where he will be treated hospitably. The older priest would do well to spend his vacation at a health resort in order to remove the gradual injuries to health.

These few examples will suffice as a general outline.

D. The Priestly Functions

1. The Sacrifice of the Mass

The priestly functions are not included in the designation of daily work. Even if the most important of these, the celebration of the Mass, takes place every day, it does not pertain to daily work. The functions are a solemnity in the highest and deepest sense; the Sacrifice of the Mass is one of the greatest sources of strength for the priest, a true fulfillment of himself.

Through his offering, the kingdom of the supernatural and grace penetrates the daily life of the priest; the ferial day of the priest is sanctified in a special manner so that, for the true priest, there are no such days as "ferial days."

No matter how grinding the daily work might be, the priest in this *"in serviendo consumor"* offers himself in sacrifice: *sacerdos et hostia* become one.

There is no doubt that daily celebration of Mass is difficult. It is, however a definite source of strength, but only for the priest who offers the sacrifice with pure heart and pure hands. When this is not the case, the pressing feeling of guilt becomes a source of serious neurotic disturbances.

In another section of this work, the author has brought attention to the "celebration neurosis," especially to that form which arises from a feeling of repressed guilt, which has been designated as "amfortas complex."

The author knew a young priest who seemed to have been affected since childhood with a serious neurosis. He suffered from a serious celebration neurosis. He seemed to remain at a standstill at the Offertory and would go no further; from the Canon on he seemed overcome with anxiety and shook all over bodily. He dared not begin the Consecration and, once begun, he repeated the same over and over until, finally, under extreme intensification of the tremor, he could finally pronounce the words of Consecration. After the Consecration he seemed a little better; however, before the priest's Communion the tremor appeared again, but in a milder form. It took him almost an hour and a half to say a low Mass. It took four hours for the recitation of his breviary.

This serious neurosis was lessened only when the priest, through the advice of the author, received psychotherapeutic treatment from a famous Catholic psychiatrist. We add with pleasure that the unfortunate priest was completely and permanently cured, but we do not know just how much the sacramental means of grace added to the psychotherapy in effecting this cure.

Even without neurotic complications the daily celebration of Mass can be felt as a serious burden. When the priest has to celebrate Mass daily all during the winter and early each morning in a very cold church, his position is definitely not enviable.

Because of a lack of priests there often arises the obligation of bination, i.e., the repeating of the celebration of Mass one or more times a day. Ordinarily bination is forbidden; it can only be an exception and not a rule. But this exception will become more necessary the less priests there are to fulfill all the Mass obligations.

Besides the sacrifice of the Mass, prayer and meditation are great sources of spiritual strength for the priest. They deeply affect the pious and wise priest so that he does not seek to acquire strength through mundane and natural means, but through supernatural means. "Seek you first the Kingdom of Heaven and all things shall be added unto you."

2. The Confessional

Sitting in the confessional and hearing confessions constitutes for the priest one of the most strenuous functions and requires great psychic force. From the purely physical standpoint it is an enormous strain to sit for hours and hours in the confessional, especially during the winter time. The hands and feet freeze if there is not the possibility of warming oneself through any heating process.

During bitter winters the priest should, while hearing confessions, have at least a blanket for his feet and gloves for his hands that leave his fingers free and, in that regard, mittens which can be put on and taken off easily. As long as the priest is free in the confessional, he will usually spend the time saying his breviary. Hence he should at least have his fingers free in order to turn the pages of the breviary.

Whatever is to be said from the standpoint of bodily hygiene in regard to the confessional, particularly concerning the prevention of contagious diseases, has already been stated in another chapter.

From the mental hygienic standpoint it is to be observed that no other activity entails so serious and so numerous psychic burdens as the hearing of confessions.

When he is confined—at times for many hours—in the hearing of many miseries and spiritual difficulties, in leading the penitents to a firm purpose of amendment, in the encouragement of the penitent and directing him to a better life, the confessor must use mental energy; and after giving to others, he feels as if he were "unloaded." Even deciding when absolution should be denied can constitute a serious mental burden for the priest. One must possess strong mental health in order to sustain this without losing courage. He who is neurotic is not able to sustain such strong demands for a long time.

In particular it is to be noticed that he who has not as yet resolved all sexual difficulties will experience a grave burden in the hearing of confessions. In confession he listens to the problems of marriage with its tragic difficulties; he listens to all the errors and failures and must remain calm.

The priest is lost and finds himself exposed to the most serious calumny of supposed "solicitation" if he even in the slightest manner allows it to be noticed that even he is only a man who has to wrestle with the instinct of nature. He must be careful when he has to ask delicate questions, even though necessary, which can be easily interpreted in a wrong manner. "For one who is pure, all is pure"; the impure and those of bad intention, on the other hand, will always find something to interpret badly. No priest, no matter how pure and noble he is, can feel safe in the presence of bad-willed misinterpretation.

The author has known in his practice not a few female penitents who, as malicious hysterics, have directly attempted to excite the priest by narrating in the confessional filthy stories which would require the asking of questions, which, in turn, were repeated by these hysterics to others in a very vulgar manner. They would go from one confessional to another, and many of them were known and feared as the "terror of the churches." Thus arose for the most part the "confessional stories" very willingly circulated against the priest. This is the recompense for the sacrifice of physical health and mental strength whose nature only a few lay people could ever comprehend. Only the doctor, who is often called upon by the priest for advice in pastoral medicine and who in his practice has learned to discern the "malicious" penitent as a truly hysterical patient, can have an idea of the serious psychic burden imposed on the priest in his duty to gather even these "poorest of all the poor."

3. Preaching

A wonderful but difficult function of the priest is also that of preaching: the announcement and explanation of the word of God, associated with the task of guiding the souls of the entire community.

In itself, preaching is an exclusively sacerdotal function. Already with diaconate the *venia concionandi* is conceded in the act of the bishop consigning to the candidate the book of the Gospels. In practice, however, the deacon, before sacerdotal consecration, rarely appears in the capacity of preaching without the assistance of someone else. The office of preaching is a task of great responsibility and, hence, in practice remains reserved to the consecrated priest. The question of the suitability of deacons to preach would be more actual if married religious leaders of other sects, converted to Catholicism, could serve the church in the capacity of deacons. If this were so, in the Roman Church the celibacy of the *ordines maiores* would have to undergo a limitation, and would thus be reserved solely to the *sacerdotium*. These, however, are only suppositions.

Even the office of preaching places great demands upon physical and mental health.

From the physical standpoint, frequent preaching constitutes an enormous strain. The same intense demand on the voice, with the variation of temperature conditions, can cause irritations and catarrh of the vocal cords (laryngitis). Once established, these disturbances are very difficult to eradicate since one must continue using one's voice.

He who has to preach often, as is the case with directors of souls in large cities, would do well to pursue a course in technical oratory. In this way he would learn to obtain the maximum vocal effect with the minimum use of effort and to use of acoustical conditions in the best possible manner.

Even in the large churches it is not necessary to preach in a very loud voice; this would not only cause strain but would lead to a rapid exhaustion of the voice. One can learn to make oneself clearly understood, even in large places, with a moderate intensity of voice. No greater strain should be put on the voice than is necessary. Moreover, even for beginners, it is no longer difficult in making oneself heard since microphones can easily be installed.

The use of loudspeakers—as with every technical innovation— presents the disadvantage that one no longer learns, by means of voice culture, to speak clearly and well, even without this technical help. The art of speaking tends to fall into deterioration.

On the other hand, the art of speaking should not be exercised in such a way that it becomes the most important matter, so that speaking artistically degenerates into rhetoric and poise, and the priest is thus transformed into an actor. This is a danger that very easily affects the famous preachers of the big cities. When a priest becomes the "preacher of fashion" in the "great world," judgment concerning him is inspired by mixed feelings.

From the psychic standpoint, the preparation of a good sermon constitutes a burden inasmuch as it requires many hours of the week.

Though the beginner should usually be advised to remember the sermon, word for word—that is, memorize—the more advanced preacher would be more effective if, after having completely elaborated the same, he would briefly outline a schema, then speak freely by following this outline.

The greatest defect of a sermon is that of being too long. Today people living in large cities do not easily tolerate hearing long sermons; their restless activity does not permit them to sit calmly, to listen, and, least of all, to reflect.

The length of a good sermon should not exceed a half hour. The sermon of beginners can easily surpass this limit, but, if it lasts too long, the beginner will finish with exhaustion.

The disciplined preacher, who has great control of his theme, can say many things in fifteen or twenty minutes. This oratorical discipline is learned very well at international congresses, where it is necessary to say as much as possible in a few minutes and where there is no greater mistake than to talk beyond the allotted time.

Moreover, in order to evaluate the mental activity of the preacher, we cannot find a better description than that given by the pastoral doctor and hygienist, Stöhr. He brings attention to the rapid exhaustion of the capacity of activity brought on by a too intensive activity of the preacher, and continues: "The priest gives us . . . the greatest multi-colored and scented flowers of his spirit formed into a garland. He offers us the most pure and noble pearls from the depths of his soul . . . and such gifts are not formed too often without exhausting oneself." [2]

We would like to confirm from our own experience the warning that Stöhr gives after having indicated the best use of vocal means and of the capacity of the lungs: "How often have we not experienced the sad outcome of a young preacher with great talent and in the flower of possibilities gifted with magnificent vocal means who, exhausted and worn out before his time, has to abandon the

---

[2] Stöhr, *Pastoral Medizin*, Herder, Fribourg, 1909, p. 249.

pulpit. How easily this could have been avoided if the fiery orator could have been advised from the first day of his career and fore-warned of the incumbent danger." [3]

The warning of pastoral hygiene should be rightly understood and well accepted. It does not wish to impede the progress of the gifted preacher, but solely to conserve as long as possible the precious strength of the preacher.

4. Other Functions

Among the specifically sacerdotal functions, exorcism, the faculty of casting out devils from the obsessed *(obsessio),* is that requiring a greater explanation from the standpoint of pastoral hygiene.

The power of exorcism is transmitted at the reception of minor orders. In the last decades the practice has arisen whereby solemn exorcism is exercised only in rare cases and by a priest especially prepared for this task and expressly authorized by the diocesan bishop.

The special preparation consists, above all, in the exact under-standing of the psychopathological borderline cases. There is no doubt that in the past many cases of hysteria and psychopathy were considered as cases of diabolical possession and were treated by exorcism. On the other hand, it is quite certain that definite cases are considered as merely psychopathological in which there is at least a participation of the devil as a causative factor. In these borderline cases, in order to distinguish where the psychopatho-logical element ends and where the diabolical begins, a special experience and complete control of this difficult matter is necessary.

The Church runs a great risk when exorcism is applied in cases in which it is simply a matter of an hysterical person desirous of making himself interesting—apart from the possible harm to the health of the apparently possessed person through a fixation of the "devil neurosis" (Freud), and to the truly possessed person through "induced insanity."

In 1936 the author, together with a professor from the clinic and a professor from the medical faculty of Graz, pursued in the Wagner-Jauregg Clinic the evaluation of a "possession" case for the ecclesiastical authorities. It concerned a woman about fifty

[3] *Ibid.,* p. 244.

years old who became the town character. She demanded that the bishop himself fulfill the solemn exorcism before the people of the town. Through the advice of the pastor she was invited to the clinic for observation where it was not difficult to show that she was simply a case of hysteria. She played the part of a person possessed merely out of need to be of worth and in order to receive attention. But unmasking of the hysterical person does not always take place.

Essentially more serious and more difficult to judge was another case in which the author was called upon during the National-Socialistic regime to give an evaluation in another diocese. It concerned a nun who had not manifested even the slightest symptoms of hysteria or psychopathy. She had been a surgical nurse in a large hospital for many years, not making herself too noticeable or inspiring great confidence. Suddenly typical attacks of demonomania became manifest in her. During calm intervals she was in perfect order and declared that the attacks of possession were expiatory sufferings. A woman doctor who examined the patient superficially stated that the attacks were purely of an hysterical nature. The author subjected the patient for three days to an accurate observation during numerous attacks and examined her during the time when she was not subject to these attacks and thoroughly explored the past history of the patient.

From these examinations there resulted not the least element which could justify the diagnosis of hysteria, of psychopathy, or of any form of psychosis. The attacks were extremely impressive, and it seemed that they were much more serious than those associated with the case that was stated above. Since the patient, even during the attacks, made prophecies which were very unfavorable toward the then reigning regime, she was transferred, by order of the Gauleiter, to a mental hospital in Bavaria. There the doctors were instructed that as soon as she manifested the slightest symptoms of a psychosis, which would be "a dangerous element to the people," she was to be transferred for "special treatment" to one of the institutions of euthanasia.

Even though the doctors were *a priori* rather opposed to the patient, they were not able to find even the slightest indication of a psychosis. After a long period of observation, she was dismissed from the institution, but was not allowed to return to her convent.

By order of the Gauleiter she was exclaustrated and sent to her mother and there betook herself to farm work. Even here the attacks occurred from time to time. Since, according to the author's opinion, it was not possible to find any medical explanation of the attacks and these "were not naturally explainable," it was advisable that an attempt be made to exorcise her. But this was not possible because of the hostile interests of the then reigning powers.

The problem of possession pertains more to the scope of pastoral medicine than that of pastoral hygiene. The norms for establishing an extranatural diabolical intervention are the same as those followed in ascertaining a supernatural miraculous healing. For this purpose the fundamental rules of evaluation elaborated at the Bureau des Constations Médicales de Lourdes, under the direction of Boissaire, Le Bec and Leuret, are decisive: first, exhaust all possibilities of a natural explanation, and only then substantiate it with the formula: *"Cette guérison (Maladie) naturellement n'est pas explicable."*

It is easy to understand how the general psychic situation of our times represents a sphere of action favorable to diabolical manifestations. If we properly understand the principle, *"gratia supponit naturam,"* then we shall also see how such a deep disturbance and a destruction of the natural order, as are those which characterize our times, present for demoniology a basis for the opposition of grace, and can exercise greater opposition than it could exert in times of order. Such knowledge can be of great importance to mental hygiene when, in this sphere, it would realize its import.

II. HYGIENE OF THE LIFE OF RELIGIOUS ORDERS

A. Special points concerning the life of the Orders

The same hygienic principles prevail for the religious as for the secular priest; they must only become integrated by certain considerations suggested by the specific elements of the monastic life.

Above all, it must be remembered that the religious Orders do not consist merely of priests. There are male orders and female orders and female branches of male orders (so-called Second Order).

In the male Orders we then distinguish religious priests *(patres)* and lay brothers *(fratres)*. The latter do not possess priestly powers, although they assume an important meaning in the life of the Order. In certain female Orders there is a distinction between the choir sisters and lay sisters.

The female branches of monastic Orders (so-called Second Order) are actually the Benedictine nuns, the Cistercians, the Franciscans, the Dominicans and the Carmelites.

The *vita communis,* the life in common according to a rule, and the monastic vows are the characteristics which distinguish the members of religious Orders from the secular priesthood.

1. Monastic Vows

a) GENERAL CONCEPT

The three general monastic vows are poverty, chastity and obedience. To these may be added a special fourth vow which confers on the Order its specific characteristic; for example, in the Jesuit Order the vow to be at the disposal of the Holy Father at all times and for any request.

The general monastic vows are normally taken only for a determined time: "temporary" vows. Only after a period of probation of several years are the "perpetual vows" taken. The temporary vows, just as the perpetual vows, can be taken solemnly or simply *(votum solemne vel votum simplex).* The canonical diriment impediment to marriage—besides Ordo and hence even for *laici*—is only the solemn vow (C. 1073).

With perpetual vows the religious becomes a member with full rights of the family of the Order. The Order constitutes a quasi-family. From then on the Order takes the place of the natural family in all points. To solemn profession is attached the symbolism of dying to the world; such references are still found in the rite of profession. At one time profession juridically removed the professed from his family and, in regard to his civil juridical capacity, he was considered as dead.

In regard to the three general monastic vows—poverty, chastity and obedience—the following is to be especially considered:

The vow of poverty is relatively the least burdensome: it obliges the professed regarding the renunciation of all private property.

Whatever belongs to him belongs to the Order. Whatever belongs to the Order belongs to all. It is a species of ideal communism which characterizes life in the Community.

In many Orders the custom still prevails in which the professed brings along a dowry since, at his entrance, the Community assumes the obligation of providing for him until death and of providing all that is necessary for life: shelter, clothing and nourishment as well as medical care; and whatever added expenses might accrue in any eventual hospitalization, and finally, for his burial.

If any priest becomes guilty of a *peccatum contra VI praeceptum,* he sins not only as anyone else, but his sin is a double sin, because it is also a sin of *sacrilegium.* The consequences are therefore more serious: exteriorly because of scandal, and interiorly because of severe guilt feelings of unworthiness ("Amfortas complex"). When, however, it is a matter of the vow of chastity, there is added the infraction of the solemn vow in which the entire personality is offered to God *("suscipe me!").*

The vow of chastity delves deeper into the human personality than the vow of poverty: it is the absolute and total renunciation of any use of the vital instinct of the conservation of the species, an instinct whose power is felt acutely by anyone who attempts to dominate it merely by natural means and improper means of repression or suppression. We realize the difficult and destructive neurosis that can arise when this instinct is not resolved.

The proper resolution of this conflict rests neither in repression, suppression, nor also in the mere sublimation according to the meaning of Freud. It rests more in the compensation of the instinct through a higher love of God which permeates the entire personality and without which the monastic life would be a dead external form without content, without a formative power understood in the sense of the Scholastic *forma.*

This compensation is to be essentially distinguished from the "transformation of the libido" in the meaning of Jung. Jung attributes to these matters a literally opposed meaning: for him, any religious aspiration is nothing else but transformed *libido sexualis;* thus the primary element "primate of the libido" is formulated by Jung in more dangerous manner than that of Freud.

In order to be correctly interpreted these associations are to be understood in the contrary sense: moved by the "primate of

God's love," even the human libido, when properly inserted in order, acquires its rightful place in the hierarchy of values.

Only by being moved by the love of God is it possible to actuate the difficult renunciation of the vital forces requested by the vow of chasity: he who has experienced an authentic calling to the monastic life and is imbued with a strong love of God which transcends all things—for him the observance of the vow of chastity is no longer a humiliating and tormenting struggle against the instinct, which is experienced only as the dominion of the devil.

In him reigns peace; for him all is understood in itself: "I can do all things in Him who strengthens me" (St. Paul, *Philippians*, 4: 13); for him prevails the words *"Ama, et fac quod vis!"*

It is such that these phenomena can no longer be understood in a purely natural manner; in order to fulfill such a difficult task, the strength of the supernatural, of grace, is indispensable. Hence, for those "who have made themselves so for the Kingdom of Heaven's sake" it is said, "let him accept it who can" (Mt. 19; 12).

Of the three monastic vows, the vow of obedience is that which delves even deeper into the human personality; it signifies the renunciation of one's freedom of decision. It places all decisions in the hands of the superior as in those of a father (or of a mother, in the female Orders); and he who observes it accepts them from these hands in humility and with absolute resignation.

If the vow of chasity contains an absolute dedication of the physical person to God, that of obedience signifies the absolute dedication of the spiritual person. It is for this reason that the vow of obedience is the most difficult of the monastic vows; and it is more difficult the stronger the spiritual personality of the one who has made this sacrifice; but it is certain that it is more acceptable to God the higher the worth of the personality which is offered in sacrifice.

This renunciation is relatively easier for the "poor in spirit." Thus many humble lay brothers fulfill in silence and with simplicity their daily duties; for them the way leading to sanctity, because of their simplicity, is much easier and more secure than for many personalities endowed with great spiritual characteristics, for whom pride can become a temptation and a weak point for the assaults of the devil who, in order to snatch the sacrificing victim from God, mobilizes all his powers, and this more intensely the more precious is the victim.

The author has witnessed the failure of priests due to spiritual pride. On the other hand, he has also seen examples of edifying humility. A religious priest who for a long time was very close to him was greatly endowed with spiritual gifts, especially in Canon Law; he could have become the glory of any university faculty. Nothing was more repugnant to him than the raising of funds and economic problems. And he was selected by the General of the Order as Provincial Procurator and in this capacity was to direct the administration of the province for many years; later he was elected Provincial and also exercised this difficult office in splendid manner. Exemplary was his humility with which he condescended to be removed from his favored scientific work and become burdened with tasks for which he had little inclination.

If one perceives these matters merely with the eyes of the world, one will not clearly understand. It is, however, more desirable and useful to take into account the natural dispositions and inclinations. But the norms of monastic life are different from those "of the world." The glance of the religious is not focused on earthly "activity," but on eternity. Hence, the criteria of hygiene are limited in judging the monastic life if it be considered only from the standpoint of health.

2. The Rules of the Orders

While the monastic vows are based substantially on the "evangelical counsels" (cf. Mt. 19, 20-23) imparted by Christ Himself, the rules of the Orders are based on a constitution which the founder of the Order has given to his family.

a) GENERAL NOTES

The monastic Orders developed at first in the Orient. The Anchorites retired in solitude in the desert ("fathers of the desert," "Stylites"), they later gathered into communities (*cœnobium*, cenobites). The first great founders of Orders were Antonius, Pachomius and Basilius.

St. Benedict of Norcia (543) formulated the Benedictine rule whose well-known principle is *"Ora et labora."* The most important duty of the monk is, according to St. Benedict, the *Opus Dei: "cui nullum aliud opus praeferendum est."*

Besides the Benedictines (O.S.B.) themselves, the following live according to the Benedictine rule: the Cistercians (O.Cist.) and their branches of the *"strict observance,"* the Trappists, and the Camaldolese Hermits who constitute a particularly strict branch of the Benedictines.

The Augustinian rule is attributed to St. Augustine. It prevails both for the regular canons and the Augustinian Hermits.

The Mendicant Orders (Mendicants) constituted in the thirteenth century a strong religious, social and spiritual movement. To them belong the Franciscans (O.F.M.), with their branches (Minorites, Capuchins), and the Dominicans (O.P.).

The Dominicans, the Order of Preachers, became in a special manner the center of the theological-philosophical science of the Middle Ages, particularly because of the works of the "Prince of Scholasticism," St. Thomas Aquinas, the pupil of St. Albert the Great. The Dominican Order, with its motto *"Veritas,"* was for centuries the bearer of systematic dogmatic-theological science.

Proper to all regular Orders is choral prayer, the *Divinum Officium* of the recitation of the Breviary prayers in common, whether according to the *Breviarium Romanum* or the Benedictine *Breviarium Monasticum.* The Benedictine Order, besides prayer, fosters work, study, meditation, and especially the liturgy both in the solemnity of Mass and in the *Divinum Officium.* Gregorian chant is used as the liturgical chant.

To the rules of the Orders also belongs the *clausura,* i.e., the most possible strict isolation from the outside world. No woman may enter the cloister of males, and no man may enter the cloister of females without special permission. Exceptions are made for doctors and for those performing urgent manual work. A very rigorous cloister prevails in the Order of the Carthusians (O.C.), of Carmelites (O.C.D.—"discalced Carmelites"), especially in their female branches.

In medieval times there were Orders of women who, according to their rule, were absolutely separated from the world by means of a wall (the so-called "recluse"). The Carthusians are accustomed to sleep in their own coffins.

Among the more recent religious institutes which arose after the Reformation, the following are to be especially mentioned: the Jesuits (S.J.), the Redemptorists (C.Ss.R.), the Lazarists, the Society of the Divine Word (S.V.D.). There are predominantly missionary religious institutes. Specific religious institutes for the care of the sick and teaching religious institutes arose as active in contradistinction to the contemplative religious institutes which formerly prevailed.

Among the religious institutes dedicated to the care of the sick, the following are especially known: The Camillians (O.S.C.), the Mercy Brothers of St. John of God, the Mercy Sister, the Elizabethians, the Vincentians and the Borromeans. Among the teaching Orders are the following: the Ursulines, the English Dames, the Brothers of the Christian Schools and the Sisters of the Christian Schools, etc.

In recent times a "lay movement" has developed which attempts to realize the monastic spirit even in the world, in the sphere of worldy professional duties. The so-called "secular institutes" request of their members the observance of definite vows, without living in a religious community life. They state that they live "in the world" even though they are not "of the world." Hence they are not distinguished from other lay people by any distinct religious habit or dress and for the most part manifest an unobtrusive sign whereby they recognize one another. Without doubt this movement can give impetus to the renewal of religious life in the world.

The positive aspect of the lay movement of the "secular institutes" is evident in the fact that, despite the abandonment of the traditional forms, which are certainly more than mere "external forms," they basically affirm the internal essence of the monastic life. Certainly, this movement is also an undeniable expression of a crisis of the monastic life in our time, but it is more than a simple crisis of the new generation. Naturally, the crisis of the new generation is the more tangible and evident aspect of a general critical situation and is a symptom that is serious and dangerous.

As regards the cause of this crisis and the means of overcoming the same, much has already been written and spoken. In this regard we shall recall only a few significant opinions.

Several nuns have taken a stand regarding the problem of why among young girls of our time there are few vocations. They are not merely negative criticisms of an immature youth that affirms that the monastic life as a whole is "out of date," that it is not adapted to our times, that it "scoffs hygiene," etc. In the objections which are posited in modern times against the monastic life, there are many erroneous judgments which require an intelligent and appropriate correction.

The objections in no way touch upon cloisters in their entirety and not even the Orders of nuns who suffer more intensely under the crisis of the new generation. In definite contrast to the statement that modern youth rejects the form of cloistered life as such, there is the statistical proof that the contemplative Orders with strict cloister register more vocations than active Orders.

In our time the convents are, in general, a model of cleanliness and neatness; the nuns are people of the twentieth century and realize the importance of hygiene in their personal and community life. The nuns, as infirmarians, nurses, teachers and even as office workers, have had the opportunity of profiting from the modern techniques offered to their lay collegues. How could they fulfill their work without observing the prescriptions of hygiene which have become a necessity?

Nevertheless, we should heartily welcome a healthful reform movement or, better, an authentic renewal movement, especially in the female religious Orders: a movement that would be truly "open" to all innovations, insofar as it is a matter of such needs of our time as have true worth, but that would also hold tenaciously to all that is truly precious in ancient traditions (not however to strict "traditionalism"), to whatever is truly essential and necessary.

That which matters is the essence and the spirit of the religious life; it is a matter of preserving the essential without precluding opportune innovations so long as these leave the essence intact. Whatever is true and genuine should be kept and accepted without preoccupation of whether it is "old" or "new." In fact, this is not the problem: it is a matter of a contrast between the old and the new generation.

If by "modern" is merely understood a form of life which is incompatible with the monastic life, then it is properly in this and not in the "old-fashioned approach" of the Orders that the gap exists between secular and religious persons. Surely the sincere objections of youth are to be taken into consideration. When this is not impeded through self-righteousness, then even young people will again begin to take serious consideration of religious vocations.

In considering the formative and didactic possibilities within the Order, the widest point of view possible should be followed; the requirements of modern hygiene can and should be followed as long as they are justified, tenable and compatible with the religious life. It will then be revealed that in the case of the most ample adaptations to the hygienic requirements, hygiene itself can not have the last word, especially when it is a matter of fundamental questions of the ascetical and mystical life. Despite all efforts, it will never be possible to avoid this in the sacerdotal and monastic state; weakness and human errors play a disastrous role. By striving to conceal this fact, and thus doing violence to truth, vocations will not be obtained; the critical conditions should be openly admitted and discussed.

Religious cannot and do not wish to claim to themselves a special Christianity. They wish, however, to ordain all their life solely to God and the Kingdom of God in a manner clearer and more unconditioned than that of lay people too burdened by the world. The more naturally they care for true humanity, the richer will the supernatural life flourish in them and the more copiously will they bear fruit.

The natural life need not become warped and destroyed by the monastic life, but can through the supernatural life become enobled, enriched and perfected in the highest manner. In fact, even in this regard the great words of St. Thomas prevail: *Gratia non tollit et destruit, sed implet et perficit naturam.*

b) MONASTIC RULES AND EXERCISES

The spiritual life in the cloister and in the world is modeled on the treasures of ancient wisdom which represent a perfect mental hygiene and originate from an era which did not know this word, yet was mentally healthy.

As examples of these treasures of wisdom we present two works selected from the major spiritual works: *The Rule of St. Benedict,* that is, the rule of the Benedictines, and the *Spiritual Exercises of St. Ignatius of Loyola.* It would be a profitable task also to peruse other famous works of the spiritual life as, for example, the *Imitation of Christ* of Thomas à Kempis and the *Confessions of St. Augustine.*

(1) *The Rule of St. Benedict*

In *The Rule of St. Benedict* we find a quantity of great riches and depth, especially in the following chapters:

4. The Means toward Good Works *(Quae sunt instrumenta bonorum operum)*
5. Obedience *(De Oboedientia)*
6. Silence *(De Taciturnitate)*
7. Humility *(De Humilitate)*
20. The Respect of Prayer *(De reverentia orationis)*
22. The Sleep of Monks *(Quomodo dormiunt monachi)*
23. Punishment and Excommunication *(De excommunicatione culparum)*
28. The Incorrigibles *(De his qui saepius correpti emendare noluerint)*
30. The Education of Youth *(De pueris minori aetate qualiter corripianture)*
36. The Sick *(De infirmis fratribus)*
37. The Old and Children *(De senibus vel infantibus)*
39. The Measure of Food *(De mensura cibi)*
40. The Measure of Drink *(De mensura potus)*
41. Meal Time *(quibus horis oportet reficere)*
42. Silence after Night Prayers *(Ut post completorium nemo loquatur)*
48. The Daily Manual Work *(De opera manuum cotidiana)*
49. The Observance of Lent *(De quadragesimae observatione)*
53. The Acceptance of Guests *(De hospitibus suscipiendis)*
54. The Acceptance of Mail or Gifts *(Si debeat monachus litteras vel aliquid suscipere)*
57. The Artisans of the Monastery *(De artificibus monasterii)*
58. The Discipline of Novices *(De disciplina suscipiendorum fratrum)*
66. The Pastor *(De hostiariis monasterii)*

67. The Brothers on Journey *(De fratribus in viam directis)*
71. Reciprocal Obedience *(ut oboedientes sibi sint invicem)*

Much could be stated concerning these chapters; the following will suffice:

In Chapter 4 the following are primarily emphasized: to love God with all one's heart, with all one's soul, and with all one's strength; to love one's neighbor as oneself. Then follows the commandments of God; then the principle: do not do to others what you would not have them do to you *(quod tibi non vis fieri, alio ne feceris* [Tobias, 4]); to deny oneself in order to follow Christ; the corporal and spiritual works of mercy; to have death every day before one's eyes *(mortem cotidie ante oculos habere);* not to cherish much talk *(multum loqui non amare).*

In Chapter 6 the love of silence is exalted.

In Chapter 22 the common dormitory is recommended in which each should have one's own bed.

In Chapter 36 the care of the sick is to precede all other things; the sick are to be served as if they were Christ Himself *(infirmorum cura ante omnia et super omnia adhibenda est, ut sicut revera Christo, ita eis serviatur).* The sick are to be bathed as often as there is need for the same *(balneorum usus infirmis quotiens expedit offeratur).* The sick may have meat to eat even when it is prohibited for the healthy, provided it is needed to restore their strength (cf. 39); the same prevails in regard to wine (cf. 40).

In Chapter 48 manual work is prescribed since idleness is inimical to the spirit *(otiositas inimica est animae; ideo . . . occupari debent fratres in labore manuum, certis interum horis in lectione divina).* This chapter contains the indications for the division of the monastic day.

In Chapter 53 is found the famous sentence that the guests are to be received as Christ Himself *(hospites tamquam Christus suscipiantur).*

In Chapter 69 the position against private friendship is taken *(privatas fugiant amicitias).*

In Chapter 73 the essence of the rule is summarized in the words: *Ora et labora*—prayer and work are the two birds that lead to perfection. *Opus Dei atque opus laboris duae sunt alae, quibus conscenditur ad perfectionem.*

(2) Spiritual Exercises of St. Ignatius

If *The Rule of St. Benedict* is the basis for the monastic life in common, the *Spiritual Exercises* represent for the secular priest and the lay person, as well as for the religious priest, the basis for individual asceticism.

The exercises, extended over thirty days, comprise principally the following practices:

1) In the first week: the general basic truths; the special and daily examination; the general examination of conscience (general examination); general confession and Holy Communion; meditation on sin; meditation on the separation from God.

2) In the second week: meditation on the kingdom of Christ; the Incarnation, the birth of the Lord; meditation on the life of Christ; consideration of the different states; the great meditation on "the two banners" (the banner of Christ and the banner of Lucifer); the Sermon on the Mount; the Resurrection; the three degrees of humility; the choice.

3) In the third week: meditation on the Last Supper; the death and agony of Christ in Gethsemane; the mystery of the Passion of Christ.

4) In the fourth week: meditation on the Resurrection and the apparitions of Christ. Contemplation concerning the acquisition of love. "Rules for the Distinguishing of Spirits."

It is a grand "dying and becoming" that is interiorly accomplished in these exercises. In any case, the *Spiritual Exercises of St. Ignatius* represents a masterful work of psychological soul guidance and a basis for soul healing.

c) LITURGICAL LIFE AND RHYTHM OF LIFE

The investigation of the laws pertaining to the "Rhythm of Life" is one of the tasks of hygiene, the importance of which has been recognized and highly appreciated only in recent times.

The first law is that of the "periodicity of the vital functions." This depends, on its part, upon the physical laws of the undulatory movement. It seems to be a basic biological law that the vital functions do not flow in a linear course, but that even their continuity manifests an undulatory course. The most common graphic

expression of this course is the sine curve. Numerous examples of
the rythmic course of the more important vital functions can be
deduced from human physiology. In this regard the following are
examples: respiration (inhalation—exhalation); cardiac activity
(Systole—Diastole); peristalsis of the stomach; the cycle of the
female generative process (ovulation—menstruation).

In the course of human life we distinguish a daily rhythm, a
weekly rhythm, a monthly rhythm, a trimestral rhythm, an annual
rhythm and even a higher rhythm.

The daily rhythm is based on the alteration of day and night, of
waking and sleeping, and demands an alternation, in conformity
with nature, of work and rest. Even the daily rhythm can be well
represented by means of a sine curve: its negative vertex (minimum) is found at midnight (Nadir); the positive vertex (maximum) at noon (Zenith). The hour of six in the morning and that
of six at night indicate the points of conversion of the side of the
curve. This normal rhythm is deeply impressed in the natural
rhythm of human life. If, because of need and extraordinary activity, this is disturbed for a short time, it would take two or three
days before the disturbance vanishes under the form of "suppressed
oscillations" and the normal rhythm is reestablished. This point
sufficiently demonstrates the importance of living in a regular manner. Hence, in the face of brief disturbances there is an extensive
capacity of adaptation.

One of the most pernicious effects of the rhythm and custom of
modern life is that the division of the day no longer follows the
natural rhythm of day and night. In the alternation from work to
rest, the time allotted to the latter is too brief. The renewal of
strength can no longer keep pace with the breakdown of strength.
This leads to the sickness of exhaustion which is typical of modern
life. If there is an habitual "exchange of night into day," in time
there will arise a total inversion of rhythm. Even when the inversion
is only partial and not total, if it lasts too long, it will lead to the
inversion of the type of sleep (inverted type).

We have already indicated the difference between the type of
sleep found in "morning" individuals and in the "nocturnal" individuals and also have stated the hygienic importance of sleep
before midnight, and even of the value of the morning hours for
the person participating in intellectual work.

When the principal burden of professional work is distributed during the hours of the day, the morning-type individual is more productive. It is just the opposite in the professions in which the principal burden must be protracted late in the night (journalists, waiters, musicians, etc.).

The examination of professional attitude must also consider these elements, and should likewise not ignore the practice of marriage counseling.

The weekly rhythm is based on the introduction of the day of rest after six days of work, according to the biblical statement: "on the seventh day God rested" (Gen. 2:2). Man, besides physical rest, is also in need of psycho-spiritual "relaxation" or, better expressed, of increasing mental energy from spiritual sources of strength.

Besides the active life, even the contemplative life must be considered. A day of the week should pertain to the Lord (*dies Dominica,* the day of the Lord)—to religion, that is—rejoining of man with the prime cause of his existence.

We have already indicated the necessity of learning anew to sanctify Sunday. If we have then presented the question particularly from the hygienic standpoint, here we must emphasize the religious aspect. The true santification of Sunday depends on it. Quite different is the spirit in which man today "enjoys" and does not sanctify his "week end." It is for this reason that on Monday he is not invigorated for new work, but is exhausted.

The struggle against the ordinary week of seven days is the expression of a very dangerous tendency. There is the attempt to offer all the workers a day of rest after five days of work, not to all the workers at the same time, but in five alternate workdays. In this way every day is a work day and there is no longer a general festive day; the noise of work proceeds without any pause.

In a society of total collectivism there is no place for the elevation of the soul of the individual toward the primary Source of Life. The result of such a disturbance of the natural rhythm of life is an absolutely shapeless, restless and collectivistic humanity. In the person of the masses there is no longer a place for the personal experiences of life nor of a force and intangible sphere of individual personality.

(1) Monthly Rhythm, Annual Rhythm

The monthly rhythm manifests itself in a special manner in the lunar cycle of twenty-eight days of the woman.

According to Fliess the male's rhythm of 23 days corresponds to this female rhythm. Such rhythmic courses of life apparently make a strong impression on man. It is probable that the phenomena of intersexuality are accompanied by an interference of these two rhythmic waves.

The man who is close to nature experiences the monthly and annual rhythm more deeply than the large city dweller. Each month has its own character. This influences the sensitive life more distinctly the closer man is to nature.

For modern man, astrology is the surrogate for the attachment to nature which he has lost. He finds access to the vital rhythm of nature only through the zodiac symbol and its relation to alchemy ("month's stones") which extends to *magia nigra.*

The yearly rhythm manifests itself primarily in the change of seasons (*quatuor tempora;* hence, Quatember). Worthy of note is the parallelism between the annual and daily curve and their concordance with the curve of human life.

After the lowest point of winter, even the curve of human life rises with the springtime, the rising of the sap flow of the trees. The highest point of the summer solstice is followed by the fall in autumn up to the winter repose. Designated by a curve, both solstices represent the vertex; the summer solstice, the positive vertex; the winter solstice, the negative vertex. The two equinoxes are the conversion points of the curve and in the parting from these toward the positive part, day prevails, and toward the negative part, night.

Even this oscillation is felt more deeply and more intensely by the person close to nature more than by him who lives in the big city. In the annual rhythm man experiences the rhythm of his life on a small scale. The farmer experiences it in a more immediate manner. In the *Oratorio,* "the four seasons" of Haydn, these experiences find expression in classical form.

For the farmer, spring, summer and autumn are the seasons of more intense work, while the winter season is a time of rest. In the life of the modern city this natural rhythm has been reversed:

summer has become the time of vacation. But this also has its advantages which we at the present do not wish to forego.

Besides the annual rhythm there are still other higher rhythms (periods), the study of which has been of great service; especially the research done by Fliess and Svoboda has studied in a special manner the meaning of the seven-year period ("the week of years" of ancient Judaism) for the human life. Besides the periods which represent a variety of 10, 25, and 50 years (so-called "jubilees"), there is also a 33-year period to be considered. It corresponds to a generation, that is, to the average difference of age between the "parental" generation and the "filial" generation. Hence, within the sphere of a century we can count three generations.

The curve of human life runs in an unmistakable analogy with the curve of the year. The "normal curve" (or, better, ideal curve) is disturbed by the various influences on life. Interruptions and flaws can appear both in the ascending as well as in descending side of the curve. The points of conversion of both sides of the curve (analogous to the equinox of spring and that of autumn) represent puberty and the climacterium. Both are critical times; puberty in particular for the male, and the climacterium for the female.

But man is not merely a biological being; he is also a spiritual being. In this regard it is quite an astonishing fact that in persons given to intellectual activity it is observed that the curve of the intellectual life continues to rise, while that of the biological life tends strongly in a downward direction. In this striking fact is also expressed the reciprocal relationship between potency and act.

Besides the general law of periodicity the curve of human life is also subject to a law which regulates the individuality of the rhythm phases. Thus, even in the course of life every moment is unique and irrevocable; no minute, no hour of life is like the others, as the sun, the moon and the stars incessantly change their "constellations" in regard to the earth, and no part (of the world's clock) is completely like the others.

A reform of the calendar which would tend to "coordinate" every year in a continuous unchangeable monotony (so that each date of the year would always fall on the same day of the week and the moveable feasts would become "fixed") would be an error, since it would not take into account a fundamental law of nature: in every year each day has its own particular character and every year has, in turn, its own irrevocable character. When we thus establish, besides the law of periodicity, also a law of individuality, we do nothing more than listen to the voice of nature.

According to the law of analogy between the orders of being *(analogia entis)*, the natural order stands in a certain relationship to the supernatural order. In the natural order the harmony of the supernatural order must find its own image. Thus the day of rest after six days of work is an image of the day of the Lord's rest after "the works of the six days"; and thus, in this, every "day of creation" bears its own character.

It is certain that man is by nature a social being, that is, ordained to a life in the community with being like himself. But he is also a rational being with the essential characteristics of a free personality. This has its own individual rhythm which can unfold itself so much more undisturbedly the more perfectly it adjusts itself to the complete rhythm of life.

In the military column on march, every "false step" causes a disturbance, but in civilian life the symmetry of the collective march required by the community cannot extend to the point of disturbing the individual rhythm of the personality. It is often the most precious and creative personalities which break down under oppression and pressure of the masses of people.

(2) *The Liturgical Rhythm of the Year*

The liturgy (from: λητον ἔργον = *munus publicum*, public service) is, according to its nature, the celebration in common of the *Divinum Officium*, of the Holy Mass, and of the *Officium* in the strict sense, according to a rigorous order, corresponding to the ecclesiastical year, always recurring, but not always absolutely the same. After having established the laws of the biological rhythm (periodicity and individuality), it is very informative in finding the same laws in the rhythm which, concerning the ecclesiastical liturgy, is introduced in the sphere of the ecclesiastical year. In it the grand law of the analogy between the order of being is continually expressed.

Analagous to the course of the four seasons *(quatuor tempora)* we find the solemnity of the "four times" with their deep lessons and the four sections of the *Breviarium Romanum: pars hiemalis, verna, aestiva* and *autumnalis.*

The ecclesiastical year terminates on the last Sunday after Pentecost (XXIV) with the Gospel concerning the end of the world (Mt. 24: 15-35) and with its exalted and conclusive words, *"Caelum et terra transibunt; verba autem mea non transibunt."* The new ecclesiastical year begins with the succeeding Sunday which is the first Sunday of Advent with practically the same Gospel which ends with the same words, but which opens a hopeful outlook: "But when these things begin to come to pass, look up, and lift up your heads, because your redemption is at hand" (Lk. 21: 25-33). Thus ends the cycle of the year harmoniously as the Christmas hymn chants: *"currens per anni circulum."*

Significant is the position of certain feasts of the year, for example, the feast of St. John the Baptist, the precursor of Christ, which is celebrated exactly six months before Christmas: at the highest point of the year, the "solstice," and from then on the days become shorter: "He must increase, but I must decrease" (John 3; 30), spoke John of himself and of Christ.

The birth of the Lord is celebrated during the winter solstice, during the darkest time of the year, that is at the moment in which the sun slowly begins to rise upwards again. The peculiarity of this negative vertex of the annual rhythm was perceived by the cult of Mitra *("dies natalis solis invicti"),* just as the Germanic feast of the winter solstice perceived the symbolism of the birth of the sun god, Baldur, who was apparently struck dead.

But even a deeper penetration is made into the unique rhythm of the ecclesiastical year from which such wisdom and clarity irradiates upon the ordinary life, if one considers not only the rhythm of the year, but also the daily and weekly rhythm and allows oneself to be carried by the same. We find priceless treasures of such wisdom in the canonical hours of the Church, in the "hours" of the Roman Breviary.

The daily hours contain psalms, lessons and hymns. The psalms are so distributed in the individual days of the week that in the course of the week all of the 150 psalms appear, and each day of the week has its own impression. The variety of the hymns of each hour express in a marvelous manner the rhythm of the day: the course of the rising and setting sun and, finally, nightfall. *"Septies in die laudem dixi Tibi"* (Ps. 118, 164)—seven times a day we give praise to God; this is the fundamental law of the canonical hours.

The first canonical hour, Matins, was originally celebrated at midnight (*"media nocte surgebam ad confitendum Tibi"* (Ps. 118, 62). Between three and four in the morning followed the first morning praise, Lauds; around six o'clock in the morning (the first hour of ancient Roman computation), the solemn prayer of the morning, Prime *(prima hora);* at nine o'clock, Tierce *(tertia hora),* at 12 o'clock midday, Sext *(sexta hora);* at 3 p.m., Nones *(nona hora).* At 5 P.M. followed the solemn evening chant of Vespers. At 6 P.M. the office of the day ended with the night prayer of Compline. After the recitation of Compline a very strict silence was imposed in the cloister.

In this original order, both the daily work and the night rest were interrupted every three hours. At present, "Matins for any good reason, may be anticipated on the previous afternoon, starting not earlier than 2 o'clock." "Lauds, since it forms morning prayer, is said early in the morning in choir and in common recitation; and it is fitting that this be done also in solo recitation."

"The Canonical hours of the Divine Office are arranged to effect, by their makeup, the sanctification of the several hours of a natural day. Therefore, it is preferable, whether for actually sanctifying the day or for reciting the Hours themselves with spiritual profit, that in the recitation one observe a time which closely approximates the true time of each Canonical Hour. However, to satisfy the obligation of reciting the Divine Office, it suffices that all the Hours be said within the 24 hours of the day." (*"Rubrical Breviarii et Missalis Romani," AAS* 52 [Aug. 15, 1960]).

The text of the "small hours" (Tierce, Sext and Nones) remains the same for the entire year. The "long hours" (Matins, Lauds, Prime and Vespers) present for each day of the week, as for the different seasons and feast, psalms and lessons that are different and impart even differing hymns.

Thus, throughout the course of the year, there is elevated a solemn crown of prayers, chants, lessons and meditations, always changing in such a manner that a permanent frame constitutes the stable element in the continuous change, and no day is completely like the other, which eliminates monotomy: *"Qui temporum das tempora, ut alleves fastidium "*

From the numerous liturgical hymns we mention only a few as examples of the daily rhythm:

1. Matins
   Nocte surgentes vigilemus omnes. . . .
2. Lauds
   Ecce, iam noctis tenuatur umbra, lux et aurora rutilans coruscat. . . .
3. Prime
   Iam lucis orto sidere. . . .
4. Tierce
   Nunc. . . . Flammescat igne caritas accendat ardor proximos.
5. Sext
   . . . Splendore mane illuminans. Et ignibus meridiem.
6. Nones
   . . . Largire lumen vespere quo vita nusquam decidat
7. Vespers
   Iam sol recedit igneus
8. Compline
   Te lucis ante terminum
   Procul recedant somnia
   Et noctium phantasmata

Even if these hymns were nothing more than a representation of the complete poetic expression of the daily rhythm and the rhythm of life, for this reason alone it would belong to highest poetry of the world's literature. But they are more since they are expressions of human life inserted in a superior order; of a harmony of existence which represents a perfect model even for mental hygiene.

B. Particular Hygienic Questions

1. Sanitary Requirements

Since life in a religious Order imposes upon the health and capacity of the religious greater essential burdens than those imposed through the priesthood upon secular priests, it would seem that the requirements in regard to physical suitability should also be greater.

In regard to physical health and according to our experience as medical evaluator, we cannot hold this view in an absolute manner.

It should certainly be required that lay brothers and sisters who have to perform heavy manual labor (in the house, garden, kitchen, fields, etc.) be in good physical health. It is clear that the cloister is not a refuge for weaklings who could not fulfill their employment in the world. For religious priests and clerics who ordinarily fulfill their studies in an institute within the Order, it is not necessary that the health requirements be more extensive than those for the secular priesthood.

In cases in which, on the judgment of competent authority, the existence of a true vocation is held, it cannot be the duty of the medical evaluator to impede the acceptance of a candidate because of health considerations. When we consider a case as that of St. Bernadette Soubirous, it would appear that her acceptance should have been refused on the basis of health: she was definitely affected by a form of tuberculosis which, after a short time, provoked a tubercular "fungus" on the knee.

In the case of tuberculosis it is necessary to ascertain accurately whether and to what extent the morbid process permits life in a community. In the case of "open" tuberculosis, i.e., expectoration with positive finding of Koch bacilli, the doctor cannot assume the responsibility of conceding acceptance since one single individual tuberculosis-spreader can infect a whole community. Even the superiors who decide in the last instance on the acceptance can, in such cases, scarcely assume the responsibility of not considering the warning of the doctor. There are, however, few cases of physical illness in which the doctor has to refuse acceptance in such a decisive manner as in that of open infectious tuberculosis.

But, in regard to mental health, the requirements should be more stringent than those required for suitableness in the secular priesthood since life in a religious Order presents higher spiritual requirements. Life in a religious community is, of its nature, fundamentally more difficult than life in a rectory. It demands much more in regard to the position of the individual religious in respect to his confreres and his superiors which is not required of, for example, the position of the curate in respect to the pastor, fellow curates and even the housekeeper. If worse comes to worse and one cannot live together with others, one can always separate. But this is impossible in the monastic life. The decision of entering an Order is definitive and binds the religious to the cloister for life.

One must, therefore, be doubly cautious and avoid the acceptance of psychopaths and hysterics into the religious Order.

We have already alluded to the difficulties that even one psychopathic priest can create for his ecclesiastical superiors and how he can endanger the discipline of an entire diocese. We add to this the fact that the author has often had the occasion to observe how a single hysterical nun was able to upset a whole community, and how her example can present a danger to the mental health of some of her psychically labile fellow-sisters.

A special danger to every cloistered community is presented by cases of *psychopathia sexualis* under which all tendencies toward an abnormal direction of the instinct are to be understood. We refer especially to certain constitutional forms of homosexuality. We are far from considering every form of homosexuality as constitutionally conditioned *(in via endogena);* on the contrary, our experience has demonstrated that the majority of cases, which we had to evaluate medically, have for the most part been caused exogenously through seduction. But this does not alter the fact that there is a form of constitutional homosexuality.

The simple predisposition toward a homosexual tendency does not necessarily mean that this tendency will actually become manifest in action. It can remain *in potentia* without ever leading *in actu* to a homosexual action.

Not rarely we encounter persons of high intellectual and moral fibre who are deeply unhappy because of their predisposition and who are completely aware that every manifestation of their tendency would place them in conflict with penal law and would bring disgrace upon themselves. Yet they wage heroic battle against their instinct and the dangers associated with it.

When the question arises concerning the suitability of such a person for the secular priesthood, the author has no doubts in declaring such a personality of high moral fibre as suitable for the sacerdotal state despite the presence of this unfortunate predisposition. In certain cases, the author has motivated his viewpoint to those interested and to ecclesiastical authorities in the following manner: priestly celibacy imposes the duty of renouncing the activity of the sexual instinct, whether this instinct is normal or abnormal. It is not the abnormal disposition as such, against which nothing can be done, which renders one unsuitable, but only the manifestation of the same. Finally, when one is a priest, one must renounce even the normal sexual instinct.

But the author has given a more severe judgment concerning the suitability of candidates for the monastic life.

In a cloister, individuals with homosexual tendencies are exposed to a greater danger since they live in closer contact with persons of the same sex, and these are the very ones who appear to them as desirable sexual objects. In cases of this nature it is absolutely necessary to refuse the candidate acceptance into the monastic life, both for the benefit of the candidate as well as of the entire community. The supreme norm of mental hygiene regarding the cloistered life should therefore be that all psychopaths, hysterics and abnormal personalities be refused entrance into the cloistered life, so that peace and the religious life will not be disturbed. The harm that is effected cannot be remedied so long as the defective personality remains in the cloister.

2. Regulations Regarding the Cloister

The essential directions regarding the construction of the cloistered edifice have already been indicated. We shall here indicate briefly some of the more important points regarding pastoral hygiene.

We have already spoken of the hygienic needs regarding the kitchen and refectory. Naturally, even in these places cleanliness is the supreme commandment. The floors should be easily washable, but not cold. The cellar compartments should be as dry as possible.

The lavoratories and wash rooms should correspond to the requirements of modern hygiene: in every cell or bedroom there should be a washbasin with running water; in larger dormitories there should be an adequate number of the same. The use of a wash basin and buckets for dirty water should be completely abolished since it is antihygienic and old-fashioned.

There should be at least one bathroom on every floor; in large cloisters there should be at least one bathroom for every twelve religious so that each religious can take a bath each week which would for the entire group total two baths a day excepting Sunday. Thus during the week one could prepare one bath in the morning and one in the evening. The too frequent use of the bathroom during the day should thus be avoided, since the program of work occupies all the hours of the day.

Today a bath tub and a shower or two on each floor of the cloister with an adjacent linen closet provide the means and opportunity of bathing or showering at the convenience of the religious.

A very important place in regard to hygiene is that of the infirmary. The author, in his many years of activity as a cloister doctor, has experienced that a quick glance through the infirmary will indicate the spirit that prevails throughout the entire house. The infirmary should be especially bright and comfortable and, if possible, facing the monastery garden; and, if possible, of white tiled walls or at least washable oil paint. There are superior, modern and washable plastic tiles for either the ceiling or the floor which are recommendable from the hygienic standpoint. An adjacent room will contain an apothecary cabinet, surgeon's dressing case and a cabinet for instruments; an apparatus for the sterilization of syringes and other instruments is absolutely indispensible for this room. There should also be a special cabinet in this room for infirmary articles.

A larger monastery will need a licensed nurse or a generally experienced infirmarian, who, in certain cases, can also be a lay brother. If it is a case of a male cloistered religious, it is recommended that the infirmary be established outside the cloister so that the nurse's room be in the immediate vicinity.

The floor of the infirmary should be easily disinfectable. Special importance should be given to the heating and ventilation. The toilet room should be easily accessible from the infirmary. The infirmary should have its own bath and toilet.

From the hygienic standpoint it is important that the monastery have a sufficiently large garden. This is ordinarily under the law of the cloister. It is very pleasant when the garden not only serves a practical purpose (vegetable, fruit and cultivation of medicinal plants), but also offers shady places, flower beds and lawns. In ancient cloisters the garden is almost always surrounded by the stations of the Cross. The tranquility of the place should be an expression of the peace of the cloister.

3. The Religious Garb (Habit)

A greater objection than that manifested against the garb of the secular priest, which gives the impression of a certain removal from the "world," was directed against the habit of religious who lead a monastic life, in that the religious habit was considered absolutely anti-hygienic and old-fashioned: a true "provocation of the hygienic sensibility of the modern man." Many voices were raised in favor of a radical reform, demanding the absolute removal of every difference that distinguishes the religious habit from the clothing of the lay people. The voices of the radical reformers were raised more strongly against the female religious garb.

It can be easily admitted that, from the hygienic standpoint, the religious habit could be improved in several aspects. Yet the objections of hygiene do not refer to the form of the habit, and, hence, not against that which distinguishes it from the lay garb, but specifically in regard to the material of the habit, especially the summer habit.

Whatever we have to suggest from the hygienic standpoint regarding the reasonable and moderate reform of the religious garb can be formulated in a single point: in all the Orders the norms concerning the habit should be reconsidered in order to establish a principle of difference between the winter and summer habit.

We cannot deny the fact that it is unhealthy for nuns to be dragging along in hot summer days with the same habit that they wear on the coldest winter days. The color and material of the summer habit could be the same as that of the winter habit, but the material could be lighter. This is the most important point of a change which we present without reservation and recommend to all religious superiors. Further, where it is still prescribed by the rule of the Order that the religious sleep in his habit (with capuche over the head), this regulation should be re-examined

A further point concerns the work habit. There is no doubt, especially for the active Orders caring for the sick, household work, etc., that the religious habit is not absolutely practical as a work habit. In the Orders caring for the sick it has been customary to wear the white garb in hospital work. The same should be prescribed not only for the infirmary, but also—eventually the color gray—for the laundry, garden work and farm work. These are understandable and natural requirements which *in se* do not in any way exclude the habit. Yet it is not exactly what one Mother Superior said concerning the matter: "Those who only sit behind a desk should at times betake themselves to the kitchen, laundry or garden—then they would no longer be so enthusiastic concerning their religious garb."

One can agree with the opinion of the above-cited Mother Superior in this that the large stiff starched hoodlike caps worn by nuns under a veil are hygienically not harmless, for doctors have stated that nuns suffer ear disturbances when the ears are covered day and night by a closely adhering cap in such a manner that no air can pass through. The adoption of a practical work habit does not necessarily imply the total renunciation of the habit which can always be worn within the convent or during the liturgical community exercises.

Pope Pius XII, on the occasion of a congress of religious held in Rome in September, 1952, encouraged the religious groups to introduce practical modifications in their garb. This encouragement was presented by the press as an order from the Holy Father. The press has, with excessive zeal, illustrated the inadequacy of the garb and has criticized the use of material for its formation as uneconomical.

If all the counsels here given are followed, all the requirements of hygiene will be fulfilled. All further suggestions as, for example, the best possible likeness to the lay garb in order not to give "an unpleasant impression" are concessions of a "world" which has no idea of the life of those who, with their garb, show that they are not "of the world." The demands of a reform of the religious garb have less to do with hygiene the more radical they are.

4. Nourishment

To the question of nourishment in a monastery, little remains to be added to what has been said concerning the nourishment of the secular priest. The nourishment in a monastery differs from that in the parish house chiefly in this point that it is a matter of providing nourishment for a much larger community. For this the principles for a collective table basically prevail even in the case of small convents. Individual tastes and desires cannot be considered as is still possible in the parish house. If it is a matter of the diet for the sick, this can be followed in the infirmary but not in the community refectory.

In regard to the preparation of food for all in the community kitchen, which is ordinarily attached to the refectory, the fundamental principle, "Simple and nourishing," should prevail. Hunger should not exist in the monastery. Every member should be able to leave the refectory table feeling satisfied. There are, however, monasteries that are very poor and in which hunger literally exists, but this is not a desirable situation. In such poor convents the guest is distressed, when, invited to dine with the nuns, she observes what they are eating and compares this with what is presented to her—often with great privation on the part of the host.

The more plentiful and better the food is during the ordinary times and on festive days, so much more rigorous can be the limitation of food be during the time of fast. During this period the prescribed fast can be advantageous even from the hygienic standpoint.

5. Fasting

Fasting, i.e., the partial or complete abstinence from food for a more or less long period of time, can be considered under two aspects, namely, the hygienic and the ascetical.

a) HYGIENIC STANDPOINT

From the hygienic standpoint we distinguish the therapeutic fast and the dietetic fast; the first represents a cure, a therapy against definite diseases and disturbances of metabolism (the cure of fasting). Inasmuch as the cure is associated with a determined diet prescribed by the doctor, it should also be considered as dietetic fasting.

By a dietetic fasting we mean, on the other hand, a rule of life for the healthy who desire to maintain their organism in good health by purifying cures practiced at intervals so as not to be affected by specific diseases. Thus one can see that therapeutic fasting and dietetic fasting cannot be clearly distinguished since one form flows into the other. The therapeutic fast represents a most energetic and important therapy and should not be adopted without definite indications and under the direction of a doctor.

There are various types of fast cures. Well known is that of Schroth, which seeks to "eliminate the waste water" from the body through hunger days, thirst days, etc. Further, there is a so-called "juice fast" in which only fruit and vegetable juices are taken. Finally, there are fast cures in which for several days one abstains totally from food (total fast). This can be practiced for only a short time.

Every type of fast cure has its definite indications. Just as no important surgical therapy can be undertaken without strict indications, so must a fast cure be undertaken with a sense of responsibility. Just as in many operations, deteriorated tissue, for example, tumoral formation, are removed by a bloody process, so the fast cure will remove, in an unbloody process, the torpid, dead tissue through a melting process. Hence the fast cure should be accurately regulated: it should remove only whatever is detrimental to the entire organism without affecting the vital substance. That this process of melting away is successively efficacious is manifested by a symptom: at the beginning of a strong fast cure there results a strong and often unpleasant odor in the mouth as well as from the pores of the skin.

The therapeutic fast also exercises an intense influence upon the psyche. After a rapid and passing weakness of concentration, the individual notices a surprising increase of spiritual strength above all of the receptiveness of mind and phantasy. The course of ideas is facilitated; the soul tends to elevate itself; mental structures acquire flexibility and agility (Buchinger); the intuition is increased. Strong sensitization can increase to the point of medical phenomena.

The physiological effects of a strict fast (only water and fruit juices) consists chiefly in the reduction of glycogen reserve in the liver, muscles and blood. The metabolism adapts itself to the law of *"vita minima."* Further, there is a reduction of exsudation, transudation, induration and deposits (for example, urate in gout, calcic salt and oxalate in rheumatic diseases, tendency toward lithiasis [stone-forming], etc.). If the fast cure is interrupted prematurely, the reduced products will again be driven back to the former places of deposit. This is the so-called "repulsion" which occurs when the fast is interrupted (Buchinger).

During the fast cure the urine is usually very turbid and thick; it contains a great quantity of *sedimentum lateritium* (principally, urate); it also contains other products of elimination and becomes strongly acidic. The fasting organism expels through all the means of elimination, that is, through respiratory air, cutaneous pores, sweat, urine and intestine. Even the endocrine glands with the internal secretions are strongly altered through fasting. Especially the thyroid and the gonads which, with hyperfunction, increase the basal metabolism, are reduced to a minimum of function, and are thus "placed in a state of economy."

In regard to the loss of weight, the principle that a loss of weight of forty per cent of the original body weight is considered dangerous to life also prevails here. The most prolonged strict fast observed in man up to the present time was that of 31 days (Levanzin; cf. Buchinger). Dewey observed a fast of 65 days duration; Hazzard, one of 75 days duration. The great reduction of weight during the first days of a strict fast is due primarily to the process of dehydration. In any case, the fasting cure effects an intense elimination and a modification of organic balance, as well as a greater loosening and distension in the psychic sphere.

The fasting cure is principally indicated in the following cases: adiposity, rheumatism in any form (arthritis, arthrosis, myalgia, neuralgia, ischias); arteriosclerosis (hypertonia); chronic obstipation; asthma; allergic diseases (e.g., hay fever, urticaria); skin diseases (e.g., psoriasis); lithiasis (e.g., kidney stones, nephrolithiasis); gastric and intestinal diseases (gastritis, ulcers, colitis); renal diseases (nephritis, nephrosis); metabolic disturbances (hepatitis, cholecystropathy); forms of vegetative dystonia; chronic exudation (pleurisy, parametritis, perimetritis), etc.

Contraindications, which must be carefully observed are: tuberculosis, Basedow's disease (hyperthyroidism), carcenoma, organic heart diseases (coronary insufficiency, myocardiac lesions, myodegeneratio cordis, (decompensation), and finally senility (marasmus senilis).

The fasting cure is efficiently integrated by physical therapy: air and sun baths; carbon-dioxide baths: brush baths, massages (caution) and homeopathic reactive means.

These brief points, generally corresponding with the opinions of Buchinger, indicate the importance of therapeutic fasting, and also the impressive effects of this therapy. They show that the fasting cure is a serious therapy which must be accurately evaluated and practiced under the guidance of an expert doctor. A rigorous fasting cure can be fulfilled only through bed rest.

The simple dietetic fast represents a very mild cure which does not require serious and precise indications. It coincides substantially with the "Springtime cures" which were in use in former times and which coincided for the most part with the time of fasting prescribed by the Church. It was, as it were, the hygienic mantle which covered the traditional practice of fasting. In the Springtime fasting cure, meat was eliminated and in its place fresh green vegetables, especially the Spring herbs, were preferred. It was also the time of blood-letting which at one time played an important role in therapy.

Through natural instinct popular and natural medicine recognized the hygienic value of the fasting cure and the season that was most opportune in fulfilling the same. It was not mere chance that the choice of time most suitable was the season which, from the earliest times of Christianity, served, in the Church, as the ascetical preparation for Easter time and which, already in the Old Testament, was considered as the time for the purifying preparation for the Passover.

b) ASCETICAL VIEWPOINTS

The fast, as prescribed by the Church for Lent, cannot be completely understood if it is considered merely from the hygienic standpoint. Certainly, as we have seen, it also has a very important hygienic aspect. But this does not constitute the essence of the fast, which has a notable part not only in Catholic asceticism, but in that of all the other religious: Judaism, Islamism, Buddhism, and in all the Near East as well as the Far East.

The Catholic Church distinguishes between abstinence and fast. The law of abstinence forbids the eating of flesh meat and broth made from meat, but not eggs, milk products or seasoning, even though the latter be made of animal fat (Can. 1250). From the age of seven, all are bound to observe the law of abstinence. The law of fast prescribes that only one full meal a day be taken. It does not forbid the taking of some food in the morning and evening, but approved local usage must be observed in regard to the quantity and quality of the food (Can. 1251). Everyone of twenty-one years of age is also bound to observe the law of fast.

The uniform norm for fast and abstinence in the United States is indicated by the Ordinaries in accordance with the requirements of Canon Law as modified through the use of special faculties bestowed by the Holy See. Each local ordinary must approve this set norm for his own diocese. According to this uniform norm: complete abstinence is to be observed on Fridays, Ash Wednesday, Holy Saturday, the vigils of the Assumption (now transferred to the Vigil of the Immaculate Conception) and Christmas. (In the decree of Dec. 3, 1959, Pope John XXIII conceded to all the faithful the privilege of anticipating the obligation of fast and abstinence. from Dec. 24—the Vigil of Christmas—to Dec. 23).

Partial abstinence is to be observed on Ember Wednesdays and Saturdays and on the Vigil of the Feast of Pentecost. On days of partial abstinence meat and soup or gravy made from meat may be taken only once a day, at the principal meal.

The days of fast are the weekdays of Lent, Ember days, the Vigils of Pentecost, Assumption (transferred to Vigil of the Immaculate Conception), and Christmas (option: Dec. 23 or Dec. 24).

As a result of the difficulties created during the years of war and post-war times and because of the food restrictions which followed, the prescriptions of fast were notably mitigated in places thus affected.

These mitigations of the fast are actually still being made. In substance, these mitigations are based on the fact that, during the time of fast, that which is of meritorious value is not only the physical abstention from food, but rather the interior intention of the penitent. Based on this premise, one should feel normally obliged spontaneously to take upon oneself a mortification even of legitimate pleasures (e.g., smoking, drinking, etc.), so that the sum total of these things will be of benefit and usefulness to the community (fast and alms).

From the ascetical standpoint, the interior intention is the decisive factor. The "solemn fast" (*solemne ieiunium* in the sense of the liturgy of the fast) is, above all, the preparation for the greatest feast of the ecclesiastical year. It should be a time of penance and should signify an internal return to God and a turning away from sin: a metanoia. Since the removal from sin necessarily implies a certain turning away from the world, its attractions and pleasures, a serious reflection of true values is indispensable.

If in all this we can even perceive a certain "escape from the world" and a certain "hostility toward the world," this is still far from being an "unhealthy" asceticism. That which the Church requires through fasting and that which she offers through it finds the most beautiful expression in the words of the Lenten preface: *"Qui corporali ieiunio vitia comprimis, mentem elevas, virtutem largiris et praemia."*

The fast, in the sense of asceticism strictly understood, therefore offers these advantages: the stifling of sin and the quelling of inclinations which drag one down; the elevation of the spirit; the acquisition of virtue and its reward.

C. Questions Regarding Asceticism

From pre-Christian antiquity asceticism meant the exercise of virtue. Christian asceticism serves the striving for perfection; in the religious Orders this aspiration is orientated toward the evangelical counsels (poverty, chastity and obedience). But, since, according to the words of the Apostles, the flesh struggles against the spirit and even one who tends toward perfection suffers under the "double law" of the spirit and of the members, the end of asceticism is to establish, confirm and assure the dominion of the spirit over the flesh.

"The law of the flesh," that is, the inordinate revolt of the flesh against the spirit is a consequence of the fallen nature of man, of the *natura vulnerata*. As man has rebelled against God, so the flesh has revolted against the spirit and has disturbed the order and harmony originally intended by God. In regard to chastity we have already indicated the fact that it is impossible to defend the same against the fallen nature, without the help of grace, and that only the supernatural can elevate the natural beyond itself *(gratia implet et perficit naturam)*. In the degree that man submits himself to God he also learns to dominate his flesh: "Obey God and the flesh will obey you" *(Tu Deo, tibi caro.")*. Thus the encyclical *("Casti Connubii"),* with the words of St. Augustine, admonishes the men of our time who hold that it is impossible to overcome the vital instincts.[4]

Asceticism substantially coincides with the requirements of the *Imitation of Christ,* as Thomas à Kempis has formulated in the *Imitatio Christi* in a valid manner and for all times. Asceticism can never be exercised as an end in itself but only as a means to the end of perfection. It would defeat its very purposes if it were practiced in the spirit of self-righteousness. If, however, it tends to leave to others that which it denies itself, asceticism then manifests itself in its deep social aspect. Asceticism should effect an increase of love of God and neighbor, otherwise it will lose its meaning. A deep *mysterium iniquitatis* is the fact that humility and pride exist so easily side by side.[5]

Genuine asceticism is, therefore, a means of clarification. The way of purification leads to illumination, to a deeper knowledge and hence to the highest love, union with God. In this way asceticism leads directly to mysticism.

True asceticism is also necessarily a struggle, a battle against the forces of fallen nature which drags one down: against sin and the lower instincts. This struggle, which is based on the very essence of asceticism, is far from signifying a flight from the world and hostility to the body, as has been charged even to our day against Christian asceticism, especially in its Catholic form.

There are, it is true, degenerate forms of asceticism, but these have not developed from Catholic sources. Unilateral asceticism, hostile to the body, rather has its origin in Manichæism and has developed a caricature of true asceticism among the gnostic-dualistic sects, the Cathari, the Albigensians, and the Bogomils. A remnant of these concepts hostile to the body is preserved in Puritanism with its sexual rigorism ("prudery").

One of the most repugnant forms of asceticism was the movement of the Flagellants who had their origin in the 13th century during the time of the plague. This was incorrectly attributed to Catholic asceticism. It is an historical fact that its aberrations were attacked by the ecclesiastical authorities and it was condemned by

[4] Encyclical *"Casti Connubii,"* n. 102.
[5] History reports of the Greek nuns at the time of the fall of Constantinople (1453) that "they were angels of purity and demons of pride."

the Council of Constance (1414-18). In the heretical sects this movement was supported until the 16th century.

These deviations have nothing in common with the extraordinary forms of asceticism which are even today preserved in the strict penitential Orders, as, for example, the Camaldolese hermits, among whom the *cilicium* and *disciplina* still have a place.

Stöhr in his *Pastoral Medizin* has basically opposed these forms of rigid asceticism inasmuch as they still prevail in our day. He accepts the use of the flagellum *(disciplina)* with certain limitations, but admonishes that the strokes should be given on the dorsal part of the body and recommends the limitation of the same exclusively to the seat. Stöhr also manifests certain preoccupations regarding the moral dangers of similar expiatory manipulations. He openly states that he has little regard for the expiatory means of the *disciplina* or the *cilicium:* "In every case they are arms adapted to a novice of asceticism but have value only in the hands of a person with character proven to virtue. More than one innocent heart, really animated by good intentions, but deprived of the prudent guidance of an experienced friend of the soul, is precipitated, by the enticing cultivation of the mortification of the flesh, into the abyss of the most degraded vice, from which it is most difficult to remove oneself."

These words of the old master of pastoral hygiene should be especially considered, insofar as they allude to the danger of algolagnia, i.e., of sado-masochism. The author, with Stöhr, accepts the *disciplina* rather than the *cilicium*. It is certain that such extraordinary forms of penance should always be fulfilled under the direction of a spiritual director who is prudent and strong in his moral principles. Otherwise it is better to avoid the same, since they can be more dangerous than useful.

From the hygienic standpoint there is more reason for the objection against the cilicium, since the extensive meaning of the same can lead to serious and obstinate irritations of the skin, to eczemas and skin infections (pyodermia).

D. Questions Regarding Mysticism

The essence of mysticism consists in a mysterious supernatural union with God *(unio mystica);* in becoming empirically aware of the divine life of grace ("infused contemplation"). The *unio mystica* is the ultimate and supreme degree of the elevation of the human soul, capable of assuming various characteristics and of manifesting itself in various forms.

Among the forms of manifestation of mysticism, the most impressionable are not always the most essential. Ecstasies, visions and revelations are only secondary forms; of primary importance is the mystical elevation of the soul. The soul is not capable of attaining actively mystical elevation by its own powers, but is in need of grace in order to become passively elevated. Physical concomitant phenomena, as, for example, stigmatization, conservation of vital functions in the case of absolute abstinence from nourishment *(inedia)*, overcoming the forces of gravity, of time and space (levitation, bilocation) are not really essential phenomena; they can also be parallel phenomena of a purely natural nature; there is further a psychopathic (hysterical) pseudo-mysticism and, finally, there is also the possibility of an extra-natural (demoniacal) pseudo-mysticism activated by the devil in order to lead human souls into error.

Mystical experience is always associated with a certain preparation of the body and the spirit. This demonstrates the close connection between asceticism (theory and practice of asceticism) and mysticism.

Even on a purely natural plane there is manifest a freer elevation of the spirit, a freedom from the bonds of matter in hunger states of higher degree; this can also arise in morbid states which present themselves with greater starvation. In order to avoid erratic interpretations, it should be noted that genuine mystical states are in no way attached to these or even to dispositions favored by asceticism or necessarily required.

They represent only a furthering factor. Authentic mystical experience is pure grace and is, therefore, not attached to any physical conditions. Nature can further it, and even in this regard *"gratia supponit naturam"* prevails. As always, even in this case we should avoid the errors of naturalism as well as those of supernaturalism.

Asceticism represents the essential part in the preparation of mystical experience. The *mortificatio corporis* should be motivated by a pure love of God and a true intention of penance. Mystical experience can and should not be sought in an active manner. The preparation is the way of purification and illumination. To illumination belongs interior contemplation which finds its fulfillment in (passive) "prayer of elevated repose." The true mystical experience is the union.

Mystical experience presupposes the state of grace. It requires further the "infused" theological virtues of faith, hope and charity. Knowledge *(scientia)*, as a gift of the Holy Spirit, is a concomitant phenomenon of the mystical life.

The passivity of the soul, abandonment without self-ambition, is expressed in the "prayer of repose." This (authentic) passivity should not be confused with quietism (unauthentic), which refuses any cooperation of the soul.

The fundamentals of Christian mysticism were set forth in a classical form by St. John of the Cross and St. Theresa of Avila. Both agree in describing how the way of purification leads first through a phase of "death" to the world of the senses ("dark night of the senses") and through states of interior aridity, to which is attached a confusing feeling of complete abandonment by God. After the supreme mystical elevation, the soul often sinks into this tormenting state of the "dark night of the spirit."

The moments of mystical elevation must be paved with a series of sufferings through which the pains of the fire of purgatory are as if anticipated.

Mystical phenomena, such as ecstasies, visions and revelations, do not belong to the essential forms of the phenomena of mysticism; but they are important for our treatment.

Ecstasies are found in the sphere of the "elevated repose." At times ecstasies are accompanied by visions. One of the best known examples is the visions of St. Bernadette during her ecstasies in the Grotto of Massabielle.

Private revelations are not necessarily associated with visions. Regarding them there is present an attitude of criticism and reservation. Private revelations complement each other as a mosaic. Even here we can notice the phenomena of "displacement" and of "condensation" as found in the images of a dream. Authentic private revelations remain internally true even if certain details are seen and reproduced erroneously. He who experiences a private revelation can reproduce the same only in his own language and according to his degree of culture. Even authentic revelations can be ambiguous. Precise indications of the time in which a future event will be verified speak against the authenticity of the revelation.

Phenomena of this nature do not occur every day, but do play a significant role in the spiritual life of the cloister. Since their appearance always produces profound disturbance in the community, it is important that definite norms be established so as to distinguish them from pseudo-mystical manifestations. Pseudo-mysticism can imitate all the secondary concomitant phenomena of the mystical life, and it is often very difficult to distinguish these from authentic manifestations.

One cannot be prudent enough in dealing with psychopaths, who for the most part feel the need to be wanted, and with hysterical mythomaniacs, who can simulate or autosuggest mystical phenomena.

That which characterizes authentic mysticism is interior experience, which develops in the interior life of man and which, therefore, is not accessible to an exact verification and control. In order to judge whether it is a case of authentic mysticism or pseudomysticism it is necessary to refer to definite criteria. One of the most important norms is that of obedience especially in regard to orders which limit the effect on the external world. The pseudomystical person wishes at any price to act toward the outside.

For comparison, recall the two cases which we have mentioned in regard to the question of obsession. In one case, theatrical actions and the need to be wanted were evident; in the other case, there was none of this; yet it was difficult in determining whether the phenomena were genuine or not, inasmuch as it was only possible in establishing that nothing was posited in a proving way, neither in favor of a psychic disturbance nor in favor of deceit. Matters are no different in the case of Teresa Neumann of Konnesreuth. In similar cases a definite acknowledgment of authenticity tends to follow only after death.

Even the pseudomystic knows at times how to imitate deceitfully the virtue of humility. She speculates with preference on the credulity and miracle mania of the masses. The mania of miracles is often the greatest adversary of the truth and true faith, which does not seek and demand continuous "miracles." Finally, there is also a species of pseudomysticism of definite demoniacal character (mysticism of the devil, *maleficium*), as well as cases of genuine obsession *(obsessio, insessio, circumsessio, possessio diabolica)*.

The spiritual atmosphere of a cloister can be infected with a true and proper induced mania when psychopathic or hysterical personalities know how to transfer themselves in the sphere of the indicated phenomena. It is therefore of utmost importance for the spiritual health that all superiors and priests of the cloister have a definite practical knowledge of these matters.

III. THE SICK PRIEST

A. Social Pathology of the Spiritual Director

Social pathology is the basis of social hygiene. It tends, above all, to recognize the social causal factors of sickness, the relation with the social conditions and the social effects of diseases, that is, their importance in society. Hence, social and professional pathology of the curator of souls is an integral part of pastoral hygiene. It teaches us, above all, to evaluate the general pathological factors inherent in the profession of the curator of souls.

1. The Historical Development of the Social Position of the Priest

The social position of the sacerdotal state has undergone a deep change in the course of the last centuries. Before 1789 the cleric, in the constitutional monarchies of the Occident, represented the first state; nobility constituted the second state; the third state *(tiers état)* was developed by the French Revolution and contained the citizen class; from 1848 there arose the fourth state, the working class. With the rise of the third class the social condition of the priest became much closer to that of the citizen class; and the revolution of 1918 which desired to overthrow, with the thrones, also the altars, transformed in many towns that which was up to that time the proletariat into the leading state.

As a result of this social revolution, the sacerdotal state became bourgeois and lost the guarantee of the existence to which it was accustomed, and participated in large measure in the fate of the proletariat, that is, in an absolutely precarious existence. In connection with this social revolution which was far from being concluded, there arose a new sacerdotal type: the spiritual director of the suburbs of the large cities, who lived among the poorest proletariats of the large city as one of them; and, in recent times, the working priest, who, renouncing all exterior conditions of existence to which he was accustomed, worked in the factories as a worker among workers and strove, through this new way of life, to regain for the Church the working masses.

2. The Worker Priest

The question of the priest workers, which some years ago impressed public opinion which, in turn, is not always objectively informed concerning the diverse tendencies, has become less actual today. It was discussed, above all, in France where the experiment assumed higher proportions than elsewhere, with favorable and contrary arguments.

Among the first, the most important was the necessity of being closer to the workmen to participate in their life in order to regain them to the faith. The inconveniences derived from the inevitable reduction of the specific activities of the sacerdotal ministry were generally acknowledged, but many held that extreme remedies should be applied to extreme evils, and that the time dedicated by some priests to work in the factory was not time lost, but, on the contrary, was used in the evangelization of the proletariat. Among the contrary arguments, the most convincing was that of the scarcity of priests which did not agree with such a conspicuous dispersion of power. Moreover, and this is the point that is of interest to hygiene, the excessive burden of work to which the priest worker had to subject himself, if he desired to dedicate himself to the care of souls at least in his free hours, was of grave prejudice to his health, so much more precious the scarcer the number of vocations. It was essentially a matter of greater interest to theology than hygiene, the solution of which could arise only from the doctrinal voice of the Church. This, in fact, although acknowledging the merits of those priests who, in order to conquer souls, subjected themselves to such sacrifices, made a pronouncement in favor of the cessation of an activity, the fruits of which were seen to be inadequate to the strain that was engendered and that could place the priests at the risk of becoming influenced by the doctrines which they intended to combat. On July 3, 1957, a letter from the Holy Office, signed by Cardinal Pizzardo, communicated to the Archbishop of Paris the decision of ceasing gradually and prudently the experiment of the priest workers.[6]

Moreover, the attempt of the worker priests neglected the true and proper cause of defection on the part of the masses. If one wishes to strike the evil at its roots, it is necessary to take into account the fact that the defection of the masses has had its origin in the incredulity of the cultured person. There was a time in which incredulity was equal to "instruction" and to "culture," and faith to "ignorance." That has fascinated the masses. Their justified attempt in bettering and instructing themselves (the motto "Culture is power" was continually impressed upon them as a stimulating motive) was thus systematically directed in a hostile sense against the Church and the faith; dialectical materialism was presented to them as the sole "scientific" Weltanschaung (a philosophy, especially a personal or racial one, explaining history in general or the purpose of the world as a whole).

In the face of such a situation there is only way of return: just as incredulity came from the "cultured" circle, in like manner the return of faith must receive its impetus from the same circle. With time even the masses must take into account the fact that incredulity has nothing to do with culture, but that, rather, true culture is accompanied by faith, and incredulity by ignorance. It is, therefore, of decisive importance that cultured persons be enlightened to the fact that the fundamentals of scientific materialism have nothing to do with true and proper science. Then and only then will it be possible to regain the masses for the Church.

Pastoral hygiene has to present its most serious objections from the standpoint of social pathology.

It can never be sufficiently emphasized that the most serious danger to the health of the priest is found in the overburden of work and that this is, in turn, determined by the scarcity of priests. We have demonstrated the burdensome tasks that the director of souls encounters in the large cities, tasks greater by far than the physical strength of any individual. And if we add the double burden imposed by work that is physically and intellectually heavy,

---

[6] For greater details, cf. G. Caprile, S.J., *"L'Episcopato francese e i preti operai,"* in La Civilta Cattolica, April 2, 1960, p. 59 ff.

it is then necessary to add, from the hygienic standpoint, that in time these labors cannot but present serious effects upon the health of the priest. To this is added the cause of disease arising from the environment of the proletarian life.

The worker priest cannot remove himself from this environment and from this form of life if he wishes to work among the workers as his equal. The doctor who is associated with social hygiene realizes the numerous and serious damages to health that arise from this very milieu. He knows that tuberculosis is a typical "milieu disease"; he realizes the severe harm to the constitution arising from lowered resistance to infection. He knows how much the overburden of work influences unfavorably the prognosis of tuberculosis; he is aware that such milieu damages can nullify the great success of the modern therapy of tuberculosis, and that, in an organism so injured, the bacilli of tuberculosis become easily resistant to the curative action of modern antibiotics and chemotherapy in a manner that the best therapy becomes powerless and the prognosis of the individual case becomes absolutely unfavorable.

That which prevails for tuberculosis, as an example, also prevails for the other diseases in which the causing factor of an unfavorable social milieu plays a role. If at present, because of a lack of priests, the priest already suffers a very heavy burden from the standpoint of social hygiene, one cannot but be preoccupied with the fact that certain priests from large cities and in the industrial centers are subject, for the greater part, to the ordinary care of souls and are also occupied with manual labor that is definitely beyond their strength. From the hygienic standpoint—and only from this standpoint can and should we speak—we find it necessary to state that the two tasks—the care of souls and manual labor—are incompatible. One will either remain a priest and thus content oneself in limiting as much as possible the time dedicated to manual labor, and this will not suffice in effecting an efficacious contact with the workers; or one will be nothing more than a "miner," and in such a case one will have to consider that in time he will run the danger of losing his profession as priest.

Just as we have from the standpoint of social hygiene formulated a law of incompatibility that motherhood and work outside the home for long duration are incompatible (Max Hirsch), so can we say the same regarding the spiritual paternity of the director of souls. If one thinks that one can ignore the warnings of hygiene and that one can lose every year a certain number of priests through professional diseases, then one should evaluate whether the advantage that is presumed is worth such a lofty place.

B. Special Pathology of the Director of Souls

We shall now indicate a number of diseases that often affect priests and which, because of their relatively higher-than-average frequency, can be designated as "professional diseases."

For obvious reasons a complete exposition is not intended nor is it possible. Nevertheless, the same diseases can also be considered "professional diseases" of the doctor, whose profession and conditions of life are very similar to that of the priest. We distinguish here between organic diseases and psychic diseases.

1. Physical Diseases (Organic)

a) ACUTE INFECTIOUS DISEASES

As the doctor, so likewise the priest through his profession is especially exposed to infectious diseases. The priest, as the doctor, who has to visit the sick at home and even in the hospital, accosts the bed of patients affected by infectious diseases, and thus has no regard, in such circumstances, for his health. The only attempt toward protection consists in making sure that the sick person does not directly breathe upon his face. The most dangerous infection that we encounter most frequently is that of the grippe (catarrh-infection). We have already indicated that the grippe should not be taken lightly, but must be considered a serious disease, the complications of which are numerous and incalculable.

The grippe (influenza) manifests itself most often during the cold season. Usually it presents two points of diffusion: the first occurs during the months of October and November; the second, during January and February. The severe complications usually manifest themselves only after a long duration of the epidemic; the first cases present, in general, a more benign course.

When the grippe waves in the course of certain decades had become ever lighter, there arose a wave of catastrophic severity and high mortality (the last was 1918-1919) such that certain epidemic characteristics, considered in the middle ages as "pestilence," have been related more closely to influenza than to true pestilence. The influenza of 1918 coincided chronologically with total damage to the European world.

There is a form which appears especially during the summer and which usually manifests itself with gastro-intestinal symptoms (grippe-enteritis).

Among the acute infectious diseases, from which not even adults are definitely immune, even if they are usually considered as "children's diseases," are: infantile spinal paralysis (poliomyelitis), the virus of which has a certain affinity with that of influenza; measles (morbilli), scarlet fever (scarlatina) and dipththeria. There is no absolute immunity against these infectious diseases, not even for those who have previously been afflicted with these diseases. Their course can be more dangerous for adults than for children.

Other infectious diseases as typhoid fever, cholera, enteritis and hepatitis infectiosa are to be classified under diseases of the digestive organs.

b) DISEASES OF THE RESPIRATORY ORGANS

Among the diseases of the respiratory organs, that of pulmonary tuberculous is to be mentioned in the first place. Concerning its association with social conditions, we have already presented its effects; its social importance consists, above all, of the fact that it seriously affects the working capacity. If, at first, the prognosis *quoad vitam* was very serious and if the disease often led to death in early age, this prognosis, thanks to modern therapeutic means, has been greatly modified; the prognosis *quoad sanationem* depends in large measure on whether the patient takes good care of himself and is able to refrain from work for a sufficiently long time. Tuberculosis is less a problem regarding the duration of life than one of disability. But if the unfavorable milieu conditions persist, even the life prognosis becomes very serious, since the pathogenic agents end up being resistant to therapy and no longer react to any treatment. Even the modern surgical therapy for tuberculosis, which does not arrest through the greatest interventions of thoracoplasty and a resection of the entire pulmonary lobes (lobectomy), cannot effect any change in the state of things created as a result of an unfavorable and persistent action of the milieu.

Individuals subject to tuberculosis (even those with hereditary disposition) should, therefore, inasmuch as the hygienic standpoint is considered, avoid the profession of the priesthood; those who dedicate themselves to teaching in schools should by all means abstain from every contact with the students since there is a danger of infection.

Chronic catarrh of the larynx (laryngitis) can easily arise as a result of the excessive use of the vocal cords (through school teaching or intense activity of preaching). Laryngitis that is not easily accessible to therapy should be watched scrupulously since it can obscure the beginning of tuberculosis of the larynx. Its prognosis was once absolutely unfavorable; today it has become more favorable. From the hygienic standpoint it is, however, incompatible with every teaching activity.

Catarrh of the trachea and bronchial tubes (trachitis and bronchitis) are to be judged under the same viewpoint. If they do not react favorably after inhalation and a medicamentous therapy, then consideration should be taken of a sojourn in a place where both cures are administered.

Bronchial asthma and emphysema are often the result of one another in the sense of a *circulus vitiosus*. Often asthma manifests itself as an allergic ailment in early youth; as such it has a certain affinity with hayfever *(rhinitis aestica seu vasomotoria)*. Emphysema is the presence of air in the intra-alveolar tissue of the lungs due to distention and rupture of the pulmonary alveoli with air and is typical of advanced age.

From the age of fifty on most priests suffer with emphysema, especially when they have to do much talking, climb many stairs or even travel steep mountain roads. Even many elderly doctors are affected by emphysema. In emphysema and chronic bronchitis bronchiectosis can be easily verified. Bronchiectosis is a chronic dilatation of the bronchi or bronchioles marked by fetid breath and paraxysmal coughing, with the expectoration of mucopurulent matter.

If to the conditions mentioned above there are added acute infectious or infections, mixed with banal pyogenic agents, pulmonary abscesses can eventuate and at times even lung cancer. The latter is distinguished by a limited expectoration and, at the same time, fetid sputum.

The pleura is in most of the indicated diseases easily affected. In every persistent dry inflammation of the pleura (pleuritis secca) or with pleuritis exsudativa the possibility of a specific pleuritis tuberculosa should be considered.

c) DISEASES OF THE CIRCULATORY ORGANS

In case of heart failures *(vitia cordis),* that is, diseases of the cardiac valves, it is important to establish whether the heart failure is congenital or acquired (for the most part from acute infectious diseases as scarlet fever or acute articular rheumatism). Individuals with congenital heart failures can dedicate themselves to the state of the priesthood only by way of exception: the patient is usually not suitable for the ordinary care of souls as a secular priest; whether and to what extent he can be of use in a cloister, either as "Mass celebrant," as spiritual father or as a scholar, is a matter that depends on the actual circumstances. In the case of acquired heart failures it is necessary to distinguish whether the failure is compensated or not.

Decompensation manifests itself especially in congestions: congested bronchitis, congested liver, accumulation of fluid (transudate) in the pleura or in the abdominal cavity (ascites), and in the extremities (edema), the so-called "dropsy" (hydrops universalis). Decompensation is a more serious pathological condition, which renders one incapable of any work.

Actually, interest is primarily centered upon the already cited diseases of the heart muscle (myocardia) and the disturbances of hemorrhage through insufficiency of the coronary vessels. In coronary thrombosis there is a formation of clots (thrombi) which provoke more or less in the myocardia extended infarcts (blocking of a blood vessel). On the extension and the seat of the lesion (whether this is in a vital place or not) depends whether there will be sudden death or whether the infarct will be absorbed and health of the patient will follow.

Cardiac infarcts have been greatly increased in frequency in the last years and this has been primarily attributed to excessive mental work to which intellectually leading personalities are subjected, and also to the rush of the modern life tempo. This complex of symptoms has been designated as the "Manager Disease" since it often strikes persons who occupy leading posts in the economic life. Even with priests and doctors, sudden death following a cardiac infarct has become horribly frequent. It often strikes during the "better years," especially around the fiftieth year of life.

The diseases of the aorta and arteries are, in general, caused by a deposit of cholesterol on the internal vascular walls (atheromatosis); in the case of secondary calcium deposits one speaks of "calcification" (arteriosclerosis). As a result of the fragility of the vascular walls there easily arises an extra-vasation of blood (apoplexies), especially in the brain, the "apoplectic stroke" *(appoplexia cerebri)*. On the extension and the place of hemorrhage depends whether death takes place immediately or rapidly, or whether there will still be an absorption and whether more or less serious paralysis will result.

The care of persons afflicted with apoplexy can, at times, present great difficulty especially when the paralysis of the extremities is associated with paralysis of the sphincters of the bladder and intestine. The *incontinentia urinae et alvi* makes this care so especially crushing.

Among the vascular diseases these are also the diseases of the veins, especially of the inferior extremities (varicose veins), the so-called complex of varicose symptoms: varicose veins, ulcus cruris, thrombophlebitis. Many priests (as well as doctors) suffer with varicose veins. If there is present an inflammation of these dilated venous textures, then this venous inflammation (phlebitis) leads to a formation of a clot (thrombus, thrombosis). If a loosened thrombus enters the blood stream, it can reach the pulmonary artery (arteria pulmonalis) and can provoke an occlusion (embolism, so-called "lung-stroke"). Besides apoplexy, angina pectoris and cardiac infarct, embolism is among the more frequent causes of sudden death.

Even when an embolism does not lead to death, the thrombus obstructs the terminal vessels of the lungs, through which a cuniform section of the pulmonary tissue is cut off from the blood circulation (so-called pulmonary infarct). This often lasts for a long time until this infarct is absorbed.

d) THE DISEASES REGARDING ASSIMILATION
AND OF THE DIGESTIVE ORGANS

Diabetes *(diabetes mellitus)* is a metabolic disorder in which the ability to oxidize carbohydrates is more or less completely lost due to faulty pancreatic activity, especially of the islets of Langerhans, and consequent disturbance of normal insulin mechanism. This produces hyperglycemia with resulting glycosuria and polyuria giving symptoms of thirst, hunger, emaciation and weakness and also imperfect combustion of fats with resulting acidosis, giving symptoms of dyspnea, lipemia, ketonuria and finally coma.

Since diabetes is due to a disturbance of the central regulation, the disease usually affects men of advanced age who are constrained to a restless and pressing life. Because of this, both priests and doctors are professionally disposed to such a disease.

Among the diseases of the digestive organs, we are to mention those of gastritis and gastric ulcer (ulcus ventriculis).

Gastritis appears in two principal forms: as catarrhal gastritis, an inflammation of the mucous membrane of the stomach, with hypertrophy of the membrane, secretion of an excessive quantity of mucus (gastric hyperacidity). The condition is marked by a loss of appetite, nausea, pain, vomiting, and tympanic distention of the stomach. The second form is that of gastric hyperacidity, a deficiency of acid: lack of normal acidity. With hyperacidity there is often heartburn (pyrosis), also associated with stomach spasms. From gastric hyperacidity ulcers can develop and from ulcers even a carcinoma ventriculi can develop. Hyperacidity and ulcers are vocational diseases which are imputed to hasty meals and insufficient rest after meals.

Among the intestinal diseases are to be mentioned, above all, that of acute infections of the intestinal canal: typus abdominalis, cholera asiatica, paratypus and enteritis. We have already treated of these in another section.

If the water supply in the parish house is not hygienically adequate, transmission of this ailment can easily be brought about through the water. When there is a suspicion of the infiltration of refuse in the drinking water, a bacteriological analysis of the water is indispensable; and if the outcome of the analysis is positive, then a hygienic examination of the water fountain or water supply is necessary.

A very frequent disturbance found in persons who lead a sedentary life is that of constipation. It consists of two forms: as spastic and atomic constipation. The former arises from an annular contraction of smooth musculature of the intestine; the latter, from the relaxing (atonia) of the intestine. The treatment is in both cases different. However, the use of purgatives is to be avoided.

A frequent and practically important disease of advanced age is the chronic inflammation of the large intestine and of the rectum (colitis chronica). In this case the urgent need of defecation overcomes the patient often quite suddenly with such incoercible force that, when evacuation cannot be immediately fulfilled, the fæces pass spontaneously and irresistibly.

Naturally, this disturbance, which is highly unpleasant, is also found in older priests. It can become aggravated by a neurotic form of "expectation-anxiety." One will try to defecate as soon as one rises in the morning or before undertaking some important function, but to no avail. One fears the well-known explosive defecation, but the more this is feared, the more surely will this be verified at a less opportune moment. This disturbance represents a definite torment for the priest if the spastic contraction of the intestine occurs just during the fulfillment of his priestly functions. A similar situation is more than painful for one teaching school, for a doctor during an operation or delivery at birth.

It should be further mentioned that hemorrhoids, piles, or vascular tumors made up of infected varices involving part or all of the hemorrhoidal venous plexus are also attributed to a sedentary life. In general they are considered a professional disease of office workers. The more the activity of the priest becomes like that of the office worker (and this is especially so with ecclesiastical authorities), so much more does the sedentary life favor the formation of hemorrhoids. Hemorrhoids are basically the same as varicose and, hence, what has been indicated concerning varicose essentially pertains to hemorrhoids.

Frequent disturbances which are not always to be taken lightly are those of hernia, the protusion of a loop or knuckle of an organ or tissue through an abnormal opening. The more common forms of hernia are: inguinal hernia, umbilical hernia and crural hernia.

When, in an inguinal or crural hernia the loops of the intestine penetrate the scrotum, we speak of a scrotal hernia. The latter types of hernia can at times attain enormous dimensions.

The treatment of hernia with hernia bandages is cumbersome and hygienically not satisfactory. The best therapy is that of surgery, taking into account the fact that, in the contrary case, sudden strangulation (incarceration) of a rupture is always possible, and this is dangerous to life and requires an immediate operation. In such a case this is much more dangerous since an extensive resection of the gangrenous intestinal part is necessary.

Moreover, a hernia operation is not completely devoid of danger especially for patients who have a tendency toward adiposity. In such cases postoperative thrombosis and embolism, especially with operations of unbilical hernia, can easily arise. Just as a hernia operation that is deferred for too long a time reacts with incarceration (unnatural retention or confinement of a part, or may occur in hernia), so a deferment of an appendix (appendix vermiformis) operation, an operation of the stomach or gall bladder, reacts with a rupture of the pathological organ (the so-called "perforation").

The infected and often purulent matter of the perforated organ spreads into the abdominal cavity and causes peritonitis, and this can be mortal. In such cases even an immediate operation cannot easily save the life of the patient.

e) DISEASES OF THE URINARY APPARATUS

The diseases of the urinary organs and their appendages are considered in the special branch of Urology. From this branch we will mention only two of the most important diseases: chronic nephrosis (renal sclerosis) and hyertrophy of the prostate.

We shall not consider the acute renal diseases (nephritis, pyelitis) in this section, since they do not present any special problems of interest to pastoral hygiene. In regard to lithiasis, the formation of calculi and concretions (kidney and bladder stones, nephrolithiasis and calculus vesicae) it is sufficient to mention them. Even the formation of varicose glomerules (varicocele) need only be mentioned.

Chronic nephrosis (nephrosclerosis, Bright's disease) is not a chronic inflammation of the kidney (chronic nephritis), as was previously thought, but a degenerative disease of the most important elements of the renal parenchyma, of the glomerules, based on an alteration of the blood pressure, of the essential hypertonia. The specific primary cause of this disturbance is not known; it is definitely not a "calcification" of the vessels; the calcium deposit is only a secondary symptom. Perhaps the primary damage is in the capillary circulation: a persistent constriction of the capillaries inevitably determines an increase of the blood pressure. The fixed hypertension reaches a maximal point (often over 250 mm RR); but rarely does this lead to apoplexy. The very restricted blood vessels can be noticed even in the base of the eyes, often associated with the degenerative alteration of the retina (retinitas albuminurica). The prognosis *quoad vitam* is absolutely fatal; in general, it can be calculated, from the moment that a definite diagnosis can be established up to the inevitable *exitus letalis,* that two to four years will intervene.

However, the author has known patients who, despite a sure diagnosis, still lived for several years; among them an old nun who rendered service as an infirmarian to the 80th year of age, although, according to the medical prognosis, she should have died at least 15 years previously.

The hypertrophy of the prostate is a disturbance that very often affects old men *(mal du villeard).* It consists of an increase in volume, often very considerable, of the prostate, which surrounds the urethra and the outlet of the bladder *(pars prostatica urethrae).* The patient suffers frequently from the urgency of urination (tenesmus) and from frequency of urination (pollakiuria), especially during the night. The difficulty of miction gradually increases. The urine is no longer totally expelled and there remains in the bladder a little of the *urina residua,* the quantity of which increases constantly.

If the patient does not provide for a regular emptying of the bladder, since he could be constrained from doing so for one reason or another (for example, obliged to attend a burial service during cold and rainy weather), so that, despite the tenesmus, he does not empty the bladder, this can lead to an overstretching of the bladder. As a result, he can no longer expel the urine; the bladder is greatly stretched *(retentio urinae);* the pains finally force him to proceed to an emptying of the bladder by means of a catheter. If this procedure is frequently repeated, the patient ends up learning to make use only of the catheter in the emptying of the bladder. Thus usually begins the second act of the tragedy. Self-catheterization is never fulfilled with the necessary asepsis. Unavoidable infection of the residual urine occurs; at first there is vescical catarrh (cystitis); gradually, the infection rises in the ureter and renal pelvis (pyelitis); and finally there is the formation of a suppurating infection of the renal parenchyma, of urosepsis, which places the patient in the danger of life through a general sepsis.

Less known than the complications already described, which can provoke urasepsis, there are other complications which cause disturbances of the function of the large intestine. They correspond to the same disturbances which can be observed in women, in the case of *retroflexio uteri* and that of *myomas:* defecation is thus disturbed because the hypertrophic prostate and the retroflexed uterus restricts, in an hour-glass contraction, the *ampulla recti.* We can designate this condition as the "sand glass ampulla." Thus there results the fact that in the morning defecation there is evacuated only a small part of the contents of the rectum which is found in the lower part of the ampulla and which first presses the anal sphincter. As a consequence, usually after breakfast, often during the hours of morning work, the ampulla stenosis has extended so greatly that the principal mass of the fæces is pressed into the lower width of the ampulla. Thus there arises a sudden pressure from above on the sphincter, which determines an irresistible and sudden tenesmus, which provokes an explosive defecation in a similar if not identical manner as that of colitis. Characteristic of the disturbance of defecation suffered by prostatics is that of fractional defecation, that is, defecation in two or more portions, corresponding to the "sand glass ampulla," the impossibility of evacuating all the fæces in one defecation.

The very close distance between the rectum and vesicle makes it easy for intestinal bacteria (bacteria coli) to travel from the intestine into the vesicle and thus infect the decomposed residual urine of the prostatic. The use of a catheter easily causes a mixed infection with banal pyogenic agents (staphylococcal, streptocaccal), through which the sad fate of urosepsis is sealed.

Today an early operation of prostatics is preferred in order to avoid, as much as possible, these serious complications. If it has reached a point wherein the catheter has become indispensable, the operative treatment, prostatectomy, is to be unconditionally preferred to the sufferings provoked by urosepsis. The results of the operation are, in general, very good. The successful operation signifies a rebirth for the patient. He will regain the joy of living and the possibility of working for many years. The urologist should be always aware of the possibility that beneath the apparently simple hypertrophy there might be a malignant tumor, a carcinoma of the prostate. Today this is treated by many with strong doses of female sexual hormones (paradox hormone therapy), and often with good results.

Concerning this, the last word has not yet been spoken regarding the possibility that this heterologous hormone therapy might not effect a certain inversion of sexual characteristics in the sense of an effeminization, and, if so, to what extent. The author is of the opinion that operable patients should undergo an operation and that the hormone therapy should be limited to cases in which the operation is contraindicated. That the mentioned disturbances belong to the frequent diseases of older priests (and also doctors) is a known fact.

f) TUMOROUS DISEASES

We have already seen that hypertrophy of the prostate and carcinoma of the prostate are diseases that present the specific problem of tumors. As is known, we distinguish between benign and malignant tumors. The benign tumors are, for example, the atheromas, often on the head, neck, face or back; the lipomas, fiberomas and the myomas. To the malignant tumors belong, above all, cancer (carcinoma) and sarcoma. The malignant character is due to the increase of the tumor superficially and deeply, an infiltrating and destructive increase which is irrepressible, and to the formation of metastasis, often in organs far removed from the primary tumor. Undoubtedly the diffusion of the malignant tumor is increased, perhaps because they usually manifest themselves in advanced ages, and the middle age of human life has today become more advanced; moreover, it must not be forgotten that today tumors are diagnosed sooner and more frequently than formerly.

There is, however, a form of cancer that is more frequent than formerly: lung cancer. This manifests itself metastatically, for example, after a cancer of the thorax, often following a primary bronchial cancer. The causes of this form of carcinoma are to be found, according to modern research, primarily in excessive smoking of cigarettes with the apparently inevitable "inhalation" of the smoke; in the second place, it is due to enormous corruption of respiratory air in the large city, due to the gases escaping from the motors burning benzine. These toxic gases are also held responsible for the frequent increase of thrombosis and of embolisms.

In any case, we are confronted with the most serious and actual problem of social hygiene. Even if it cannot be held that the definitely increased motorization can be reduced, yet it would be useful to substitute combustive motors with electrical motor power. In this way, besides the problem of air corruption, another important city problem, from the social standpoint, would be solved, namely, that of the "plague of noise."

The anxiety that modern man has concerning cancer has developed into a true panic. One speaks correctly of a cancer psychosis. The popular illustrative conferences concerning tumorous diseases—which is exaggerated—contribute to the increase of panic and the psychosis of carcinoma. The influence of anti-cancer guidance centers and centers of cancer examination has increased, and these elements are very useful from the standpoint of social hygiene.

Man attains a more advanced age today than formerly, and the higher mortality rate from cancer is the price that humanity must pay for the increase of the average age of life, in other words, for the phenomenon of longevity which, on its side, stands in close association with birth decline, with the limitation of natural rejuvenation and its substitution through "artifical rejuvenation" and with the artificial retention of the process of old age. Hence, behind the increase of tumorous diseases serious problems of social hygiene are hidden.

g) DISEASES OF THE LOCOMOTORY ORGANS

The extremities very often suffer from rheumatic diseases. Among these we distinguish forms, the seat of which is predominantly the musculature (muscular rheumatism, myalgias) and others, the seat of which is predominantly the joints (articular rheumatism, arthritis, arthrosis). Muscular rheumatism often affects the dorsal muscles of the Erector trunci; if the pain is predominantly localized in the lumbar region, we speak of lumbago. The neurolgic pains of the sciatic nerve which pass from the hip to the feet are designated as Ischias (Ischialgia). The pains determined by flat feet can in turn pass to the dorsal section under the form of static myalgia (pseudo-Ischiac).

In the articular rheumatic diseases we distinguish above all those of an acute nature (arthritis) from the chronic-degenerative process (arthrotis). The acute articular rheumatism is, of its nature, acutely infectious (rheumatic polyarthritis). The uric gout (arthristis urica) is a metabolic disease due to a deposit of uric acid as a result of a too rich diet of purin (predominantly meat diet). In practice the most important form is that of arthrosis deformans, which usually manifests itself after the fortieth year and moves along with degenerative alterations of the articular surface. The movement of the joints becomes painful because, in place of smooth bone surfaces, rough bone surfaces come in contact in the movement; thus there arises a reactive thickening and tension of the joint capsule which renders the articulations rigid and immovable. The joints most frequently affected are those of the knee.

With the great frequency of arthrosis deformans even among older priests, it is obvious that the painful stiffness of the knee constitutes a serious obstacle in the celebration of Mass. During the Mass the priest has to genuflect more than a dozen times. In genuflecting, the priest with arthrosis must support himself with his hand since the knee lacks elasticity.

The diffusion of rheumatic diseases has become a question of great importance to social hygiene. Social insurance uses enormous sums of money for the treatment and rehabilitation of rheumatics in health resorts. The research regarding the basic causes of rheumatism has not as yet brought any satisfactory results despite all the research institutes for rheumatism. Suppurative foci in the tonsils and at the roots of the teeth play an important but not the exclusive role in the cause of rheumatic diseases.

Foot deformity and nail diseases have already been mentioned in another section. In the case of severe foot deformities, orthopedic footwear is absolutely indispensable.

h) DISEASES OF THE NERVOUS SYSTEM

Among the organic diseases of the nervous system it is important to distinguish between those of the central nervous system and those of the peripheral nervous system. The central nervous system includes the brain *(cerebrum)* and the spinal cord *(medulla spinalis)*. Among the appropriate diseases the following are to be mentioned: in the brain, tumors, abscesses, and hemorrhages (apoplexies, traumatic hemorrhages, e.g., hemorrhages from the arteria meningea media caused by an accident): diseases of the cerebral and apinal menix (Meningitis); on the part of the spinal medulla, poliomyelitis (so-called "infantile paralysis"), multiple sclerosis, spastic spinal paralysis, etc.

Only for the sake of completeness do we mention Tabes dorsalis and the so-called "softening of the brain" (paralysis progression). As metatuetic diseases they do not play a noteworthy role in the social pathology of the director of souls. An authentic brain softening, that is, the formation of centers of softening as a result of circulatory disturbances, is found in arteriosclerosis of the brain. This has absolutely nothing to do with paralysis progression; since we often find this in cases of apoplectic strokes and not rarely in the course of dementia (dementia senilis).

The author has often witnessed multiple sclerosis in priests. Among these there were cases in which, despite the unfavorable prognosis *quoad vitam,* the patients attained a very advanced age. One of the priests died at the age of 86 years, after almost 40 years of sickness. Although he was totally paralyzed and for many years could not celebrate Mass, he was regularly carried in his chair on casters to the convent chapel where he read his breviary with fervor. He could scarcely speak, but was still animated by intellectual interests and was surprisingly vivacious.

Among the diseases of the peripheral nervous system we find the following with relative frequency: neuralgia, neuritis and polyneuritis. The neuralgia of the sciatic nerve (Ischias) has already been mentioned. Extremely painful is the neuralgia of the sensory facial nerves (trigeminus).

A patient of the author belonging to high hierarchy of the clergy became sick in 1942, during the war, of a serious neuritis of the plexus brachialis. The examination of the patient revealed suppurative foci of the tonsils. It was not easy, considering the age of the patient (who at the time was 66) to assume the responsibility of a tonsillectomy; yet, after removing the tonsils, there was a rapid and complete recovery, and the patient remained surprisingly vigorous until a mature old age.

On the border between the organic diseases of the nervous system and the mental diseases, there is a case of Cushing's Disease, which the author witnessed in a priest. As a young priest, he was intellectually interested, especially attached to music, the arts and sciences, and was in every respect an exemplary priest. About the age of forty there occurred a complete deterioration of spiritual interests: he was interested only in eating, and this he fulfilled with great avidity. At the same time his countenance changed and lost its former characteristic and was transformed into a large and insignificant "full moon face." The neurological examination confirmed the diagnosis of "Cushing's Disease," that is, an organic brain disease, which had its seat in the pontine angle of the cerebellum. The patient failed intellectually so rapidly that he was incapable of any professional activity of the priesthood and thus had to be pensioned.

Epilepsy has already been considered as a cause of irregularity.

2. Mental Diseases

On the border between organic diseases and mental disturbances there are, on the other side, neuroses which are designated as organic neuroses. The rigid differentiation between organic neurosis and psychoneurosis has been definitely overcome since depth psychology has taught us that every neurosis is of psychogenic origin and is based upon a situation of conflict between the subconscious and the superior conscious psychic strata. That even among priests cases of neurosis cannot be excluded has already been demonstrated by our considerations concerning the neurosis of Mass celebration.

Here we are to give greater consideration to the psychoses than to the neuroses. The fact that a psychosis is not always immediately differentiated from an organic cerebral disease has been demonstrated in the already cited case of Cushing's Syndrome. The patient mentioned above definitely suffered from a phychosis. His behavior presented a surprising similarity with that of paranoia: the patient felt persecuted by the doctor (persecutory delusional ideas); he imagined the doctor to have been "corrupted by the Freemasons," for no other reason than that of removing him from his priesthood.

Schizophrenia essentially consists in the increasing self-enclosement and removal from the external world (psychosis of introversion); its extreme form is catatonia, a stuporous state of negativism.

The manic-depressive mental disturbance manifests, on the contrary, a most extroverted behavior, which can intensify to the point of raving madness. Shock therapy has produced a progress in comparison to the therapy of the past insofar as it succeeds in tranquilizing the very agitated patient and thus helps the patient to become more useful in society.

Under Amentia, in the meaning of Canon 984, all mental diseases are to be understood.

Dementia is a state of intellectual deficiency, the various degrees of which are debility, imbecility and idiocy. Since these states of deficiency are most congenital, they are not considered in the pathology of the priesthood. Only the secondary state of deficiency as found in dementia senilis can at times, but not too often, be verified in advanced age. It seems that intellectual activity exercised to advanced age is the best protection against the decadence of intellectual strength in old age.

If a priest becomes afflicted with a serious mental disease, there is no other choice than that of institutionalization. In general, hospitalization is necessary only when the patient presents a serious social danger or when it is presumed that he may attempt suicide. In judging the danger, the profession exercised by the patient is to be taken into account: if it is a priest, teacher, or doctor, the danger is evidently greater since it is incalculable what they, with disturbed mental powers, can cause in their professions. Even the question of care plays an important role. The care of a mentally diseased parish priest in the parish house in absolutely impossible. In this case hospitalization is the only means of care. When the secular priest has recovered and has left the hospital since there is no further need of therapy, he should be pensioned, since there is always the possibility of the psychosis recurring, and because of harm that a mentally sick person in a responsible position can cause. In regard to a religious priest one can hold a milder view since, with mentally sick persons who are tranquil, care within the cloister is possible. But agitated patients should receive clinical care.

C. The Care of Sick Priests

The necessity of care for mentally sick priests presents another important problem of pastoral hygiene: To what extent is there provision for the assistance of sick priests? The difficulties are not too serious when there is, within the cloister, a well-established infirmary, or when it is a case in which hospital care is of immediate necessity, as, for example, in cases requiring a surgical operation. A problem that has not been satisfactorily resolved is that of caring, within the parish house, for secular priests afflicted with acute diseases. If it is a case of the pastor himself, it is possible to provide in some way a capable housekeeper, and intelligent relatives can always fulfill at home, through the instructions of the doctor, the care of the sick pastor. But it is just the opposite in the case of a sick curate since he is ordinarily badly assisted especially in the turbulent rectory in the large city which is not organized for the suitable care of the sick. The fact that a curate becomes sick represents, under more than one aspect, a disturbance and calamity.

For this reason the author has for many years been influenced in holding that, at least in large cities, and, above all, in dioceses, a house under the direction of a few religious nuns be established for the care of sick priests. Of course, serious cases of sickness would not be considered here, but only acute diseases of short duration, as the grippe, minor surgical diseases as inflammations, etc., for which, because of actual scarcity of beds, it is difficult to receive hospital care. Even in cases in which the diagnosis is still indefinite, the sick can be held for several days for medical observation before being placed in a hospital. A small laboratory for the simple examination of urine, blood and secretion (sedimentation, sputum, etc.) could be established without great difficulty and would greatly facilitate the fulfillment of the diagnosis by the doctor.

It seems to the author that it is a task of exceeding importance that a similar place for the care of priests be established in every diocese. This institution could essentially contributed in the care of sick priests, in a more rapid recovery of the same, in the avoidance of more serious diseases and their consequences, and in maintaining the health and working capacity of priests. If these modest needs in favor of the sick priest cannot be fulfilled, then pastoral hygiene will have failed in its scope and purpose.

D. A Warning against Hypochondria

The present work would fail in its purpose, if whatever has been mentioned concerning the social pathology regarding the director of souls has the effect of causing in the clerical reader a hypochondriac anxiety of disease as we have mentioned when speaking of the widespread anxiety concerning cancer. The reader should be aware of the fact that it is not a rarity with young students of medicine, who in the first clinical semesters learn to distinguish the different morbid symptoms, to experience the following phenomenon: almost every young medical student imagines in the beginning that he has all the symptoms described in the preceding lecture; the more advanced medical candidates smile at this weakness of the younger students. Since this work is designated principally for priests, it can be assumed that a spiritual director of souls, endowed with stability and maturity, does not become too anxious concerning the necessary description of the various diseases. It is not worthy of a priest to be overcome by an anxious hypochondria which can affect the young medical student only in his first clinical semesters.

A hypochondriac anxiety concerning disease no longer becomes a doctor who has to face the same with the calmness of experience and wisdom; and it does not become a priest who is called to announce the word of the Lord: *Non solliciti estote!* The priest knows, more than the doctor, that health is a precious gift—definitely the greatest of the earthly gifts—but by far not the "highest gift."

If it is the duty of a doctor to consider these problems, above all, from the hygienic standpoint, the priest observes the same from even a higher position: he sees them *sub specie aeternitatis*.

IV. ACTUAL HYGIENIC QUESTIONS OF PASTORAL ACTIVITY

A. Organizational Questions

We have already considered the hygienic inconveniences resulting from the overburdening of the spiritual director of souls, of the dispersion of the care of souls, of the excessive application due to detailed daily activity and excessive organization which has even disturbed the peace that once prevailed in the rectory through the rush and agitation that is characteristic of our times, transforming the care of souls into an object of "business" and of "organization." We may characterize these inconveniences with the designation of "activism" or "pragmatism," but we do not wish that these be misunderstood as if we wished by this designation also to indicate a complete restriction of wholesome activity. The designation "pragmatism" is less susceptible of being misunderstood. It designates the concept of life which values only external activity, the "act," thus overlooking the fact that the act must be preceded by being and knowing: *agere sequitur esse*.

We are of the opinion, however, that the minimum of external organization of the care of souls as that of Caritas, which renders possible a maximum of activity, is also to be considered as the optimum even from the standpoint of pastoral hygiene. For this reason it is no longer necessary to say anything more concerning questions of organization; it will only be stated that Caritas, as an ecclesiastical welfare institution (Catholic Charities), must maintain its autonomy toward organizations of secular (public and private) welfare care, but must closely work with them. The common duties are abundant; the division of strength is to be avoided.

B. Caritas

The task of Caritas is not fulfilled in an organized and centralized collecting and distributing of alms. If Caritas rightly understands its great temporal tasks, it then represents one of the most powerful organizations which is also of service to social hygiene, community health and world health. Because of this reason, so as not to divide strength with small alms, is a methodical management necessary, which places the material means where something great can be attained.

Small alms are only temporary palliative means. One should not lose sight of the fact that these small daily alms accumulate through frequency into an enormous sum of money. In a large city the parish caritas as well as the diocesan Caritas have their home beggars who are dismissed with alms of a small amount. Because of this, sums of money are often lacking with which serious and pressing emergencies could have been assisted. Thus the so-called "social indication" for abortion is merely due to critical conditions which often can be helped by an adequate deposit of money. A human life is always at stake. Caritas, however, does not have the means for such greater share (restoration of living conditions, shelter in a maternity home, etc.), if it distributes this in small alms. The so-called "SOS" societies for "immediate help" of Caritas together with that of Catholic Action suitably assists with immediate and unofficial help in cases of pressing emergency. In these cases the tedious investigation which is often required before every greater help is given is diminished to a minimum.

Caritas has important tasks to fulfill in the following spheres:

1. Care of the alcoholic and of the addicted

Here there is concern, above all, for the restoration of family and social relations, for the assumption of expenses for custody and treatment in suitable institutions (Antabus cure, etc.). The establishment of special institutions which are not annexed to public insane asylums can be suitable for the object in view.

2. Care of those who are tired of life

With proper organization this can be effective in the rescue from suicides and the prevention of suicidal actions (e.g., Rescue, Inc., Boston, Mass., Rev. Kenneth Murphy, Director). This is most effective when closely associated with psychiatric institutions and arranged so as to supply psychotherapy (Ringel).

3. Care for the endangered

It interests itself in neglected youth, especially of girls, in order to prevent their falling into prostitution, and even boys as a prevention of criminality. If care comes too late so that such moral failures have not been obstructed, it then accepts the fallen and seeks to restore their physical and spiritual health. This work is essentially promoted by the "Sisters of the Good Shepherd." They work in close relation with the public youth care and youth legal aid. An essential means of help for the care of the endangered is that of the Railway Station Mission. It discreetly watches over those arriving at the railway station, especially young girls; it leads travelers from the country back to their parents' home, as far as this is possible; it concerns itself with employment mediation; it takes care of girls, especially in large city railway stations, so that they will not fall into the hands of white-slave traffickers who promise the girls good positions abroad, but in reality have them shipped to foreign brothels.

4. Student care

The situation of young students is not so controlled that negligence and risk is definitely avoidable. Hence, Caritas concerns itself with student homes, with genuine formation during free time, as long as the large firms continue to be of help in this matter. In Vienna the firm of Julius Meinl has been very cooperative in this matter. The cooperation of the organizations founded by Kolping and of homes (friendship societies) has been excellent.

5. Care for the bodily encumbered

This includes not only the "cripple" in the higher sense, that is, those crippled from childhood—whether from a hereditary cause (hereditary deformities), or also as a result of hereditary Lues, early childhood infantile paralysis—but also the bearer of all the acquired bodily injuries: blindness, deafness and dumbness; lameness, for example, arising from organic disease of the nervous system, traumatic lameness; war injuries, the victims of air attack, political terror (the latter is partly included in the care of political victims). It includes all institutions of "rehabilitation," that is, re-employment and efficiencies in the highest possible degree.

6. Family care—family help

Here we deal with one of the most important spheres of charitable care, in which Caritas is at present more advanced than the public care and welfare, which has not understood the nature of the family and thus in this regard has much to recover.

Caritas continues thus by establishing housekeeping help to aid sick and exhausted mothers, as well as suitable care for those sick at home and for lying-in women.

In cooperation with the marriage counseling bureau and care of pregnant women, Caritas has assumed the manifold duties which are associated with family care. It is concerned with maternity homes and children homes, in which expectant mothers in a helpless situation are accepted, without a time limit, usually until three months after the birth of the child, in which even the children receive further care, and thus make it possible to eliminate in many cases the so-called "social indication" toward abortion.

Maternity instruction courses and maternity recovery care complete the varied picture of the social work in this sphere. Added to this are the modern nurseries (also with directives of modern techniques and care regarding premature children), homes for children, vacation arrangements, etc. All these institutions reestablish in a more complete manner the social functions which in former times were fulfilled in foundling hospitals. A concentration of power in the well-known Catholic work organizations for national health has manifested itself well in the sphere of Caritas.

The helper in the Caritas organization must be well instructed in all the phases of social and health care in order efficiently to fulfill her manifold tasks so as not to be inferior to the public lay worker for social welfare. When she fulfills the tasks of this marvelous vocation with tender heart and proper spirit, she can then with the strength of Christ-like Caritas surpass the public social worker. Extensive material means are needed in order to fulfill the tasks of Caritas. At present there is more of a need for purposeful application and proper direction than for means. Moreover there is a great need of much schooling and review of the wide sphere of social hygiene and social welfare as well as a deeper insight into the sources and associations of human intensive needs of our age.

C. The Protection of Youth

The protection of youth is one of the most important tasks of the care of souls at the present time. Considering the extensive working of women outside the home, this must begin in early infancy.

1. Religious Instruction

The infant is active in play schools; children a little older, before scholastic age, are gathered in kindergartens. For the child attending elementary school and for youths of higher age and attending more advanced schools, the care of the soul is to be predominantly oriented toward a solid and complete instruction in religion.

The well-known difficulty which intervenes in the satisfaction of this great need is due for the most part to the lack of interest on the part of school authorities regarding religious instruction. In dictatorial nations this instruction is not allotted the same safeguard as other forms of instruction. Fruitful results arising from religious instruction are also made less possible because of the growing lack of discipline of our youth. Hence, the imparting of religious instruction becomes, at the present time, more a source of struggle and agitation for the director of souls and catechists than of joy in instilling the light of faith into the hearts of the youth.

In view of the ever-increasing difficulty that is encountered in the education of youth and of the serious mental harm arising from the lack of early religious education, we are to strive, even from the standpoint of mental hygiene, for the imparting of religious instruction to all. For those who have left school and for adults it would be desirable to have in common a renewal of instruction in Christian doctrine. Where there is a need, certain actual and contemporary problems could be treated in specific circles, for example, for young girls, for engaged couples, for young mothers and fathers of the family. But the strong basis for the care of souls of youth must be religious instruction and its continuation, general Christian doctrine.

2. Questions Concerning the New Generation

One of the most serious problems of our time is that of the lack of priests in the new generation. We have already indicated the manner in which this problem is closely associated with the problem of birth decline. Many families today "have only one son," and they do not allow this only son to become a priest.

Seminaries and other places set aside for the preparation of candidates for the priesthood and religious life in a community can become, from the hygienic standpoint, model institutions. Concerning this matter and in the last decade, great progress has been made especially regarding cleanliness and bodily care of the young seminarians. Today greater emphasis is given sports activities than in the past. It is, however, necessary that exaggeration be avoided. Moreover, from the hygienic standpoint, it is essential that all seminarians receive the opportunity of participating in physical exercise for the purpose of invigorating the body. Good average performance of the same is better than any individual record performance. Toward this purpose, long walks, trips, swimming and mountain-climbing are more useful than certain sport activities with their inevitable record tendencies. As precious as the hygienic value of physical exercise is, yet it is not the purpose of a seminary to form sport champions, but priests who face the problems of the day with clear eyes and who are able to resolve the same.

The young generation of priests should realize the particular needs of physical and, especially, mental health.

3. The Care of Souls in Regard to Apprentices and Students

In the spiritual assistance of youth there also arises the care of souls in regard to apprentices, that is, the care of souls of the youth who have finished school and dedicate themselves to a working activity, and the care of souls for students in colleges and universities. In both cases it is a matter of a group of young people who are still in a stage of preparation and professional formation and who are morally exposed to many dangers, and therefore have definite need of spiritual direction. But between them there exist notable social differences.

Since the social differences of the two groups were formerly very cogent and the family milieu presented a very notable difference, the apprentices were less of a problem in regard to spiritual direction. The dangers, which even for them were not trifling, could be overcome with relatively simple means.

It is quite a different matter in regard to the spiritual direction of students. Considered from a purely material sense, the situation of the college student of today is little different from that of the apprentice and worker of former times. The college student is a proletarian and is at times constrained to procure the means for study through manual labor. Because of this, his problems have become more complicated than formerly. For the director of souls the greatest preoccupation consisted, above all, in this, that the intellectual youth, removed from the discipline of school and the paternal home, was completely abandoned from the standpoint of religion, at least if the student did not belong to a Catholic student group. The moral and religious conduct of students is not endangered through a dissolute life as was the case forty or fifty years ago. However, it has not yet become better so as to compensate all the difficulties that arise from the actual situation of college students. Moreover, the fact that many women have taken to higher studies has definitely contributed to the diffusion of sexual liberty among the students. In place of the free relations of former times there is the situation of extensive marriage among students. These marriages represent a severe problem regarding the children who are brought into the world without any security of existence; and even more serious because such early marriages last, in general, only for an extremely short time. An astonishingly high percentage of these marriages end, after a few years, in separation or divorce. Occasionally these lead to a social deterioration and decline which removes any hope of future resolution, since the mental and spiritual powers are prematurely exhausted and crushed. The fact that a good number of young students lack the proper philosophy of life orientation adds difficulty to the task of spiritual direction for students, and makes this one of the most difficult tasks of our times.

D. Prison and the Care of Souls

The care of souls in prison is one of the most difficult tasks of the spiritual director since he has to deal with hardened souls, and in order to reach the same is in need of special charisma.

An association between the care of souls in youth and convicts is represented in the care of souls in criminal youth.

The custody of delinquent youth represents more an act of precaution rather than an act of penal justice. The educational institutions connected with social welfare should, above all, be formative of character in the sense of a curative educational action for psychopaths who are difficult to educate, and not of a punitive character. Moreover, the modern pedagogists overlook the fact that the mental healing of the criminal youth is made more difficult because of the nature of the age of youth, which is like a "period of storm and stress," through their spirit of rebellion against all authority which also easily causes them to become criminal. However, it must not be concluded the entire life of a youth can become ruined by a single mistake. But the fact still remains that, having once fallen into the hands of the "infernal world," the youth is held strongly by the same and becomes obdurate against all benevolent attempts to help him return to the right road.

In general, the young person is in need of authority and guidance and the psychopathic youth is in greater need of the same. But he is also in need of love and inexhaustible patience, of the capacity of a sympathetic understanding of a sick soul which can arise only from a deep understanding of normal and abnormal psychic life. Almost all criminal youths are psychopaths. This does not imply that they are not responsible for their actions, but they are to be treated rather as unfortunates than as delinquents. One must be aware of the fact that a greater percentage of criminal youths and of antisocial psychopaths are from broken and disturbed marriages, from "imperfect families," and that they, in many respects, are merely the product of their parents' fault.

That which often does not succeed for institutional educators and also less so for justice officials, namely, the winning of the pupil's confidence (he should be considered more a pupil than a prisoner) is precisely the difficult task of the spiritual director of the institute against whose priestly garb complete diabolical spite and hatred is often directed and which inflames the corrupted soul of youth with sinister flames.

There are basically two distinct types of adult prisoners: the occasional delinquents and the old habitual delinquents. This distinction does not regard the gravity of the crime. The occasional delinquent who bitterly repents his crime and desires to adjust to an orderly life may be a murderer or an assassin, and the habitual delinquent may be a vagabond and an habitual thief who has become indifferent to all things. Nevertheless, the latter may be socially more dangerous since he has allowed himself to fall and has no intention of arising from his fall.

When habitual delinquents are designated as delinquents by profession, an intentional discrimination is indicated. It is intended thus to express that crime is their profession in the same manner that an honest man exercises an honest profession. It is thus overlooked, when even crime is designated a "profession," that this implies a depreciation of the very concept of "profession." Profession in its basic meaning signifies "vocation." The habitual delinquent is certainly an individual who has followed the "calling from below." But one should not designate this as a "profession."

It is very dangerous to imprison the novice delinquent in the same prison cell with habitual delinquents. The "old" delinquent, who for many years has become accustomed to all the conditions of every prison, immediately takes the "newcomer" under his protection, gives him plentiful advice regarding practical behavior; at first, harmless advice and, little by little, always more daring. He proceeds systematically to draw the novice delinquent into the underworld so that he can no longer free himself from the same.

The repenting occasional delinquent is usually appreciative of the spiritual direction given in prison, while the habitual delinquent is usually ungrateful. Nevertheless, even he has moments in which he is more flexible and accessible and is thankful for the good word spoken at the opportune time.

A special art of the spiritual director is the celebration of the major feasts of the year for the prisoners so that the obdurate delinquents will not become more obdurate but will become more accessible to recollection.

More serious than the position of the convict is that of the prisoner on trial. His position is more pressing if for no other reason than the fact of the uncertainty of the outcome of the process. That is the reason that segregation in the imprisonment on remand should be much more rigorous in order to impede any danger of collusion.

In these cases the spiritual director should be particularly prudent so that his kindness is not abused, as, for example, when the prisoner strongly begs him to deliver a letter to his wife or another relative.

Clandestine communication by a prisoner held for trial is more dangerous than that of the convicted prisoner. Whatever the imprisoned person intends to communicate to his relatives should be communicated through the direction of the prison, which is the only authorized means.

The hygienic conditions in prison often leaves much to be desired: the wash places, the latrines and sleeping bunks are often of such a nature that it is a wonder that infectious diseases (especially parasitic cutaneous diseases as scabies) are not more frequent. Vermin and bright lights which remain on in a community room do not permit any sleep at night. The latrine often consists of a plain bucket found in the cell. The air in a community cell is such that the inmates have no other choice than to bear the stench or to leave the window open even in cold weather. The bed blankets are often horribly dirty and during the day are gathered and placed in a pile so that the inmates seldom receive the same blankets. The common bath is also often unhygienic. The food is monotonous, insipid and often disgusting; the prisoner is "disgusted," so that he can no longer partake of the mush and prefers to cast it into the lavatory. Hence, he seeks to satisfy his hunger by smoking. This is strictly forbidden, but the old prisoners who undertake certain service work know how to smuggle in smoking commodities. When smoking is prohibited and there is a separate lavatory in a cell, the prisoners gather there, two or three at a time, and in these circumstances there arise homosexual aggressions. Homosexuality in penal institutions is also a sad chapter which the spiritual director must realize.

It is no wonder then that sensitive persons react to these impressions with a prison psychosis (the so-called "prison explosion"). It is not just, especially in regard to political prisoners, to consider the outbreak of a psychosis as a proof of guilt feelings. It is really the grave mental shock due to the sudden removal from one's work and family which disposes one more easily to a prison psychosis.

The old prisoner is no longer overcome by a prison psychosis. He has no shame and "has navigated at length." Whatever he does or leaves undone is well considered and, from his viewpoint, is useful. If he produces a prison psychosis, it is simulated for a definite purpose. Criminals of this kind present a definite characteristic, a repugnance toward work. This is often the primary cause of their criminality. It is the tendency toward social parasitism, the tendency of living comfortably without working and at the cost of others.

While the normal prisoner welcomes any occupation which corresponds in a certain measure to his strength and capacity, the prisoner who shuns work fears nothing more than work and is inexhaustible in his tricks to avoid work. As oppressive as isolation for a long period can be, so that it can also lend to serious depressive melancholia, yet it is for sensible persons more bearable than group imprisonment. Especially for subjects who are more intellectually inclined it would be considered a privilege to be able to live in a separate cell and thus participate more comfortably in reading and writing. Medical care for sick prisoners is usually inadequate. In the case of a fever lasting for a short time, this is occasionally found in the community cell, so that the grippe often rages in the overcrowded places. The prisoner is isolated only in the case of *angina purulenta* and infection. Infirmaries should be present in all prisons; for more serious and perduring diseases arrangements should be made for the transportation of these cases to a central prison hospital. It is obvious that the prison doctor should be careful that he not be deceived through simulation; for he who has intention of escaping believes that it would be easier to do so from a hospital than from prison.

A prison hospital cannot and should not be a sanatarium, yet every prisoner should be given the opportunity of being healed of a disease which he has contacted in prison without permanent harm to his health.

An important question is that of the possible custody of criminal psychopaths who, after serving their term, are set free. These cannot be held in prison after fulfilling their term, nor can they be committed to an insane asylum, since they are not insane but psychopathic, that is, individuals who react abnormally, whose responsibility is diminished but not completely removed. They are, however, usually antisocial and hence a danger to society. Institutions of detention which do not have the nature of institutions of punishment should be formed for such cases. The inmates should be under custody as long as they are dangerous to society—in other words, for an indefinite time.

The necessity of detention should be periodically controlled by a committee composed of psychiatrists, lawyers, representatives of social welfare, and this should be terminated as soon as the need of protecting society no longer exists.

The chief educative means in the institutions of detention for the purpose of restoring these persons to human society can only be work, since it is the very pathological shunning of work, the basic instinctual force, which has caused these persons to become criminals. Naturally the work, as an educative means, should not be presented in such a manner that it becomes more repugnant. This is inevitably the case when work assumes the character of forced labor. An institution of detention should therefore be equipped with a psychological laboratory for tests in which the inclinations and aptitudes are ascertained in order to give the person in detention the opportunity of work that is suitable to him and which would make him again aware of his usefulness. A progressive system, which gradually diminishes the rigor of isolation and redirects the one in detention little by little into society, guarantees a complete return into society.

It is better that such an institution be located in the open country rather than in the midst of crowded homes in a large city. That in a camp of detention of a social nature there should not be any cruelty and inhuman methods of a concentration camp and that here it is merely a matter of fulfilling a social task arises from the very nature of an institution of detention. And it is quite evident that in such institutions tasks of great importance arise for the chaplain. The prison chaplain must recognize these social problems.

E. Spiritual Direction of the Sick

It is difficult to compare the duties of the spiritual director of the sick with those of a prison chaplain despite the fact of the many parallels that exist between the stay in prison and that in a hospital.

A certain analogy does exist insofar as the stay in the hospital is more or less involuntary and imposed and is felt to be an intrusion upon daily life. The entrance into a hospital depends upon the will of the sick person; dismissal no longer depends upon him but upon responsible medical directors. But the differences are greater than the similarities: sickness is imposed on the sick person by fate, while imprisonment is caused by the guilt of the prisoner. The stay in a hospital benefits the health and welfare of the sick; imprisonment is an evil that must be inflicted upon the delinquent for the protection of society.

1. Spiritual Direction of the Mentally Sick

It is only in one case that the analogies appear greater, and that is in the case of committal in a mental hospital because of mental disease. In former times the mental hospitals were more like prisons than hospitals.

The history of the care of the mentally disturbed demonstrates the long road that had to be traversed in order to arrive at the present state.

In Germany the Teutonic Order founded in Elbirg in the year 1326 the first "madhouse." The treatment of the sick in the so-called "lunatic cages" of the middle ages was inhuman. They were not treated as sick people and were often treated more severely than convicts.

The following was part of the treatment given to the mentally ill of that time: corporal punishment, chains, strait jacket, mouth-gag, suspensors, constraining chains, rotating chairs, shower baths, emetic cures, burning with hot irons, etc.

During the time of the processes against the witches, the mentally disturbed were considered by many as "possessed." It was only in the sixteenth century that doctors began to make systematic use of psychiatry. Pinel is considered the "father of the modern care of the mentally disturbed." His precursor was St. Vincent de Paul who fulfilled the pioneer work. Pinel was the first to liberate the mentally disturbed from chains (1798). Esquirol modeled his system for the care of the mentally ill upon the example of Pinel.

From the work of these early pioneers to that of modern clinical psychiatry and present institutions of health and care a great distance had to be traversed. Great results have been accomplished especially through the efforts of the schools of Charcot and Wagner-Jauregg.

Since Wagner-Jauregg, diseases which lead to complete mental debility and hence to mental death, as the disease of *paralysis progressiva,* can be cured and the deterioration of the personality can be arrested. Even the prognosis concerning schizophrenia and of manic-depressive diseases has become, in comparison to the former prognosis, essentially better.

Although serious concern cannot be denied concerning shock therapy and its systematic application as well as concerning the operative methods of so-called "psychosurgery" (lobotomy, leukotomy), yet the fact of the definite success of modern methods of psychiatry can be confirmed.

While in former times the "agitated wards" in the mental hospitals, with the numerous furious, agitated patients, and the wards with their completely dull and rigid catatonics retained their characteristic impression and could do nothing without their cells with grated windows and doors without handles, today the situation is basically changed. The patients in the hospitals feel themselves to be sick, seek to be cured and are treated as such. Strait jackets are no longer used. Grated windows and closed doors disappear more and more.

It is far from our intention to approve indiscriminately the false progress of shock treatment that is unilateral and schematic, as well as the excesses of "psychosurgery." But the fact cannot be overlooked that the indisputable improvements which we have described are due in greater part to the progress of psychiatry through its modern physical, surgical medicamentous therapy.

The mental hospitals (health and care institutions) have become hospitals like all other hospitals. The care of souls in mental hospitals does not differ in any essential point from the care of souls of the sick. The chaplain for the mentally disturbed must naturally know the clinical psychiatric syndromes (a symptom complex) and be able to judge what is presented by the patients; for example, a manic-depressive, with ideas of guilt, will mention the terrible sins which he claims to have committed; the paranoid will speak of the systematic persecution which has led to his committal or will explain that powerful enemies impeded his dismissal from the hospital, etc. The chaplain should acquire a notable knowledge of pastoral psychiatry. A treatment of modern pastoral psychiatry can naturally be compiled only by a psychiatric specialist.

In France, Abbé Gebus has outlined, on the basis of his psychiatric study, some directives for the systematic construction of the care of souls regarding the mentally disturbed which take particular consideration of the spiritual life of the sick. Among the problems associated with the chaplains' work with the mentally sick are the following:

How can we bring confession closer to the mentally disturbed? What is considered good and evil by the patient? When is confession advisable and not advisable? With what expressions of sorrow may the chaplain be satisfied? Which patients are absolutely incapable of receiving Communion even in danger of death? How can these patients be recognized? If a patient refuses Extreme Unction, when can it be assumed that his refusal is merely a symptom of the disease and can therefore be ignored? What can the chaplain do to eliminate any disrespect toward the sacrament on the part of the patient? How can symptoms of anxiety be calmed through religious means?

The general directives of Abbé Gebus are an important basis for the formation of modern pastoral psychiatry. Thus the care of the souls of the mentally disturbed is no longer a purposeless activity, but has become a fruitful phase of the spiritual care of souls and can no longer be considered outside the scope of mental hygiene.

2. Hospitals and the Care of Souls

The care of souls in the hospital is characterized by the fact of helping persons afflicted with diverse diseases. A large hospital contains the following principal departments:

1) Intern Department
2) Surgical Department
3) Gynecologico-Obstetrical Department
4) Pediatric (children) Department
5) Dermatologico-Venereological Department (for skin and venereal diseases)

6) Urological Department
7) Ophthalmological Department (for eye diseases)
8) Otorhinolaryngolgical Department (for larynx, nose and ear diseases)
9) Neurological Department
10) Tuberculosis Department
11) Special Department for Infectious Diseases
12) Department for X-Ray, Radium and Physical Therapy

In small hospitals we often find only the intern and surgical sections; to the latter also belong then the tasks of a urologic and gynecologic-obstetric department. It is evident that this is not desirable, but is only a solution of expediency. The special departments (7-12) are found only in large hospitals.

A department for pathological anatomy with a laboratory for chemical, microscopic and serologic research should be present in every hospital when this is within means. We mention it for the sake of completeness. It is of interest to the hospital chaplain insofar as he is to preserve the dignity of the cadaver and be concerned regarding the treatment of the body during an autopsy. The chaplain should also make sure that deceased fetus arising from abortion is placed in a becoming place.

The operating room with its adjoining rooms (preparation room, sterilization room) is the principal center of action in any hospital. The nurses of surgery and anesthesia (if narcosis is not fulfilled by a specialized anesthetist) are the principal assistants of the chief surgeon. Of similar importance, and this for the departments, is the central X-ray institute; besides this, in large hospitals, the individual departments also have their own X-ray station. The personnel attached to the X-ray room are exposed to serious danger to health because of the continuous exposition to the radioactive irradiations. Protection against irradiation has increased in modern times and makes it possible to avoid the damages which at one time were very frequent: burns and ulcers from X-ray; irradiation castration and serious anemia. The personnel attached to X-ray work should be frequently changed.

The care of the sick is almost exclusively fulfilled by female persons (nurses). The nurses have been employed in special tasks which require great strength, especially in mental hospitals. The nurses were, up to the time of the first World War, predominantly nuns belonging to the different nursing orders as the Vincentians (Mercy Sisters), Elizabethians, Borromeans, the Sisters of St. Joseph, the Franciscans, etc.

Since about 1918, the picture of hospital care has basically changed in this regard. Already during the first World War the nuns were mostly integrated by the Red Cross nurses. From 1918 on we are faced with the systematic secularization of the care of the sick which is often favored, through political considerations, by state authority and by its sanitary and hospital offices. In relation to this phenomenon the care of souls in the hospital is definitely made more difficult. From 1945 matters, in this respect, have really become better, but are not yet completely satisfactory. In an International Congress (Lucerne, 1955) it was established that the tendency of eliminating the care of souls still persists.

There exist today schools for professional nurses in which lay persons are taught the art of caring for the sick. These schools for nurses are of great worth since they inculcate in their nurses a culture of the first class from the scientific and technical standpoint. It is obvious that the nurses belonging to the different religious orders realize this and do all to avoid lagging behind the lay nurses in efficiency. If this were ever the case, it should be decided that the religious nurses be definitely disbanded.

The spiritual care of the sick will be essentially promoted by the religious nurses. They will remind the priest of the serious and impending operations, of complications or of grave danger to life. The comfort of the priest's words will not be imposed on anyone. But, when willingly accepted and when added to the administration of the sacraments, it always becomes for the sick a source of consolation and of strength.

In the obstetrical and gynecological departments, the chaplain is not only concerned with the baptism of the newly born but also with the problem of abortion; at times concerning the evaluation of the "indications," but more often concerning the stage of the intervention that has already been initiated or concerning the treatment following an *abortus completus*. Every embryo or fetus prematurely expelled from the womb should be baptized absolutely if life is certain, conditionally if life is uncertain, and not at all if certainly dead. In cases of apparent death, an aborted fetus or newly-born child should be conditionally baptized unless putrefaction is present. When there is doubt concerning the presence of life in a fetus, it should be baptized at once and conditionally. Abortion differs from premature delivery. Abortion is the expulsion of the inviable fetus from the womb of its mother while premature delivery is the birth of a child before the normal and natural time, but after the period of viability has been reached. Premature delivery of a child is morally justifiable whenever there is a sufficient reason for this procedure. When there is a reasonable fear that the viable fetus will die before delivery, it should, when possible, be baptized in the uterus as long as the life of the mother is not endangered. When a cesarean section offers the only chance of saving the mother's life, the operation is permitted. It is open to serious doubt whether a dying mother is morally obliged to undergo the operation. The operation may be suggested to her in a diplomatic and cautious manner, but insistence on a moral obligation to provide baptism for the child is to be avoided. In the dermatology and venereology department the chaplain will encounter victims of venereal infections, the latter effects of which he will encounter in the department of neurology.

The chaplain may encounter special problems in the department of tuberculosis. Even from the standpoint of therapy and prognosis the conditions have definitely become better so that the atmosphere of the "enchanted mountain" no longer constitutes a danger to the will to live and work on the part of the patient.[7]

As manifold as the problem of spiritually caring for the sick appears at first sight, because of the manifold nature of the diseases, yet they all have a common basis: it is a matter of treating with people who are suffering, some of whom need the comfort given by the priest, others who reject the priest and still others who are indifferent or who seek the same but do not find it. In all these cases, however, disease disturbs the foundation, and hence spiritual care of the sick is to be considered, in its entirety, as a sphere in which the chaplain can find great satisfaction.

---

[7] Thomas Mann, in his novel *Der Zauberberg* (*The Enchanted Mountain*) has described in accurate manner how the prolonged stay of the tubercular patients in a sanatorium diminishes the will to live in them and affects them morally. The patients who physically succumb to the tuberculosis are usually first overcome mentally.

3. Care of the Sick at Home

While in former times the greater part of the sick confined to bed was cared for at home and hospital care was administered only in serious circumstances—above all, in the fulfillment of an operation (many operations were at one time conducted at home)—the modern hospital, with its technical resources, with its asepsis and organized assistance down to the minutest details, has taken over from the home for the most part the assistance and care of the sick. At present only temporary acute diseases or chronic diseases concerning which nothing more can be clinically done are cared for at home. Hence, even the priest in his spiritual work has little association with such diseases. In case of acute but temporary diseases either a cure takes place soon or, when complications arise, the sick person is taken to the hospital. It is rather the patients who have little or no chance of living who still call the priest to the bedside.

These patients are also accepted in ever-increasing numbers in hospitals for chronic diseases and in nursing homes, that is, homes for the incurables *(maisons de pitié)*. These patients are no longer subjects for medical treatment, but rather have need of spiritual assistance. Among these we find old people who for years have been confined to bed and who are no longer on their feet; patients with inoperable and incurable cancer for whom even radiotherapy is no longer of any avail; patients in the last stage of multiple sclerosis or with total paralysis from apoplexy; in brief, patients for whom there is nothing more that can be done and who await the end which is, however, not proximate. In these cases the task of the priest consists merely in helping the sick prepare well for death. But since these patients are more easily accessible to spiritual care, they are usually appreciative and hence a consolation to the priest.

Thus, prescinding from the consolation received by the patients, spiritual assistance represents not only a very precious means of mental hygiene, but it is, at the same time, one of the most efficacious means of the mission.

Such missionary tasks must never be forgotten nor lost sight of; yet, on the other hand, this task should not be excessively placed in the foreground. It would otherwise endanger the confidence already entrusted and give occasion to the objection of making use of physical and mental suffering for the purpose of "hunting for souls" at the bedside of the sick. The enemies of the faith have objected that the sick have become "agitated" and suffered through this means.

F. The Missionaries

1. Foreign Missions

By missionaries we here mean those priests who travel to foreign lands for the purpose of announcing the Gospel among the infidels. Protestantism distinguishes this sphere of the missions as "external mission" from that of "internal mission," which has for its purpose the alleviation of social conditions.

The activity of the missions in foreign lands is still very dangerous to the life and health of the missionaries. As the mission doctor, the missionary must have an adequate knowledge of the more important tropical diseases and their prophylaxis, that is, he should have a basic knowledge of the specific nature of tropical hygiene. Among other things, he should know especially the symptoms and the prevention of trachoma (the "Egyptian eye disease"); certain forms of tropical diseases which are associated with dermatology and neurology, as beriberi and leprosy; disease provoked by microorganisms and parasites, as malaria and its forms, the tropical amoebic dysentery, yellow fever and blackwater fever, the plague, cholera, typhus and spotted fever, the sleeping sickness and intestinal diseases as bilharziosis and filariasis (a diseased state due to the presence of filariae [nematode worms] within the body); further, the divesting proceeding forms of tuberculosis, syphilis and framboesia (skin disease like that of syphilis).

Missionary work in the leper colonies requires a very special dedication and at times a complete sacrifice of life. In this regard we recall Father Damien De Venster.

A knowledge of endemic medicine and its methods is also important for the missionary—even the witchcraft medicine of the medicine men in order to be able to oppose it more efficiently. The greatest difficulty of the mission arises from these medicine men; further, from the disdain of the colored people by the whites and the immorality of the white person (alcoholism, syphilis); finally, from the lack of native clergy.

Concerning questions of tropical hygiene which are of importance to the missionary, we mention the following:

The climate of the tropics as such is less harmful to health than is usually believed. The danger lies in the specific tropical infectious diseases and in the lack of resistance on the part of the white people against these diseases.

Even our harmful infectious diseases (measles, scarlet fever) affect the natives disastrously when they come in contact with them for the first time. The more frequent tropical diseases which cause death to the white people are yellow fever and the serious forms of tropical malaria (quotidiana, tropica). The acclimatization is made more difficult by many diseases, especially through the humidly warm air which leads to heat accumulation. The white person is exposed to a serious danger because of alcoholism which in the tropics manifests itself as a mania. Sleep is often disturbed in the hot nights while the sexual libido often is unhealthily increased, which leads to a mixture of whites and blacks. The race and half-breed problems will be treated later.

Important for the suitability of service in the tropics are the following points. The maximum age for the first attempt toward acclimatization is forty years; absence of adiposity, negative Wassermann reaction. The vaccinations against smallpox, cholera, typhus and dysentery should be well tolerated; absence of abnormal reaction to quinine (proof of tolerance for quinine): absolute exclusion of epileptics, neuropaths, psychopaths, drug addicts, etc. Arteriosclerosis, liver disease, diabetes, and gastric ulcer exclude suitability as does any sickness that requires a particular diet.

The nutrition of the whites in the tropics is extremely difficult: the white person should be able to remove himself completely from his habits of nutrition and way of life to which he was accustomed in his homeland. Even the problem of a dwelling place is often very complicated. A notable complication is provoked by the plague of noxious insects. The dwelling places are often exposed to the dangers brought on by tropical ants and termites which are difficult to combat. The fleas are dangerous inasmuch as they transmit epidemics. Mosquitoes transmit malaria, flies (Tse-

Tse) sleeping sickness, and gnats the yellow fever. DDT has made the struggle against the insects more effective.

The clothing in the tropics should be arranged according to the climate. The wearing of the same heavy religious habit which the missionary wore in his homeland, e.g., the heavy Franciscan habit, will not be practical in the tropics. Going barefoot should be definitely avoided in the tropics because of the sand fleas, filaria, poisonous insects, spiders, scorpions, and snakes.

For the hygiene of the natives it is of utmost importance that a hospital be erected and, if possible, that it be closely associated with the mission station. The mission doctor is the most important helper and associate of the missionary. It is very important that the mission doctor be adept not only in tropical hygiene, but in surgery, obstetrics and dermato-venerology.

In summation, it is to be said that the missionary should possess strong health. He should be aware of the fact that a good part of the missionaries succumb to the dangers of health and other dangers associated with the mission and should be prepared to sacrifice his life for the missions. He should observe the norms of hygiene as far as possible; in case of necessity, however, he can take these norms into consideration in the same manner as a soldier in combat.

2. Parish Missions

The parish missions serve to reanimate from time to time the religious life in the parishes, especially when certain signs of weakness manifest themselves. They consist basically of a series of mission sermons of the nature of public exercises, having as their scope the preparation for the worthy reception of the sacraments. Preaching and the hearing of confessions are the principal functions of a parish mission. A parish mission successfully conducted can bring about a deep religious revival. Parish missions, as extraordinary means toward the care of souls, are especially effective among the rural population.

In the customary Sunday sermons the pastor, especially in the rural parishes, is wont to complain reasonably that his sermons are heard by a small part of his parishioners, by those who fulfill their duties faithfully and spontaneously; but those for whom the sermons are mostly intended manage to remain almost always outside the church.

The parish missions place great demands on the pastors and his assistants as well as on the missionaries themselves. They are exercises of great value, even from the mental hygienic standpoint. In case of epidemics with grave danger of contagion the gatherings of people connected with the mission should be opportunely postponed.

3. Pilgrimages

Pilgrimages, i.e., tours or travels to a shrine (place of grace) take place under the direction of a priest and should be primarily dedicated to prayer, meditation and edification. It is of no importance whether it is a matter of a pilgrimage to a nearby shrine, which can be reached on foot, or very long pilgrimages by train or other conveyance. In the latter case there are for the most part arrangements for reserved buses, trains or planes.

In the pilgrimages organized by the Marian Lourdes Committee, even the sick in bed are transported in special sleeping conveyances for the sick, and in such a case medical and infirmary care must be provided. The author can attest to the fact that a pilgrimage to Lourdes entails notable medical and nursing assistance. These cases are usually very serious cases in which all means of natural cure have been used and are, for the most part, hopeless cases. Nevertheless, it is wonderful to notice how the psychological reaction, even in those returning without a cure, is completely different from that manifested on their way to the shrine. All, without exception, return to their sufferings with absolute calmness and complete resignation. The most seriously sick persons from all over the world congregate in the sanctuary of Lourdes; a similar reunion of acute and chronic sickness and of human suffering cannot be found in any hospital. In no place however—and this can be said in a definite manner—is there found such fervor in prayer and unconditional resignation to grace. But the greatest graces of Lourdes are not the visible healings but the interior conversions especially in the attitude toward sickness and suffering.

From the hygienic standpoint, the concern regarding the use of the fonts, especially the baths, is understandable. But the very circumstance that every concern pertaining to hygiene is intentionally ignored and yet no transmission of disease has arisen from the use of the fonts should cause serious thought even to the infidel orientated in positivistic tendencies.

It is quite evident that we are here concerned with elements which are different from those which can be rationally comprehended from the hygienic standpoint. In this regard one can also answer another question, namely, whether pilgrimages should be absolutely avoided during the time of epidemic and contagion. To this proposition we answer that they should be definitely avoided until there is the assurance that the epidemic can be eliminated by the natural means of hygiene. But if an epidemic assumes such proportions that hygiene would be forced to capitulate and the people become desperate, that there would be nothing else to do than to invoke heavenly aid, then the concern for hygiene should take a secondary place. In such a case there would only be one imperative: pray!

As long as the emergency has not reached its highest point, the hygienic norms should be observed and the pilgrimages and gatherings should be avoided. But if the natural means show themselves to be insufficient, then a spiritual director conscious of his duty should not fear to assume the responsibility which entails the adoption of extreme means of emergency.

G. Spiritual Director and Doctor

That which we have indicated concerning the spiritual director in his activity in prison work, in institutions of detention, in mental institutions and hospitals, in regard to pilgrimmages and the missions, as well as the association between the missionary and mission doctor has clarified only a few of the many associations which occur between priest and doctor. Only a short résumé is here permitted.

1. "Medical-Priests"

In very ancient civilization we find the priest and doctor united in one person, the so-called "medical-priest." The "medicine men" of primitive people still represent a remnant of this primitive relation. They exercise an extraordinary power over their tribe and are, therefore, the most bitter adversaries of the missions.

In our day the doctor who professes a materialistic-positivistic medicine has again acquired a strong power over people. At times he is still one of the most influential adversaries of a re-evangelization of our times, especially if he has become indifferent to the scientific progress of the last fifty years. On the other hand, there is a tendency of reviving the "medical priest" of former times. It was felt that the "rationalism" in medicine could be overcome by resorting to an "irrationalism" and to a "natural myth" by which one allowed the resounding recalling of the "medical priest." Here truth and error are dangerously mingled. Here truth is dangerously confused with error. In the ancient association of religion and medicine, if well understood, there is profound truth. Its reintroduction should be welcomed. But there should not be a resurgence of elements proper to a "magical" epoch in which a natural primitive demonology prevailed. The need of a "medical priest" is a contradiction in a time which ever seeks to laicize the priest and which seeks to bestow priestly tasks upon lay people.

2. Delimitation of Competences

In more recent times one has gone too far in stating, in view of the progress of psychotherapy, that in the future the doctor will render the priest superfluous and that he will become the "future director of souls" (Grosschopf). These tendencies, which manifest themselves under the banner of a modern irrationalism, have had their parallel in the age of Rationalism, but in an inverse direction. While the modern era seeks to attribute to the doctor the functions of the director of souls, it seeks to make a doctor of the priest. Thus the State has authorized the priest to assume, when there was a lack of doctors in the country, the treatment of the sick in order to "render them useful." The designation, "pastoral medicine," was well adapted to those "manuals of medicine" which strove to give to the country parish priests the medical knowledge which was useful to them (medicina ruralis). Marx rejected this confusion of competences: "A pastor medicus is as absurd as a doctor acting as a pastor."

Such a confusion of competence does not correspond to the

spirit of pastoral hygiene and has been definitely rejected by the same. The doctor cannot and should not tend to be a "substitute spiritual director" in the same manner as the priest should not play the part of a "substitute doctor." This does not mean that in extraordinary cases of necessity circumstances could not arise in which the priest is called upon to intervene in a decisive manner. A similar eventuality can be verified in mission sections where the mission doctor cannot be reached. In itself such "substitution," which is nothing more than a substitute, that is, an emergency, is not auspicious. It would be definitely erroneous basically to restrict this possibility of emergency through motives of prestige as it would be erroneous to foster these competences basically.

Even the doctor can find himself in a situation in which he will occasionally undertake the part of a "substitute director of souls." Such a situation is very possible in psychotherapy. But the doctor can dedicate himself to this task only in a subsidiary manner, that is, only until the patient has found his way to the priest. But the doctor should never claim for himself tasks which belong to the spiritual director.

The more the limitations of these competences are correctly respected and the more any exaggerations are avoided, the more satisfactory and fruitful will be their collaboration. It is advantageous toward the cure of the sick and serves toward the reciprocal spiritual fructification of both spheres.

3. "Medical Care of Souls" or Medical Help in the Care of Souls

The title of the famous work of Frankl, *Artzliche Seelsorge (Medical Care of Souls)* can give the impression that the author wishes to attribute to the doctor tasks which pertain to the care of souls. Frankl has rejected such an interpretation as a misunderstanding of his viewpoint. He has accepted the formula of the subsidiary spiritual function of the doctor.

Thus Frankl rejects with reason every "concession" by which the doctor attempts to influence his patient's philosophy of life. It is not compatible with the liberty of the personality which the doctor has to respect no less than the priest. If a patient seriously seeks help in his life problems and cannot resolve the same alone, the doctor can and should be a guiding light for him inasmuch as the doctor possess the necessary orientation and the patient explicitly seeks his counsel. His task of direction ends where that of the competent priest begins.

It would be more accurate to indicate the cooperation of the doctor in the sphere of practical pastoral work as "medical help in the care of souls." In view of certain actual questions of pastoral and social hygiene, it seems particularly important that this cooperation be formulated according to determined plans. It represents an analogy of the mission doctor's tasks as medical helper of the mission itself (not however as a "medical missionary").

Medical aid in the care of souls, by means of its human and charitable results, opens the way for the spiritual director. For the most part, the doctor presents himself to men estranged from religion as a helper in corporal and social needs, and also as a psychotherapist in psychic needs. At present three circumstances determine the particular necessity of a medical aid in the care of souls: 1) the social critical states of the large city and its border spheres, suburbs *(banlieue);* 2) the confusion and the aberrations in the sphere of the sexual life; 3) the increase of serious alterations of the physic life.

The cooperation between the doctor and the priest can thus result in a twofold direction: in the direction from the priest to the doctor, and in that which goes from the doctor to the priest.

The first case is that in which the patient (as a penitent) first seeks the priest and is directed by him to the doctor: It is here a matter of limited questions between pastoral medicine and pastoral hygiene difficult to resolve without the technical cooperation of the doctor; for example, the question of impotency, of the difficulty in the consummation of marriage, of the practice of the Rhythm, of aid in pregnancy complications so as to avoid a spontaneous abortion or miscarriage.

The second case, which ordinarily presents a psychotherapeutic character, is that in which the patient first calls on the doctor. The latter often comes to the conclusion that the patient "has greater need of the priest than the doctor," especially when there is not only a morbid feeling of guilt, but real guilt actually exists.

An important sphere of common collaboration between the

priest and the doctor is that of marriage counseling which we shall consider later.

4. Quackery

Nothing can more disturb the necessary relationship of confidence between the priest and the doctor as an inadmissible overstepping of competence on one or the other part. As the priest rightfully chides the doctor when he begins to play the role of a "spiritual director," so does the doctor disapprove with equal reason when the priest attempts to treat the sick. The priest would thus commit a punishable act of quackery, at least in places in which the practice of medicine is prohibited by anyone who does not possess a medical license recognized by the State. The problem of quackery is one of the most serious and controversial problems of social hygiene. We are to judge it here from the standpoint of pastoral hygiene.

The very definition itself of "quackery" is difficult and controversial. We here understand it in the sense of an unauthorized practice of medicine by persons who "without receiving medical instruction and legal authorization to treat the sick, exercise the same professionally in the capacity of doctors and of surgeons."

If the priest occasionally gives some advice to the sick or even "goes about doctoring a little"—which, from a simple form of dilettantism, can easily become a passion—it involves an action which does not present the character of the "professional practice of medicine"; he, therefore, does not run the risk of a conflict with penal law. A danger can exist insofar as it pertains to legal authority to establish at what point the frequent acceptance of gifts can indicate the characteristic of "professionality."

The acceptance of gifts becomes inevitable, especially in country places, when the priest often intervenes with counsel concerning the curative treatment of the sick. If he does not accept the gifts, he will offend the persons who have no other means of demonstrating their appreciation; if he does accept the same, he can incur the sanctions of law, especially when the doctor reacts with hostility and resorts to law.

We have to admit that there have been many priests who have begun as "healers" and have become great benefactors and helpers of humanity. But, even in these cases, one cannot ignore the admonition *"admirandum quidem, sed not imitandum"* ("It is definitely to be admired, but not imitated."). Hence, it is better for both parties if each limits himself to the task designated by the nature of his profession. It is not the place here to consider in detail the remote origins of the problem of quackery and its ineradicability. We indicate that these origins are found in the sphere of the "irrational" in which medicine moves with her "older sister," magic; it is of the essence of medicine that it is not only a science, but also an art, and, at the same time, a charisma.

There are personalities who possess this charisma in far greater measure than those who have been scientifically approved and have obtained a degree. But the State, in the interest of public hygiene cannot permit the medical art to be exercised by persons other than those who have obtained their license after having appeared before examiners authorized by the State. Therefore, in the interest of the priest himself and in order to have the proper cooperation between the care of souls and medicine, we again place a guard against quackery prohibited to clerics by Canon 139, §2 of the Code of Canon Law.

V. CELIBACY

A. Juridical Questions

The celibacy of the priest (from *caelebs,* not married) is the state of non-marriage regulated by Canon Law to which those ordained in the major orders are obliged. Celibacy is an institution of Canon Law *(ius ecclesiasticum)* and not of divine law. Insofar as this institution is regulated by positive ecclesiastical law, it is basically susceptible of modification. Against this change is the tradition of the Church and the fact that, despite the many difficulties associated with it, celibacy has been realized in practice. In the Oriental rite, in which celibacy is not obligatory for secular priests, but only for monks and bishops, the marriage of priests has led to greater difficulties than those that have resulted from celibacy in the Latin rite.

B. Hygienic Questions

It would be one-sided to judge an ecclesiastical institution (as celibacy) merely from the hygienic standpoint. The considerations of an ecclesiastical, disciplinary and moral nature will be evaluated at the end of this chapter.

From the hygienic standpoint especially, two questions should be studied: from the standpoint of individual hygiene, the question whether celibacy implies for the individual priest a harm to health; from the standpoint of social hygiene, and especially of eugenics, whether celibacy can signify a harm to public health.

In regard to the first question we observe that the presumed damages to health through sexual abstinence have not been demonstrated. If abstinence could in general provoke some inconvenience to health, it is more a matter of mild nervous disturbances, and even these are verified only in persons of a labile nervous system, especially in psychopathic personalities, who are not adapted to bear the sacerdotal burden and who should be prevented from taking major orders. For normal persons, with a normal intensity of the instinct and with normal strength of will, the domination of the sexual instinct without serious harm to health is not only possible but definitely necessary even under the hygienic standpoint. Even today is valid the famous opinion of Forel: "I have seen many victims of sexual excesses but have not yet seen any victims of abstinence." It has been a bad habit, which is not scientifically justified, for doctors to impute every possible and imaginable morbid phenomenon among celibate patients to the "unnatural mode of life" of celibacy.

In this regard the statistical findings of social hygiene cannot be omitted that the average life-age among married persons is much higher than that of the celibates.

This fact would speak in favor of an antihygienic action of celibacy, if we did not take into consideration the fact that in the majority of non-married persons the reasons for a shorter life are completely different from those found among priests: above all, the anti-hygienic mode of life of the greater number of "bachelors" with their habitual excesses in Bacchus and Venus and the high tribute paid by them to venereal infections. Celibacy as such cannot be held responsible for the shortening of life affected by the irregular mode of life which the unmarried priest as well as the married doctor undergo.

In recent times attacks upon celibacy from the psycho-hygienic standpoint are becoming more numerous.

It is objected that man, in order to perfect his personality, has need of "contact" with the opposite sex; without this man remains psychically incomplete; it pertains to "full humanity."

If man represses this need of nature, conflicts and faulty neurotic behavior arise, and these can lead to disintegration of the personality. This objection overlooks the value which interior and external virginity can offer for the supernatural maturity of the personality; it ignores what grace can do for nature and what enrichment of the human personality it can signify. Yet such objections are instructive for a critical orientation of our times against celibacy, an orientation which has penetrated into the ranks of the clergy. Of celibacy no less than of the monastic life it is said that "it is no longer adapted to the present time." It is by no means accidental that the objections against celibacy utilize the conceptual formation of the philosophy of Existentialism and of the psychology of C. G. Jung.

Even more deplorable is the attitude of certain medical circles regarding the presumed "dysgenic" effect of celibacy.

In this regard one speaks readily of the phenomenon of "differentiated reproduction"; if in a national organism "inferior individuals" are reproduced without limitation, persons of great physical and spiritual worth who evade the duty of reproduction cannot be tolerated, especially in view of the contraselective effects of the war, which has indiscriminately destroyed a hereditary patrimony of inestimable value. Even certain authors who have, under other aspects, affirmed the legitimacy, the possibility and the necessity of sexual abstinence, have made use of the racial hygienic argument against celibacy (Abderhalden, Lockemann and others). Johann Peter Frank, the social hygienist of Josephinism, had combatted celibacy with this form of argumentation. Hartnacke designated it as the "source of social biological damage"; authors who were defenders of eugenic sterilization have rejected celibacy as "moral sterilization."

The true cause of the deplorable "differentiated reproduction" does not lie in celibacy, but in birth decline, especially in the general decline of marriage fertility; further, in the serious generative damages of social strength through venereal diseases, through abortion and the increase of sterility, especially of secondary sterility caused by all forms of sexual abuses. The deficit of a healthy new generation, conditioned by this fact, is far superior to that which can be attributed to celibacy. This could be a point upon which the forces of true eugenics can be used with success. In the healthy body of a population, deficiency of births ascribed to celibacy cannot play a role and is not even worthy of mention.

If attention is given to the importance which large families have upon civilization and if at the same time the family of the Protestant pastor is added as a model, these considerations must definitely be taken into account; but as an argument against celibacy they lose their value. The majority of priests came, up to recent times, from large families; and it is their decline which is basically the cause of the lack of priests.

Among the numerous families of Protestant pastors, the author has observed many who lead exemplary lives; but the author has also had the opportunity to observe the preoccupations which oppress the married pastor and force him to dedicate his time, for the sake of supplementary gain, to work that is extraneous to his ministry (substitute teaching, farming, cattle-breeding, etc.). More than one have admitted to the author their admiration of the Catholic Church for her law of celibacy and deplored the banality of the arguments posited against it. These arguments fail to recognize the great and deep association between celibacy and the Catholic Church's conception of marriage, between the two sacraments of Holy Orders and matrimony.

Celibacy and the Catholic conception of matrimony are closely associated. The ideal of virginity and that of sacramental marriage constitute an essential basis for sanctity and the fecundity of matrimony. The deep meaning of this association has been greatly evaluated by the freethinkers and the adversaries of the Church.

Krafft-Ebing emphasizes the emancipation from the lower sensual instincts in order to completely preserve the spiritual forces in the ministry. Sved Ribbing calls attention to the significative example of the control of sexuality and considers it as a "moral cultural force" of extraordinary importance.

Finally, the example of numerous learned men and researchers, who have decided to live exclusively for their science shows how they are prepared to sacrifice, through love of this mission, their life, marriage and the family.

The Catholic concept of marriage is the native soil of a genuine eugenics. If it becomes again common patrimony, marriages will again become prolific and fruitful. The number of priests who, because of celibacy, do not contribute to the increase of population, cannot represent a deficiency in a healthy national organism, but rather constitutes an inestimable increase of strength for spiritual paternity and bulwark in defense of the purity of marriage as a basis of society, and thus also a basis of the true health of the people.

C. Moral and Religious Questions

The objections of a hygienic nature alleged against celibacy have manifested themselves, as we have seen, to be devoid of any basis. It now remains to consider these objections from the moral and religious standpoint.

From the standpoint of ecclesiastical discipline there are more reasons for celibacy than against it. Above all is the fact that only the priest, not obliged to the care of a family, is in the position of intervening in any moment, with liberty and necessary independence, in favor of the purity of doctrine and morals, "opportune, importune," even against the power of dictatorial states.

The priest cannot be divided; his mission demands total dedication, an absolute "vacare Deo." The number of tasks which such a varied spiritual paternity requires is with difficulty compatible with the serious duties of physical paternity. Surely there is here no absolute law of incompatibility, but the marriage of priests does not represent an advantage for the sacerdotal ministry.

Among the clergy of the Oriental Rite, as also in Protestant communities, there are undoubtedly families that lead an exemplary life; but even in these cases collision of duties too often arise which are not advantageous to the ministerial state. But if the family relations—even without any fault on the part of the cleric —are disturbed, there arise inconveniences more serious than those imputed to celibacy.

From the moral standpoint the inconveniences resulting from the infraction of celibacy are indicated. Prescinding from the fact that these inconveniences are often notably exaggerated, if for no other reason than a single fall makes more of an impression than hundreds of cases in which the commandment of the Church is quietly and faithfully followed, so it can in no way be said that, with the abolition of celibacy, the inconveniences will vanish.

The marriage of priests is by no means the simple and infallible panacea that it is indicated to be. If it is held that human nature is too weak to fulfill the heroic demands of celibacy, then it must not be forgotten that every Christian marriage imposes upon human nature such grave demands that celibacy appears as the easier form of life. No state of life can fulfill its duties without grace. No human being on his own strength can remain completely pure either in the celibate or matrimonial state; but *"omnia possum in eo qui confortat me."*

One can object that it would be better not to have celibacy rather than a bad or scandalous celibacy. But this institution is not of its nature such that it should necessarily be represented as bad or scandalous. On the contrary, a good celibacy is an edifying example of the power of the spirit over the instinct and is therefore a protective bulwark for the sacrament of matrimony. Celibacy, obligatory throughout the Latin Church after the reform of Cluny (c.1100), has proven itself. Continual attacks by the enemies of the Church against this point give testimony of the fact. Hence a good celibacy is by far better than no celibacy at all. Strength and grace flow from a good celibacy. After mature reflection it can be stated that it is not possible to point any serious argument against celibacy either from the hygienic or moral standpoint. The profound nature of celibacy cannot be completely understood on a purely natural basis but can only be understood when considered on a supernatural basis; *"qui potest capere, capiat"* (Mt. 19, 12).

The nature of virginity and celibacy cannot be completely understood solely from the moral standpoint. It is definitely a matter of sacrifice offered to God for the salvation of souls: of a sacrifice of the highest value.

In this concept there is no underevaluation of sexuality; in fact it is highly evaluated as a value of life, as a *bonum excellens* (St. Thomas). In fact, only a sacrifice of high value is worthy of God; when it is offered with intense resignation, the mortification of asceticism is united to the supreme illumination of mysticism.

4 Actual Problems of Social Hygiene in the Light of Pastoral Hygiene

Pastoral hygiene would be incomplete if it did not contain a study of important problems of social hygiene.

I. PREMARITAL INSTRUCTION AND MARRIAGE COUNSELING

The so-called "investigation of the spouses" to which the priest subjects the couple before he assists at the religious celebration of marriage serves a twofold purpose:

1) to exclude in the most secure possible manner the eventual existence of matrimonial impediments;

2) to ascertain, as a matter of duty, whether the spouses have a sufficiently clear idea of the nature of the marriage consent and the relative consequences.

Ad 1) the existence of marriage impediments can only be established with proximate certitude since it is always possible that some impediment could be concealed.

Marriage swindlers, who are already validly married, know how cleverly to hide the fact of the existence of an *impedimentum*

221

ligaminis. It is very difficult to establish the existence of the *impedimentum impotentiae* before the contracting of marriage. Even in regard to the *impedimentum ordinis* there have arisen at times dissimulatory maneuvers. Because of this, there is required, on the part of the priest, special attention and experience.

Ad 2) Many so interpret this part of the investigation of spouses that the priest is expected to undertake the delicate task of instructing the couple concerning the reciprocal marriage duties. But it is essential that the priest be assured that the couple has understood the nature and content of the matrimonial consent. The priest must be convinced that the engaged couple is capable of consent according to the requirements of Canon Law, that is, that they are *personae iure habiles* in the sense of Can. 1081.

It is, therefore, necessary to ascertain:

1) whether the spouses can in general give a valid consent;
2) whether they have a clear understanding of the nature and content of this consent. They must be instructed that it is a matter of *traditio mutua* and precisely of a complete, reciprocal physical and spiritual surrender for the purpose of fulfilling the *finis primarius matrimonii,* that is, the *procreatio et educatio prolis;* to explain this with the words of Canon Law: *"in ordine ad actus per se aptos ad generationem prolis."*

In this connection the question of the so-called "matrimony of St. Joseph" is to be briefly explained. Widely diffused is the erroneous idea that a so-called "matrimony of St. Joseph" exists when a woman marries a man who is impotent or no longer is capable of fulfilling the marriage act. This is not a valid marriage since the essential requirements for the validity of marriage are lacking. In this case the *traditio mutua* is not present since there is nothing to hand over. Impotence is in every case a matrimonial impediment of natural law.

Essentially different is the case in which the matrimonial right *(ius matrimonii)* is not denied or the right is not excluded, but only the use of the right *(usus iuris)* is renounced. But it must be a case of voluntary renouncement. We can speak of a marriage of St. Joseph only when a so-called voluntary renouncement takes place because of supernatural motives. It presupposes, however, the *potentia coeundi,* since, when this is not present, there is neither a renouncement nor a *traditio mutua.*

Even in such cases the priest should be careful that he will not be deceived by the illusion of religious motives.

Hence it is not the duty of the priest to "enlighten" the spouses concerning the nature of the marriage union; but he is definitely obliged to procure the certitude that they are able to respond concerning the essence and the import of the duties assumed through consent. This is necessary, for otherwise there is no possibility to demonstrate later the validity of matrimonial consent.

Notwithstanding these obligatory prescriptions, cases are repeatedly presented in which invalidity is claimed on the basis that one of the parties did not have the intention of contracting and fulfilling a marriage according to the Catholic marriage norms; one had, for example, from the beginning, the intention of excluding the procreation of children, the *bonum prolis,* or the unity and indissolubility of marriage, the *bonum sacramenti;* that the will was directed merely toward a "temporary marriage" or toward a revocable marriage. In these cases we speak of a *simulatio totalis vel partialis* of the will to marry.

This is the essential task that the priest has to fulfill in the investigation of the spouses: to exclude through precise questions, a possible future nullity. In view of these two points, the investigation of the spouses remains indispensable, as it was at first, and represents an official act of the pastor of great juridical import. Of great importance, from the pastoral and hygienic standpoint, is the course in preparation for marriage, the direction of which, besides the priest, is entrusted to a doctor and a father and mother of a family. Not absolutely necessary, but desirable, is also the participation of a lawyer. Books and pamphlets on the subject can also serve the purpose.

A. Formation of a Modern Pre-marital Instruction

The investigation of the spouses is not and should not be substituted or supplanted but completed by a modern premarital instruction. From the pastoral hygienic standpoint it is of great importance that such an instruction be formulated in a manner adapted to the times. It is opportune that the instruction be given to separate groups directed by specialists. In practice one group should be directed by a doctor, another by a lawyer, a third by a father of a family and still another by a mother of a family, and all, under full direction of the priest.

The premarital instruction adapted to our times tends to impart to the spouses an introductory guide to the problems of marriage and family life. In order to demonstrate how indispensable is the participation of the doctor we have only to mention the numerous medico-pastoral problems which have also been treated in the encyclical *"Casti Connubii,"* as, for example, the questions of birth control, ryhthm, abortion, eugenics and the measures of selectionistic race hygiene; they are complemented by the important problems of social hygiene and politics which regard the protection of the family and which have been officially treated in the encyclical *"Quadragesimo Anno."* There results for the priest the task of not limiting his premarital instruction merely to the ascertaining of the fact that impediments do not exist and that both parties intend to give valid matrimonial consent. His participation in this instruction should, above all, consist in the interpretation of the encyclical on marriage *"Casti Connubii,"* with reference to the social encyclical *"Quadragesimo Anno"* and to the encyclical on education *"Divini Illius Magistri."* The quantity of ideas contained in these three great papal encyclicals also gives the priest a deep richness of inspiration so as to transform the premarital instruction into an instrument of spiritual direction and orientation of life.

B. Marriage Counseling

The difficult problems of marriage life in our days has also brought marriage counseling to the notable actuality which it now enjoys. Without doubt, there has always been marriage counseling (tacit), partly exercised by the priest in the confessional and in the rectory, and partly by the family doctor by his medical prescriptions, and as a family counselor in his home visits.

Systematic and organized marriage counseling has definitely developed only in our times. Centers of marriage counseling and centers of sex counseling have arisen in great numbers but are not completely under the direction of such persons that there is a guarantee that these centers fulfill their activity according to the spirit of a correct concept of matrimony. In no other sphere as this can incorrectly orientated counseling affect such disastrous harm. We have in another place more than once brought attention upon the serious iatrogenic damages arising from the fact that the doctor, as a marriage counselor, permits himself to lack the orientation in the necessary and wholesome philosophy of life. If he has a materialistic-evolutionistic philosophy of life, he will not acknowledge the basic difference between human and animal sexuality and he will trace back the marriage of human beings to the sexual community of animals. He will hold the opinion that the control of the sexual instinct is impossible and detrimental to health. He will attribute functional sexual disturbances to abstinence and will declare that the patient should give up his "unnatural life" (thus alluding to the state of virginity or of celibacy), otherwise more serious illness will arise. He thereby is unaware of the serious psychic traumatic effects that can in this manner affect the youth and celibates. When the occasion presents itself, he will rather advise birth control and will establish an "indication" for abortion even in the case of mild complications in pregnancy. He will not only declare that masturbation is unimportant and harmless, but will directly advise the same and will tend to minimize even the more serious sexual anomalies.

In regard to masturbation, we have known of cases in which the doctor has explained to the patient that masturbation is not harmful in itself but only the feeling of guilt associated with it, and that the patient could continue masturbation with tranquility, remaining in peace with his conscience, but he should never feel sorrow afterwards and should not permit the appearance of guilt feelings, since only these and not masturbation are responsible for eventual neurotic states.

The examples show how dangerous it is when sex and marriage counseling are entrusted to persons who do not guarantee the correct and blameless exercise of the same. Marriage counseling should be both scientifically and morally unobjectionable; it is preferable not to have marriage counseling than to have erroneous counseling.

From this standpoint it appears absolutely necessary that marriage counseling and its organization become the interest of the spiritual director. In this way a universalistic marriage counseling could be established with the purpose of treating problems not only biological but also social and moral problems.

There has actually been an attempt, especially in view of the inconveniences associated with sex counseling, to limit marriage counseling to purely eugenic tasks, that is to say, to the prevention of a hereditary tainted progeny. Without minimizing the importance of this task, we must state that this represents only a minor part of all the complexities of marriage counseling. It is only a partial sphere and not the most important of marriage counseling. Medical marriage counseling is in turn only a part of the entire complexities of a universalistic marriage counseling. As the universalistic mode of considering pastoral medicine consists not only in the consideration of the biologico-medical aspects of problems, but also of the social and legal and finally even the ethico-metaphysical aspect, so a universalistic marriage counseling should, of its nature, contain the following sections:

1) A section concerning spiritual direction.
2) A section concerning the legal and juridico-social assistance.
3) A section concerning the biologico-medical aspect.
4) A section concerning the physcologico-pedagogical aspect.

The direction of the first section is the task of the spiritual director, who is to also undertake the complete direction.

It is opportune that the direction of the second section be assigned to a lawyer. To his competency belong, besides legal counseling concerning questions of marriage law, the settlement of marital controversies, the prevention of marital processes that can be avoided, and, when these are not avoidable, also a continual process of counseling orientated in the sense of *favor matrimonii*. A social assistant is associated with the legal director. His task is, above all, social counseling and the aid in social needs of every kind and in cases of broken marriages; partly even in cases associated with social medicine, for example, in cases of supposed "social indication," the establishment of a way of helping to avoid abortion, etc.

The direction of the third section should be entrusted to a doctor who will guarantee an unobjectionable direction both scientifically and morally.

The director of the fourth section should be a specialist in psychology or one with a degree in pedagogy; and where this is not possible and the general conditions permit it, this section may be entrusted to a spiritual director instructed in psychology and pedagogy.

In a marriage counseling center under the direction of a spiritual director, all of the four sections should be coordinated. A certain pre-eminence of the section assigned to spiritual direction arises from the fact that general direction is entrusted to it. It also imparts directives in regard to all the basic problems. Hence in regard to principles, the other sections are therefore subordinate to that of spiritual direction, but not so in regard to technical problems. In technical matters each director of a section is responsible only before his own conscience. Only in this way will any possible conflicts be avoided.

The difficulties that can arise in the sphere of marriage mediation can be easily overcome by forming centers of marriage preparation in close association with centers of marriage counseling entrusted to spiritual direction.

Now we have only to consider the biologico-medical aspect of marriage counseling from the standpoint of pastoral medicine and eugenics.

II. HYGIENIC MARRIAGE COUNSELING AND EUGENICS

A. Eugenic Viewpoints

1. Positive and Negative Eugenics

Hygienic marriage counseling is the most important sphere of practical eugenics.

Eugenics is (from the scientific standpoint) the theory of hereditary health and is (from the practical standpoint) the care of hereditary health. If it is a matter of caring and furthering hereditary stock, one speaks of positive eugenics; but if it is a case of eliminating tainted and diseased hereditary stock (prevention of diseased hereditary progeny), one speaks of negative eugenics.

The following pertain to the positive means of eugenics:

1) The furthering of marriage contracts and the establishment of families on a healthy basis (loans for expenses associated with the contracting of marriage and for the establishment of a household, funds for household furniture, etc.).

2) The furthering of healthy and large families, above all, through social political means: family remuneration and burden compensations. These basic measures render a unilateral system of "small patronages" superfluous.

3) Protective laws for mothers and protective provisions for the extra-domestic work of women; the most possible return of women to domestic work by recognizing and acknowledging her household work as a profession and vocation.

4) Centers of marriage counseling. These should pursue their activity in the spirit of a positive eugenics and not that of a negative eugenics.

The following are among the negative measures of eugenics:

1) Rendering more difficult the marriage of hereditary-tainted persons.

2) Legal prohibitions regarding marriage.

3) Legal sterilization of hereditary-tainted persons (hereditary diseases).

4) Castration of the asocial and sex delinquents.

5) Permanent custody (asylum, house of detention) of psychopathic criminals and of asocial persons.

6) Elimination of "life not worth living" (euthanasia) and abortion on the basis of "eugenic indication."

A glance over the negative (eliminating) measures shows that they operate, almost without exception, with immoral means. In the face of these measures we can do nothing else but recall the principle: "Nothing can ever be hygienically correct which is morally false."

Among the negative measures only the first and fifth points can be discussed: impeding the marriage of hereditary-tainted persons is a task of marriage counseling. If serious hereditary deficiencies are present, marriage should be discouraged as is established in the encyclical *"Casti Connubii."* This case is specifically indicated when there is present in both parties a homologous hereditary disease. We will return to this point. Marriage counseling should remain completely free. We reject an obligatory, forced counseling with a prescribed certificate of good health for marriage. This is in effect the same as marriage prohibitions. But marriage prohibitions should be completely rejected at least if it is not a matter of marriage impediments which have their basis in natural law and which are sanctioned by civil and Canon Law. The rigorous observance of these marriage impediments is absolutely in the interest of eugenics, especially when it concerns the following impediments:

1) Age (lack of prescribed age)
2) Consanguinity (blood relationship)
3) Impotence (incapacity regarding the consummation of marriage)

There is no need of introducing other "eugenic marriage impediments." When mental diseases are present (amentia in the sense of Can. 2201), there exists the incapacity of giving consent, according to the meaning of Can. 1081.

2. Racial Problems, Race Hygiene

Marriage prohibitions are to be rejected since every person, on the basis of natural law, has the right of contracting marriage, insofar as he is *sui compos,* that is, capable of expressing a periodically obliging declaration of the will. The contracting of marriage should be permitted to every person capable of responsibility and action *(matrimonia libera esse debent).* This freedom cannot be taken away even when, in a concrete case, the contracting of marriage manifests itself as an act of irresponsibility. It would lead to incalculable consequences if one were to impede every irresponsible action with constrictive measures. The sum total of all the evils arising from such an action would always remain less than the evil constituted by the privation of freedom. We have in recent times experienced the enormous dimensions assumed by legal marital prohibitions: to the prohibitions regarding hereditary diseases, the establishment of which brought with it legal sterilization,[1] there was added the marital prohibitions regarding persons of different races or of mixed races.

Marriage counseling is education regarding responsibility; to it

[1] In the *U. S. News and World Report* of September 24, 1962, under the article entitled: "Sterilization: New Argument," it is stated that "A Virginia law now sanctions free surgery for needy mothers to prevent further childbirth—if they request it. A pioneer program under way in one county has strong local support, but is under heavy fire from some nationally known churchmen."

"In his condemnation, Archbishop Patrick A. O'Boyle, of Washington, D.C., referred to the program as one which obtains the induced consent of the individual." The prelate also declared: "If we cannot eliminate occasional abuses of public assistance without resorting to immoral means of sterilization, the only conclusion that one can logically come to is that our unprecedented material prosperity has sapped our moral fiber and has made us soft and flabby."

belong the respect of the difference in races on the basis of natural order. But respect is quite remote from any form of discrimination. One should avoid speaking of "superior" and "inferior" races. One can speak of "superior" and "inferior" individuals, but the races, as such, are never by nature "inferior." Certain races can remain socially and culturally backward; in this case it is the duty of civilized races to further the progress of the same.

For this reason we should, without reservation, reject the concept of race hygiene and refer to that of eugenics. Since we approve of eugenic marriage counseling, marriage counseling inspired by race hygiene is for us too unilateral. Where it is a matter of relevant differences (white and colored people), the racial problem is to be evaluated as is proper. But even in this case there should not be a legal prohibition but only a responsible evaluation of the difficulty that a "mixed marriage" presents among different races. That which, as an exceptional case, can have satisfactory results should be avoided as a rule. Racial laws, according to which, for example, colored people are treated as citizens with limited rights, and, for the purpose of racial separation, are threatened with isolation ("separate quarters"), are immoral. These laws have nothing to do with hygiene even when they appeal to "race hygiene." Moreover they render the "mission" more difficult to the point of becoming impossible.

B. Universalistic Viewpoint

But even a marriage counseling exclusively eugenic still seems to us to be too restricted and unilateral. We consider it essential for a rightly oriented marriage counseling that it be based on a universalistic end. In order to confer this universalistic form it does not suffice that the medico-hygienic section be united with a juridical section and with one associated with spiritual direction for the purpose of "team work," but that the medical section have a universalistic character, so that it does not limit its activity exclusively to the sphere of eugenics.

Marriage counseling has a very important pedagogical function in regard to the people and should, therefore, include also the sphere of sex life in general, above all, for the purpose of leading back to normality the anomalies that are verified in it. According to this we distinguish the tasks of premarital counseling from those of marriage counseling strictly speaking (intramarital).

C. Premarital Counseling

1. Hereditary Diseases

In this section of marriage counseling, eugenic viewpoints are taken into consideration and it is estimated just how justifiable and tenable these points are. The theories concerning hereditary diseases (hereditary pathology) forms the basis of this section.

a) GENERAL HEREDITARY PATHOLOGY

The principal task of general hereditary pathology is the prevention of homologous hereditary taint on the part of both parents. This factor can become manifest when the spouses are consanguines and both originate from a hereditary tainted line; and, even if they are not blood relatives, when a homologous hereditary taint, manifest (dominant) or latent (recessive), is present in both parties. In this case, when the hereditary factor is dominant, the unfavorable hereditary prognosis is clearer; but, even in the recessive hereditary process where the manifestation is hidden, the presence of the disease in both parties can render it manifest in a fatal manner.

Hence, when it is a case of bilateral hereditary taint with recessive characteristics, the same prudence and perhaps even a greater prudence should be shown than in the case of disease with a dominant hereditary process. Moreover, it must be firmly held that an "homologous" disease does not mean that in both parties or in their ascendants the same disease is present; for example, cleft palate. Instead the concept of "homologous hereditary taint" should be understood in a wider sense, if for no other reason than, instead of genes univocally determined, we are faced more exactly with hereditary potencies which, of their nature, are polyvalent and pluripotent. This can be clarified by the following case: a split uterus (uterus duplex) was reunited in a mother through the Strassmann process; the mother could thus bring a pregnancy to term; the child born by a caesarean section (because of pelvic presentation) manifested a congenital dislocation of the hip (luxatio coxae congenita). There was present here a simple polyvalent hereditary potency toward physical malformations in general, but not a determined disposition toward a certain malformation of a determined organic system. In other cases in a hereditary line the following could be established: hare-lip, cleft of the hand, a fissure of the eyes (coloboma), in alternated order. Under the concept of "homologous hereditary taint" is also included the case in which, on the side of one party, schizophrenia or another mental disease is present and, on the other, only mild defective states, as debility or psychopathy, hysteria or serious neurosis.

Particularly difficult questions arise in diseases with a recessive hereditary process associated with species as, for example, the blood disease (hemophilia). This is transmitted through heredity from the mother (apparently healthy) to the sons. The female members of the hereditary stock are phenotypically healthy but genotypically sick: they function as conductors of the recessive hereditary disposition. The theory of genes supposes that in this case the "sick gene" is united to chromosome Y, which determines the female sex, which is activated by the chromosome X, which determines the male sex. Thus there are the descendants of the male sex whose heterochromosomes are exactly "heterozygote" (XY), while the descendants of the female sex react as "homozygote" (YY).

In the hereditary process of hemophilia there are still many problems to be resolved before being able to contribute, by means of marriage counseling, to the prevention of the hereditary transmission of this disease.

The laws of Mendel concerning hereditary transmission permit, within certain limits, a definite hereditary prognosis even in men. Man is no exception to the general rules of amphimixis, with the sole difference that in him matters are more complicated, as has been surmised in the first enthusiasm for a hygiene of race.

The practical application of Mendelism in animal and plant breeding is far more complicated than had been at first perceived.

It is rare, in pairs of characteristics simply and easily perceivable, that the verification of the law of the dominant and recessive hereditary process is encountered without some deviation. Higher Mendelism has made use of many keen explanations in order to justify the innumerable deviations from the expected verification of the law. Man is definitely a "polyhybrid, indefinitely heterozygotic, and from the innumerable combinations of hereditary unity which are possible in each pair, only few are realized" (Schallmayer).

For this reason human genetics and hereditary pathology are satisfied with an "empirical hereditary prognosis" (Ruedin); that is, they refuse, in the individual case, to explore the hereditary process which should be theoretically considered according to the Mendelian rules and are satisfied with the fact that, according to the indications of experience, in a hereditary disease the n o/o of the descendants are carriers of the disease.

But even in this manner it is impossible to give a definite prognosis of the individual case. It has, for example, been estimated in the case of schizophrenia that (with extensive diagnostic position, that is, with the inclusion of all limited cases and all minor disturbances), when there is a unilateral hereditary taint, 10% of the descendants are carriers of the hereditary characteristic, and, when this is bilateral, 25% of the descendants are carriers of this characteristic. This signifies that even in the case of bilateral hereditary taint there is still the probability that 75% of the progeny will not be affected, and that, when there is a unilateral hereditary factor, the probability rises up to 90%. But in this matter the following has been overlooked: the 10% of the tainted signifies that among 100 children it is expected that 10 will be carriers of the hereditary characteristic. But in order that these appear within the maximal number of the children practically present, they must be compared within the number of the first ten children of the hypothetical 100 children. Thus it signifies that the probability of this event amounts in turn only to 10% of the 10% of the empirical hereditary prognosis, and hence, in practice, it is only 1%.

There is still another basis of hereditary pathology that is questionable, namely, that of the research concerning twins. This presupposes than in man there exist authentic uniovular twins, that is, twins that arise by successive division from the fecundation of a singular egg cell—and which therefore have the same (identical) "hereditary mass." Hence when these twins are "concordant," such characteristics are to be attributed to the common and similar hereditary predisposition; when they the "discordant," this phenomenon can be explained by the influence of the environment.

Even in this regard matters are not so simple in man. So far it has not been proven beyond doubt that true uniovularity exists in man. The findings concerning the vitelline membrane cannot be of service for the diagnosis of uniovularity because of the numerous deviations. The "concordance" of certain pairs of twins can also be explained by the common vascular connections in the placental circulation (anastomosis). The conclusions treating of uniovularity and the method based on it, and limiting the effects of predisposition and environment, are based on a hypothesis which has not been demonstrated in every case.

We will notice that in the sphere of hereditary pathology many matters are still problematic and hypothetical.

b) SPECIAL HEREDITARY PATHOLOGY

Hereditary diseases, or such that at least the causal concurrence of a hereditary factor is present, are found in the more diverse spheres of human pathology. Since a complete enumeration of these is out of the question, we shall limit ourselves to certain examples among them which are of the greatest practical importance.

(1) *Eye Diseases*

In this sphere we encounter, with relative frequency, malformations, defects and deficient development which are greatly hereditary. Congenital absence of the eyes (anophthalmia); a mutilation or defect, especially a congenital fissure of the eye (coloboma); abnormal whiteness of the eyes (albinism); absence of the iris (aniridia); congenital defects of refractions (myopia, hyperopia, astigmatism); dimness of vision without detectable organic lesion of the eye (amblyopia); position anomalies (strabismus); congenital forms of glaucoma and star (cataract); night blindness (nyctalopia).

Under the concept of "congenital blindness" are contained diverse diseases which we have already mentioned. The Tay-Sachs amaurotic family idiocy is a congenital blindness conditioned by race and which up to the present time has been observed only in Jewish children.

The red-green blindness (Daltonism) is cited as a typical example of the recessive hereditary process associated with species.

(2) Ear Diseases

The following are hereditary in a high degree: the cretinistic hardness of hearing and deafness, congenital deaf-mutism and otosclerosis. The latter generally manifests itself in advanced age, but it is probable that a hereditary factor concurs.

(3) Skin Diseases

In this category belong "moles" (birthmarks, angioma), cutaneous fibroma, etc. The formation of multiple pedunculated soft tumors (neurofibromatosis, Recklinghausen's disease) belong more to nervous diseases than to skin diseases. Symmetric gangrene (Raynaud's disease) is a disturbance of the capillary circulation of the extreme parts. Psoriasis is not simply a skin disease but is due to a constitutional internal dysfunction of assimilation (arthritism). It reacts in the same manner as ichthyosis, a disease characterized by dryness, roughness and scaliness of the skin, due to hyperthropy of the horny layer. It is called also fish skin disease and xeroderma. Any onychogryphosis (a deformed overgrowth of the nails) definitely does not depend solely on endogenous hereditary factors but is also conditioned by exogenous factors (nutrition, wear and tear). A hereditary factor concurs in several forms of eczema and cutaneous allergic reactions (Urticaria, etc.)

(4) Deformities

In regard to the hereditary-pathological evaluation, the first place is held by all deformities of the genital organs (in the male: hypospadias, epispadias, cryptorchism, atrophy of the testicles; in the female: atresia and aplasia of the uterovaginal tube; double deformities: vagina duplex, uterus duplex, bipartitus, etc.; hermaphroditism, pseudohermaphroditism; cases of so-called "erreur de sexe," etc.).

The subjects with serious deformities (monstra) do not generally live long and hence, despite the gravity of the deformity, are of little interest in hereditary pathology (for example, acranii, anencephali); double linkages (cranio—and thorasopagi, xiphopagi; so-called Siamese twins) are too rare to be of any practical importance. Frequent, and hence practically important, are the deformities of the extremities, as clubfoot, talipes equinus, cleft foot, cleft hand, the lack of fingers and toes (polydactylia, syndactylia); congenital defects of parts of limbs and bones; congenital dislocations (e.g., luxatio coxae congenita).

Of importance are all the degrees of divided formations of the dorsal spine (rachischisis-congenital fissure of the spinal column), even in a latent form (spina bifida occulata), "cerebral hernia" (encephalocele) and spinal cord hernia (meningo-myelocele). In the sphere of the abdominal organs we have the "umbilical hernia" (hernia umbilicalis congenita) and, in more serious cases, a more or less total evisceration (ectopia viscerum); fissure formation of the bladder (ectopia vesicae), etc.

(5) Constitutional Anomalies, Diathesis

The exsudative diathesis of early infancy probably depends more on nutrition that hereditary predisposition. To what degree the hereditary factor concurs with the environmental factor in cases of lymphatism, scrofulosis, rachitis and spasms (spasmophilia) is a question that requires greater definition.

In certain constitutional anomalies which are associated with dysfunctions of internal secretion the concurrence of a hereditary factor should be indicated: for example, dwarfish and gigantism (nanosomia, gigantismus): in severe cases of adiposity (adipositas), especially in cases of dystrophia adiposo-genitalis and, finally, in cases of infantilism. Even in the case of intersexualism the hereditary factor could also concur. Among the systematic diseases associated with the skeleton of the body the following are to be mentioned: abnormal fragility of the bones (osteogenesis imperfecta, osteoporosis, osteopsathyrosis, chondrodystrophia foetalis), the "hypertrophy of the bones disease" (Leontiasis ossea, Albers-Schöenberg).

In this category also belong, when it is not a case of malformation, the case of the inverse position of internal organs (situs inversus). Some authors consider in this group of diseases even those diseases which are wont to manifest themselves solely in advanced age and which sometimes indicate an anticipated hereditary transmission: the manifestation of the diseases intervenes in anticipation from generation to generation. This phenomenon is encountered in arteriosclerosis, diabetes mellitus; in bronchial asthma and emphysema. Finally the predisposition toward cancer and other malignant tumors has also been included in this group.

Despite its infectious genesis and the great importance of the environmental factor, even tuberculosis has been included among the "hereditary diseases." With the aid of the "method of the twins" both Diehl and V. Verschuer have attempted to place the factor of the hereditary predisposition in the foreground. Hence it has been concluded that the battle against tuberculosis should not be limited, as formerly, to means of hygienic care, but should be extended in the sense of "excluding from reproduction the inferior constitutions."

(6) Nervous Diseases

To the organic nervous diseases in which the hereditary factor can be supposed belong the following: the hereditary degenerative nervous diseases as syringomyelia, progressive muscle atrophy, spastic spinal paralysis, myotonia congenita (Thomson), cerebral ataxia (Friedreich) and, finally, even multiple sclerosis.

The functional nervous diseases are included in part in the group of mental diseases. Among these even epilepsy has been considered a "hereditary disease." According to the more recent opinion this disease is to be considered as an organic disease of the cerebral cortex. Insofar as hereditary forms exist, it is of definite importance that the endogenous conditioned forms be distinguished from those that are of exogenous origin, for example, from forms of traumatic origin. Hysteria, neuropathy and psychopathy belong to the functional diseases. Paralysis agitans (Parkinson disease) is mostly a sequel of encephalitis, of hereditary origin as the hereditary St. Vitus dance, chorea major (Huntington), while the youth Vitus dance, chorea minor (Sydenham) are more of an exogenous basis of an infectious nature. In the disease of Pelizaeus-Merzbacher, which is a hereditary progressive diplegia, the hereditary factor seems to be more in the foreground.

(7) Mental Diseases

Among the practically more important mental diseases from the hereditary standpoint are the following:

1) Congenital dementia
2) Schizophrenia
3) Manic-depressive insanity
4) Hereditary epilepsy
5) Hereditary St. Vitus dance (Huntington's chorea)
6) Hereditary blindness
7) Hereditary deafness
8) Serious hereditary bodily deformities
9) Serious alcoholism

Concerning the above the following is to be observed:

In regard to 1). In congenital dementia the greatest difficulty consists in distinguishing the hereditary, endogenous forms from the exogenous, non-hereditary form conditioned by the environment (peristaltic). The same can be said for all degrees of oligophrenia: debility, imbecility, idiocy. Intelligence deficiency can be congenital without having to be hereditary, as is the case, for example, of brain lesion as a result of birth trauma.

In regard to 2). Schizophrenia is, next to dementia (oligophrenia), practically the most important mental disease of this group. We have already alluded to the fact that an extensive diagnostic position also included limited cases and reached a hereditary empirical prognosis of 10 per cent, or 25 per cent. For the prognosis of schizophrenia it is important that even this disease has become susceptible to a cure through modern therapy (electric shock, insulin shock and, in part, hormone therapy).

In regard to 3), manic-depression (circular) insanity, a dominant hereditary process is presumed. The hereditary force is apparently very important. The empirical hereditary prognosis indicates a relatively high percentage of diseased factor carriers. But even in this, matters are not so simple: the same distinction between an endogenous depression and a reactive depression can be very difficult. The circular oscillations of feelings are also found in the sphere of normality.

In regard to 4), the task of distinguishing the forms of epilepsy of exogenous environmental origin from those of endogenous hereditary origin has not been completely resolved despite the use of electric encephalography (EEG). In regard to the predisposition toward convulsions, a hereditary factor may concur. In regard to suitability of marriage, great prudence should be had in these cases.

In regard to 5), Huntington's chorea is relatively rare and hence is today of no practical importance.

In regard to 6) and 7), whatever is important has already been indicated in the chapter concerning organic diseases.

In regard to 8), in the general critique we shall allude to a noteworthy case.

In regard to 9), social causal factors concur in serious alcoholism and we are not to ignore the possibility of a cure and the success attained in modern times through clinical treatment associated in part with the antabus cure. The sterilization of chronic alcoholics imposed by law in Germany in 1933 for the prevention of progeny affected by hereditary diseases, which included all the above-mentioned mental diseases, is as doubtful a means as castration of sex delinquents. The unrestrained instincts and addiction are not cured by this means, but to the already disturbed personality there is added another disturbance resulting from imposed sterilization. The late postpuberal anomalies of the instinct are not cured by castration but rather aggravated by it. In regard to marriage counseling in the case of alcoholism the principle prevails that the question of sanitary suitability concerning marriage can be resolved in the affirmative if there is positive proof of the betterment of the social and moral situation. The contracting of marriage with an alcoholic who continues to drink is a serious disaster. But this can be avoided through marriage counseling. In regard to the eugenic problems in marriage counseling it must summarily be said that in practice the problems are more complicated than is apparent from the standpoint of the theoretical hygiene of race unilaterally tending toward the hereditary factor. Moreover, of greater importance in marriage counseling is the judgment of the personality in its fullness and the avoidance fixating of one's glance or consideration solely on the hereditary factor.

This can be illustrated by an example: the author had the occasion of counseling a young man concerning marriage suitability from the hereditary hygienic standpoint. The candidate had a serious cleft hand; the hand was cleft to the wrist and this was very accentuated. Considering the hereditary factor in this deformity, he was advised against marriage. But notwithstanding this serious deformity, it happened that he passed the examination for master of precise mechanics with an outstanding mark. He therefore more than compensated his physical hereditary defect with excellent intellectual quality. The author therefore no longer felt authorized to counsel the renunciation of marriage and progeny to one who, besides the possibility of a physical defect, also could transmit through heredity many other qualities of a moral and character nature.

The pure eugenicist could reject this viewpoint. But he who evaluates man as a personality and as a totality would have to admit that only that marriage counseling is justified which does not consider the "hereditary factor" in a unilateral manner.

2. Infectious Diseases

Besides the hereditary diseases, premarital counseling must concern itself with the establishment and evaluation of certain infectious diseases. Its task is, above all, to establish with certitude the absence of infections before being able to certify the sanitary suitability to matrimony. Since there exists the danger that the marriage partner can become infected through marital relationship, the sick partner should be advised and the doctor should make use of his authority in preventing him from contracting marriage while he still finds himself in the contagious stage of the disease.

The most important diseases here indicated are the sexual diseases (venereal infections) and tuberculosis.

Contrary to the authentically hereditary diseases, that is, those conditioned through predisposition (endogenously), the infectious diseases are essentially of an exogenous origin. But even here the hereditary factor can play an important part as, for example, when there is a familial accumulation of tuberculosis. This factor should not be overlooked.

The establishment of the moment when the infection is removed is in practice much more difficult than the lay person imagines. However, it constitutes a task of great importance, for the solution of which all the means at the disposal of clinical investigation should be used.

a) VENEREAL DISEASES

The question that implies the greatest responsibility for the marriage counselor is the following: when can he declare with a clear conscience, after a venereal infection, that marriage may be contracted or that those married may resume marital relations without any danger? The establishment of a definite cure after a venereal disease is always difficult; it can be more difficult after gonorrhea than lues. As dangerous as it is to declare a cure too hastily, so it is not free from danger to delay longer than is strictly necessary.

The establishment of gonorrhea is easy in the fresh acute stage. It is also relatively easy to exclude, when, for example, in a *virgo intacta* the examination of the secretion presents the typical I° degree of purity (pure culture of the lactic acid of Döderlein's bacillus). Between these extremes of surely positive and surely negative detection of gonococci the greater number of findings presents all the gradations with partly doubtful findings. In case of doubt besides the methods of "provocation," those of the "culture" should also be used. In women gonorrhea is no longer to be considered contagious, when, after a suitable treatment and weekly examination of the secretion, the result is negative even immediately after menstruation. In men the absence of infection can be established when, after a suitable treatment, with weekly examinations gonococci are no longer found in the secretion of the urethra and the prostate as well as in the urinary threads. The examination becomes difficult because of the postgonorrheal catarrh which often persists for a long time.

Syphilis can be considered no longer contagious if, after four years have passed since contagion and after an adequate and sufficiently long cure, the symptoms of the disease are no longer present, at least for two years.

These precautions are, in general, sufficient. In the individual case it would be well eventually to take into account even the ulterior requirements.

It is most important for marriage counselors to consider the legislative dispositions existing in many places concerning the campaign against venereal disease. These laws provide the possibility of coercive recovery and obligatory cure in the hospital for patients obstinate in the observance of medical prescription.

Marriage counseling has, above all, the task of education, regarding responsibility.

b) TUBERCULOSIS

The task of marriage counseling in regard to tuberculosis is similar to that concerning syphilis. When it is a matter of contracting marriage, the danger consists primarily in this, that the "open" tubercular person constitutes a grave danger to persons around him. In marital and familial life he will with almost absolute certainty infect his wife and children.

The difference between "open" and "closed" tuberculosis is not longer so fixed as formerly since the limits have become more flexible. A "facultative" open tuberculosis can be temporarily "open," that is, it can manifest itself with a diffusion of bacilli and can be temporarily "closed" again. A "closed" tuberculosis can become active again. Hence it is better to distinguish between "active" tuberculosis and "inactive" (latent) tuberculosis. But it is important to know that latent tuberculosis can become reactivated by any kind of influence.

It follows that marriage counseling will not have fulfilled its task if, in the case of open tuberculosis, marriage will have been delayed until a harmless stage of inactivity has been certainly reached, but must even follow the cases in a catamnestic manner, that is, be concerned with the ulterior course of the disease.

This is done through successive assistance especially through the collaboration between marriage counseling and antitubercular assistance. This is an important task of social hygiene. In comparison with the past the prognosis of tuberculosis has undergone a notable advance because of modern therapeutic procedures, especially through the modern medicamentous combination treatment (streptomycin, hydracid and PAS), through which the operative therapies (pneumothorax, pneumotomy, lobectomy, thoracoplasty, drainage of the caverns, etc.), have somewhat taken a secondary place.

The principle, valid at one time, of prohibiting matrimony to single girls affected with tuberculosis, pregnancy to young women and breast feeding to young mothers *("jeune fille, pas de mariage; jeune femme, pas de grossesse; jeune mère, pas d'allaitement")*, consequently degenerated to the point that tuberculosis was used as the principal "indication," and practically most frequently for the "interruption of pregnancy" (more correctly: murder of the fetus). Too often the "indication" was simply a pretext.

Through the modern therapy of tuberculosis this abuse of medicine has definitely lost ground. Clinical treatment and the therapeutic measures mentioned above can be executed with success in every phase of pregnancy.

Notwithstanding the essential betterment of the prognosis of tuberculosis *quoad vitam,* the prognosis *quoad sanationem* and hence the work capacity still remains doubtful. It therefore follows that even the matrimonial prognosis can be established only with caution. In cases in which there is added an unfavorable hereditary prognosis, that is, when there is a high familial predisposition to tuberculosis in association with an asthenic constitution and other organic defects of hereditary origin ("organic deficiency"), it would be better, *in dubio,* to discourage marriage.

3. Sexual Anomalies

To generative hygiene also belong the question of sexual anomalies especially from the standpoint of marriage suitability.

a) IPSATION (MASTURBATION)

Actually many doctors do not consider ipsation as an anomaly, and, if they consider it as such, do not attribute much importance to it. From the standpoint of marriage counseling and generative hygiene, the opinion which tends to minimize it is not admissible. Temporary ipsation proper to the period of puberty can be considered as relatively harmless since it can be completely and definitely overcome with the entrance of full maturity. But habitual ipsation is by no means of no importance for the prognosis of marriage. It produces an habituation to inadequate sexual stimulation and, consequently, because of this there often arises a difficulty in the fulfillment of the marital act, that is, in the male, disturbances of potency and, in the female, disturbances of sensibility (dyspareunia—difficult or painful coitus in women).

In cases of habitual ipsation it would be an error to hope that marriage would be a remedy against this evil. This could be the case if ipsation has not yet become a habitual fixation. Habitual cases are always suspects of potency disturbances. There is the additional fact that habitual ipsation always indicates psychopathy. This case is similar to other fixated addictions.

Ipsation must therefore be unconditionally overcome before suitability of marriage can be declared. It is, however, the duty of the marriage counselor to avoid every form of discouragement since this represents a serious psychic trauma; he should be encouraging and, when necessary, should advise the help of a capable psychotherapist.

b) HOMOSEXUALITY

In the case of homosexuality it is preferable, *in dubio,* to resolve the question of marriage suitability in the negative. In this case it is a lesser evil to prevent marriage than to allow it too easily.

A careful distinction should be made between obligatory and facultative homosexuality. This distinction coincides for the most part and not always with that between primary (endogenously predisposed) homosexuals and secondary (exogeneously influenced) homosexuals. Obligatory homosexuals are incapable of fulfilling the marital act with a person of the opposite sex, and are therefore impotent *(impotentia absoluta).* They cannot contract a valid marriage nor can they consummate marriage. In spite of this fact they sometimes contract marriage partly to hide their homosexuality from strangers and partly for economic reasons. In such "marriages" the wives are always very unhappy and are merely utilized. Homosexual friendships act as an explosive of marriage. This can also be said for lesbian "friends" of female homosexuals. It is important for the spiritual director that he realize that female homosexuality *(amor lesbicus)* has assumed in our day an extensive diffusion. It is a case for the most part of intellectual and emancipated women who do not wish to bind themselves to a man and believe that they are protecting their freedom and independence by attaching themselves to a lesbian friend.

Facultative homosexuals are unsuitable for marriage in an absolute manner but are not so in a permanent manner. They are absolutely unsuitable for marriage only insofar as the homosexual inversion of the instinct exists. A cure, especially by means of psychotherapy, is not to be excluded.

The cure must be established in a definite and certain manner before the contracting of marriage can be permitted. Even in this case the marriage counselor finds himself faced with decisions which imply extraordinary responsibility.

That which has been said in regard to homosexuality also prevails for other sexual anomalies (perversions), provided that these do not justify absolute unsuitability because of their gravity as, for example, in severe cases of sadism.

4. Psychological Questions

Psychological counseling is essentially important in a twofold sense: in regard to the psychological requirements for the qualification of marriage for each contracting party and in regard to the reciprocal adaptation of both parties. It is possible that each party, considered separately, appears psychologically qualified for marriage but that both parties are not suitable to each other. This aspect of the examination regarding suitability should be reserved to a specialized psychologist.

Test-methods (for example, the Szondi test) can occasionally give good results, yet they should be applied with extreme prudence. With tests alone one cannot judge whether two persons can adapt themselves to each other in the common life.

Hence even the psychologist, if he wishes to formulate a sure judgment must evaluate the complete personality of both parties. He will utilize for this purpose the experience acquired through research of the constitution, the rhythm of life and characterology.

It has been recently recommended that even astrology and graphology be included in the sphere of research regarding the judgment of reciprocal adaptation of both parties. If this can be considered a serious matter, it is a case of limited spheres in which the doctor is competent only in very rare exceptional cases.

Since these are spheres which are difficult to control and in which charlatanry reigns supreme, greater prudence must be imposed. Hence the most severe criticism and prudence can never be sufficiently recommended in the face of these tendencies which often surreptitiously pervade marriage counseling. Very suspicious are certain matrimonial mediation institutions which, in order to please the public, make use of the indicated methods. In order to eliminate the inconveniences that arise in this sphere, we can do nothing else but recommend the union of centers of preparation for marriage with charitable institutions of spiritual direction for marriage counseling.

D. Intramarital Counseling

Premarital counseling treats of hygienic questions regarding the contracting of marriage. The subject matter of intramarital counseling is the questions relative to the manner of conducting conjugal life. One can also speak of premarital or postmarital or intramarital counseling.

1. Difficulties Regarding the Consummation of Marriage

The initial difficulties which can arise in the consummation of marriage are not yet to be considered as disturbances of potency and, respectively, disturbances of sensibility and should be definitely distinguished from the same. In the majority of cases there is no need of treatment but only a need of definite patience on the part of both parties.

The impatience of one of the spouses—frequently on the part of the wife who has to deal with a man without experience and for the most part confused—can easily transform initial difficulties, that can be overcome, into irreparable damages. If the spouse is discouraged because of the expectation anxiety mechanism, the initial difficulty can be developed and become fixated into a disturbance of potency.

With patience and with an adequate and psychological treatment, the prognosis of such a difficulty is absolutely favorable— much more favorable than that which is had when the difficulties are based on a premarital association with a former sexual partner or on the fixation of inadequate sexual stimulation. In every case one should be warned against declaring impulsively initial difficulty as a case of impotency.

2. Potency and Sensibility Disturbances

For the etiology and the curative prognosis of potency disturbances and of the disturbances of sensibility it is important to know if these are of organic (somatic) origin or of functional (psychic) origin.

If it is a matter of forms of organic origin susceptible to operative therapy (for example, phimosis, slight degrees of hypospadias), the prognosis *quoad sanationem* is favorable. The forms of psychic origin susceptible to psychotherapy have a more doubtful prognosis but still a relatively favorable prognosis. On the other hand, very unfavorable is the prognosis of forms *depending* arising from deep-oedipus fixations and even of those based on a fixation upon the first premarital sex partner, especially in the case of the female sex. The prognosis is also relatively unfavorable when the disturbances of potency are based on a fixation of inadequate sexual stimulation (masturbation). Obligatory homosexuality is almost always the basis of absolute impotency, that is, in respect to every partner of the opposite sex. The doctor often encounters complaints concerning dyspareunia and frigidity of the wife, and, with particular frequency, after the birth of the first child. The husband complains that the wife has become "frigid" toward him and has interest only in the children; very often for the child in marriages with an only child. The wife, on the other hand, complains that the husband is no longer capable of satisfying her. The "difficult excitability" of the wife is often due to the precocious ejaculation on the part of the husband, which, on his part, represents a sexual neurosis and a potency weakness.

Even vaginism can be the cause of the impotency. Prognostically favorable are the cases in which hypnosis and dilatation are applicable. We are opposed, however, to the discussion of the hymen in the case of vaginism since we consider this procedure useless and dangerous.

In many cases of deep psychological causes both parties are in need of psychotherapy. If the disturbances depend exclusively upon an *abusus matrimonii* of many years, the cause can be eliminated once and for all by means of an adequate explanation and spiritual direction concerning the proper concept of marriage.

The husbands should learn to comprehend up to what point

they themselves are at fault in regard to the presumed frigidity of the wife. The wives on their part should understand how they can contribute by an erratic behavior toward the husband's formation of a fixation of even light initial disturbances, and what a mistake it is for her to shun her husband after many years of marriage and thus awaken in him tendencies toward "polygamy." The fact that the woman is too occupied with professional and extra-domestic activities exercises a most harmful effect in this matter. To be reproved is the situation in which the modern woman, occupied in a profession, is placed before the husband, especially when she "maintains" the family. She often refuses to fulfill her conjugal duties. The modern woman rejects the concept of "matrimonial duty" for particularly sentimental reasons. He who understands correctly knows that duty and love do not exclude each other, but one presupposes the other. When such conjugal difficulties are not overcome through reciprocal love, they easily lead to an irreparable ruination of marriage.

3. Counseling Concerning Sterility

Counseling in regard to sterility is a particularly important task of intramarital counseling.

Of particular importance is the distinction between primary and secondary sterility. The following causes and conditions come into consideration in primary sterility: high degrees of hypoplasia and infantalism of the internal organs; anomalies of formation (aplasia, atresia): general constitutional defects and disturbances of the endocrine system.

The more frequent causes of secondary sterility are the inflammatory ailments of the uterus and oviducts with consequent adhesions. These inflammations are frequently caused by gonorrhea, abortion and the use of contraceptives, and hence by sexual abuse; even appendicitis can cause sterility. These can also be caused by cryptogenic septic focal infections; also by lues and tuberculosis, nutritional and developmental disturbances, avitaminosis, etc.

Secondary sterility often manifests itself in the form of "sterility after the first birth" as the result of the development of a latent infection after the first puerperium (arising from gonorrhea, abortion, etc.). In every case it must be established if the sterility is due solely to the wife or to the husband or to both parties.

When it is a matter of establishing whether the husband is capable of procreating, a microscopic examination of the sperm is indispensable. For this purpose only a moral method can be used.[2] Of particular importance is a previous examination of the sperm, before applying to the wife a more energetic method of investigation or therapy (perturbation, hysterosalpingography, for the purpose of controlling the potency of the oviducts; surgical means.)

4. Artificial Insemination

Often the sperm examination indicates that the sterility of the marriage is not due to the wife, but the husband (azoospermia). In such cases many women request from the doctor that they be helped toward conception by means of artificial insemination with the sperm of a "donor," a stranger to the marriage. It is a principle of natural law that a woman has no right to receive into her vagina the semen of any man except her husband.

Here we prescind from the decisive arguments of a moral nature which can be posited against such a procedure; we prescind, therefore, from the incompatibility of this procedure with the essence of marriage which makes of this artificial insemination an action in itself illicit.

Pope Pius XII has pronounced with definite decision the condemnation of artificial insemination, especially with the sperm of a person other than the husband, in the allocution given at the International Congress of Catholic Doctors which took place on September 29, 1949. Here we are to formulate a judgment concerning artificial insemination solely from the hygienic standpoint.

The hygienic considerations against artificial semination with sperm from a stranger donor are not only based upon the immoral method of obtaining the sperm, but they are based rather on the very nature of this intervention, which is a degradation in the manner of generation. The origin of the procreated child (so-called "test-tube baby") remains and must remain unknown. For

[2] Cf. *Compendium of Pastoral Medicine,* Niedermeyer, Wagner, New York, 1961, pp. 111 ff.

obvious reasons neither the marriage partners as juridical parents of the child must know the name of the donor nor must the latter know the name of the parents.

Since in America the number of children thus generated already reaches the tens of thousands, it is possible later that these contract marriage with a person who is actually a close consanguine (half-brother or sister). The serious preoccupation that arises against this procedure from the racial hygienic standpoint is more than justified.

Where special counseling institutions regarding sterility are established, it should be arranged that they are placed near a gynecological clinic in unison with an ambulatorium of endocrinology. In order to exercise an efficient control, it is necessary that the examined cases be followed catamnestically. Toward this end the possibility of successive assistance should be arranged.

5. Counseling Concerning Birth Control

From the hygienic standpoint every form of birth control (anti-conception, prevention) is, in the long run, harmful to health. The degree of damage for the health increases proportionally to the degree of certitude of success. It can be established that there is no method of birth control which is for a long time absolutely sure and, at the same time, absolutely harmless. Hygienic marriage counseling could perhaps refuse *a priori* to discuss the question of birth control in general.

But such a negative stand is not to be recommended, since experience teaches that, in doing so, more harm than good is done. If the marriage counselor does not concern himself with the difficulties and problems presented to him by those who consult him, the same will turn elsewhere and will be counseled in a harmful and immoral manner and in the manner that is contrary to their wishes.

Such a problem makes evident the educational task which marriage counseling has to undertake in regard to people. It does not suffice to send people away with moralistic self-righteousness and to show indignation concerning their wish. One should rather instruct the clients concerning the immorality of their desire and show them the way to face the difficulties of life in another manner.

Moreover, if one explains the harm done to health through birth-control, one could then make them understand that nothing can ever be hygienically correct if it is morally false. The fulfillment of such a task is naturally much more difficult than giving in to the desires of the patient. The obligation of educating the people requires the protection of the entire personality of the counselor. He must not only know how to instruct and guide the counselee, but must also know how to convince him.

The task of counseling in regard to questions associated with birth control should not be rejected *a priori*. Despite the fact that it is a difficult and unpleasant task, the counselor should undertake the same. The purpose of this counseling should be that of guiding the spouses in overcoming the abuse of matrimony. In order to attain this end, marriage counseling should collaborate as closely as possible with all the branches of hygienic and social assistance. Its leader should possess the complete control of all the problems of family protection. The protection of the families should not limit itself to an amplified assistance for large families (so-called familial assistance), but should include far-reaching means of social politics intent on a basic restoration of the social conditions of the family: above all, the introduction of the family remuneration for the head of the family, legislative provisions in favor of the mother of the family, and, above all, an efficient compensation of the family burdens.

The assurance given to the head of the family that the social question can be resolved according to social justice is the most efficient means of combating the spirit of Malthusianism and birth control.

6. Counseling and "Periodic Abstinence" (The Rhythm)

If marriage counseling cannot avoid the questions of contraception, it definitely cannot avoid discussions concerning rhythm *(observatio temporum)*. If the moral illiceity of contraception would seem to indicate that this theme should *a priori* not be discussed, the same cannot be said in regard to the discussions of rhythm, since it is, according to the general doctrine of the Church and according to the various doctrinal decisions of the supreme doctrinal offices of the Church, not illicit *in se*. This, however, is far from signifying that the use of the Knaus-Ogino Method (rhythm) should represent, without further consideration, a "licit birth prevention."

Even the question of moral liceity should be accurately evaluated in every individual case. This may be done by the couple. In case of doubt the advice of a spiritual director should be sought.[3]

The duty of the doctor is that of indicating whether the application of the method should be considered and whether the method is applicable and even if contraindictions exist; and, in a positive case, of establishing which are the days that are to be designated as "sterile" (more accurately: days in which conception is least possible). It is this latter task which is most difficult and which requires a complete knowledge and control of the matter. Every specific case requires a precise observation and a great number of accurate considerations on the part of the doctor. If there is present a serious medical indication which suggests the avoidance of a new pregnancy, only a method substantially limited in respect to the original method of Knaus can be considered.

From the list of the "free" days which should be compiled for each case, the first ten days should be absolutely eliminated. The spiritual director should avoid giving advice concerning the practical application of the method; he may direct the spouses to a reliable doctor who possesses an absolute mastery of the method and its circumstances. This does not mean that this should always be a doctor who is a specialist in women's diseases and, much less, that all gynecologists should necessarily possess a complete mastery of this method. But it is necessary that in each individual case the doctor realize the limits of the method, the source of its defects, the dangers that it implies, and that he select with utmost concern the cases that come to him. It is a "different" method which should be prescribed only after an indication has been rigorously established. The doctor must also know—and instruct his patients in this regard—that even this method cannot be considered without limitations as a "natural" method and hence definitely harmless in the prevention of birth.

That this method is not "according to nature" is demonstrated by the following consideration, confirmed by experience: The

[3] Cf. *Compendium of Pastoral Medicine*, Niedermeyer, Wagner, New York, 1961, pp. 140 ff.

libido sexualis of the wife is strongest during the time of ovulation. She must, therefore, abandon sexual coitus at the time when she is disposed, and bear it when she does not have any inclination toward it. Thus marital relations become in time a torment and a repugnance, and disturbances of the sexual sensibility result, as dysparennia and frigidity, which in time lead to the disintegration of marriage.

From the generative hygienic viewpoint it can be objected against the method that it is the safest in women who are completely healthy, in whom the monthly cycle occurs in a very regular manner and can be calculated beforehand, that is, in women who are "ovarian stabile." In sick women the cycle is much more disturbed the more serious are the alterations of the entire organism; their cycle is labile and the calculation is very difficult to the point of almost being impossible. These are the cases in which the method registers the greater number of "failures." The result is that healthy women do not have children while the sick women, whom one would want to spare a new pregnancy, have the children. From this results a sort of "differentiated reproduction" which is anything but desirable from the standpoint of sanitary eugenics. One can speak of a contra-selective effect (dysgenic) of the method, which is stronger the more an indiscriminate propaganda is diffused among the masses.

Prescinding from the objections of an hygienic nature, we must bring to attention a serious pastoral consideration. The fact that the method is not of itself illicit tends to bring about a certain propaganda among Catholic spouses. This propaganda among Catholic couples utilizes, under the mask of benevolence, this method as a Trojan horse in introducing the mentality of Malthusianism, with its destructive tendencies, into the bulwark, which up to this time was impenetrable, of the Catholic concept of marriage.

This serious preoccupation is answered with the argument that there is an attempt to "withhold" the "heavenly gift" of new knowledge from the young married people through "obscurantism." In 1955, on the occasion of a congress of Catholic families, the author was present for a conference on the "licit regulations of birth." The speaker for the young couples reproved the author for limiting the "rhythm" solely to cases of extreme necessity and of wanting to reserve counseling exclusively to the specialist. The author has always held that the method is not of itself illicit in individual cases in which there are present serious reasons, but that only the doctor, who is truly the master of the method, can give advice regarding its practical application.

The episcopal director of this conference closed the same by affirming that the propagation of the rhythm system is certainly the more convenient way, while the viewpoint of the author constitutes the more difficult way. But it is not a matter of what is more convenient, but rather of what is just, even if it is difficult.

To this we include by way of an addition the method of the so-called "chemical inhibition." It consists of the oral use of hesperidin, which is a substance similar to the vitamin from a citrus fruit (grapefruit). Hesperidin renders hyaluronidose, which is a ferment very important for fecundation, inactive. It is said that it can be taken for a long time "without harm," and that the inhibitory effect upon the hyaluronidose disappears when the medicament is no longer taken.

A too materialistic opinion already stated that in similar cases there was nothing morally wrong since the marital act was not altered in its nature and was performed in its "full integrity." But he who takes into account the moral relevance of an *actus humanus* and judges the action not only on its external characteristics, but according to its total structure, must acknowledge that here the complete act and behavior demand serious moral consideration.

In fact the use of a medicament for the sole purpose of inhibiting an important ferment for reproduction represents nothing else but the behavior condemned by the encyclical *"Casti Connubii"* in the words: "Those who in exercising it deliberately frustrate its natural power and purpose sin against nature and commit a deed which is shameful and intrinsically vicious." [4] There can be no doubt that there exists a deliberate frustration of the marital act when, by means of hesperidin there is present the intention of impeding the formation of hyaluronidose. Only a very materialistic and formalistic opinion can hold that the act is moral since the act is fulfilled according to nature.

Moreover, it can in time be harmful to health when the forma-

[4] Cf. *"Casti Connubii,"* encyclical of Pope Pius XI, The America Press, New York, p. 17.

tion of a ferment so important for the vital function of reproduction, such as hyaluronidose, is impeded. This method has been known for only a short time and because of this fact it is difficult of knowing in a certain manner whether its use even for a long time will not be harmful. We can, however, foresee that in time a new form of secondary sterility based on a disturbance of the production of hyaluronidose, will have to be taken into consideration. While in the therapy of sterility there is promised a favorable effect by the increase of hyaluronidose with the use of hesperidin here, the very advantage that one expects is repressed when, at a later time, children are desired but in vain, after having done, at the beginning, violence to nature. Even in this matter we can do nothing else but repeat the principle: Nothing can be in time hygienically correct which is morally false! [5]

Three general types of medication are to be distinguished:

1) Medication whose one and only purpose (finis operis) is induction of a temporary state of sterility (e.g., phosphorylated hesperidin). The use of drugs whose one and only immediate purpose is to induce temporary sterility (child-bearing incapacity) by suppressing or diverting the generative function is a violation of the fifth and sixth commandment and absolutely forbidden.

2) Medication whose one and only purpose is an attack against the fertilized ovum (e.g., to prevent proper preparation of the endometrium as a nesting place for the ovum). The use of drugs whose one and only immediate purpose is to prevent the natural development of the already fertilized ovum or which is directed to this end by the agent is gravely sinful as feticide (if the ovum, embryo, or fetus is destroyed in the womb) or, theoretically, as abortion (if it is ejected to die outside the womb).

3) Medication capable of achieving a plurality of immediate effects, one of which is sterility (e.g., Enovid, Norlutin). Medication capable of admitting a plurality of effects, one of which is temporary sterility, is licitly used according to the principle of the double effect: that is, provided sterility is not directly intended and there is a proportionate reason for this particular medication (a simpler and equally effective nonsterilizing treatment is not available).

[5] Cf. "Anti-Fertility Pills," Richard A. McCormick, S.J., THE HOMILETIC AND PASTORAL REVIEW, Joseph F. Wagner, Inc., May 1962, pp. 692-700.

a) THE CORRECTION OF MENSTRUAL DISORDERS

Theologians unanimously agree that it is morally permissible to use progestins to correct menstrual pathologies of any kind as, for example, dysmenorrhea or menorrhagia. Though ovulation may be suppressed even intentionally in such a use of the steroids, the relief of the pathology is attained not through the suppression of the ovum as the germ cell of human life, but through the control or suppression of the endocrine activity which precedes and accompanies ovulation.

b) REGULARIZATION OF THE CYCLE

It would be permissible to use these drugs to regularize the cycle in such a way that it would always be, for example, a twenty-eight day cycle with ovulation always taking place on the fourteenth day. It is, however, well to remember that as yet no drug has been discovered which will achieve such a result. If the cycle is pathological or abnormal, treatment to regularize it is a *remedium defectus naturae* and any sterility produced in the process is a non-intended by-product, hence an indirect sterilization. Even if the cycle is not pathological, but varies only within a range considered to be normal, thus making rhythm less secure, competent theologians have suggested that fertility-related drugs may be used to regularize the period so it would always be predictably exact. Pope Pius XII in his Address to the National Congress of the Family Front, November 26, 1951, said that "one may even hope (but in this matter the Church naturally leaves the judgment to medical science) that science will succeed in providing this licit method (rhythm) with a sufficiently secure basis and the most recent information seems to confirm such a hope."

c) SUPPRESSION OF OVULATION DURING LACTATION

The question of whether it is permissible to use progestins to suppress ovulation during lactation in order to better provide for the proper spacing of children is still being debated in theological circles. Available medical opinion is anything but convincing on the point that a certain period of lactation is normally anovulary so that ovulation during this period must be viewed as abnormal. The moral theologian, however, is totally dependent on sound medical opinion. But even if ovulation during the period of lactation were regarded as an abnormality or pathology of the endocrine system, the question of whether it would be permissible to suppress it in order to avoid conception is still engrossing the attention of theologians. Some feel it would be permissible, but others are very reluctant to admit this for several reasons.

d) THE OVULATION REBOUND

Doctors are of the opinion that in some cases, if ovulation is suppressed temporarily, then permitted to resume, fertility can often be restored. Theologians who have written on the point generally believe that it is permissible for a woman to take medication which suppresses ovulation temporarily in order to render chances of conception better.

e) DELAY OF MENSTRUATION

Theologians agree that, where there is no contraceptive intention and no undue delay of menstruation, it is permissible to use hormonal therapy in order to delay or suppress menstruation because of an important athletic event or some other very important event. It is, however, necessary to note that some of the analyses given above regarding the use of the progestational steroids are tentative and subject to immediate revision consequent upon further medical or theological clarifications.

f) COUNSELING REGARDING PREGNANCY AND PREGNANCY COMPLICATIONS

Counseling concerning pregnancy and pregnancy complications is no longer strictly the task of marriage counseling but belongs to the vast sphere of assistance to expectant mothers. But it often happens that cases are first presented to the center of marriage counseling and it is expected that the first phase of counseling be fulfilled here.

The first consultation is often decisive in regard to the fate of the pregnancy, that is, for the life or death of the fetus. This fact indicates how important it is that marriage counseling and assistance to expectant mothers be placed in the hands of doctors who are medically and morally well orientated.

In this phase of counseling it is important that a clear idea be given to women of the serious physical and psychic dangers of abortion and of the disastrous *effects* that it has upon the marriage state (ruination of marriage).

In cases of hygienic complications of pregnancy (so-called "medical indication") and of social conditions of emergency (so-called "social indication"), it is necessary to utilize and exhaust all the means and resources of social and hygienic assistance as well as those of medical therapy. In order to fulfill this task it is absolutely necessary that there exist a close cooperation between marriage counseling, assistance to expectant mothers and their numerous ramifications. Serious social and psychological difficulties arise in cases of pregnancy resulting from rape. In this case it is of decisive importance that the future mother be placed in a well organized home or shelter and later that the child be also placed in a good children's home until the mother is able to take the child with her.[1]

The establishing of adequate maternal and child homes (in place of the foundling homes of former days) is one of the important tasks of the assistance to expectant mothers. In this manner the major difficulties arising from extreme social needs, to which one appeals in the justification of a "social indication," could be overcome. Here it appears most clearly how marriage counseling

---

[1] An innocent victim of unjust aggression may eject or destroy the semen provided it is done before conception takes place; but once conception has taken place, nothing may be done.

The victim of a criminal attack is entitled to use a spermicidal, vaginal douche as quickly after rape as is possible. Since conception does not occur in the vagina, there cannot be any time limit on a woman's right to destroy this semen in her vagina. No new human life is possibly involved in a purely vaginal douche. Intrauterine douche is, however, gynecologically contraindicated today. It is considered a dangerous procedure because such a douche would flow through the fallopian tubes, enter the peritoneal cavity and create a serious danger to the woman. If, and when, medical science does discover some method of destroying sperm within the fallopian tubes prior to the producing of conception, the moralist will have to offer some norm on the span of time after rape beyond which such a procedure could not be used. (Cf. *Medical Ethics,* Charles J. McFadden, O.S.A., Ph.D., F. A. Davis Co., Philadelphia, Pa., pp. 142-143.)

and assistance to expectant mothers occupy a key position in the entire system of social and hygienic aid.

7. Other Questions Concerning Intramarital Counseling

It is impossible to formulate the questions of intramarital counseling into an exhaustive system. We can only indicate further some questions which present themselves with greater frequency and which are already partly on the border betwen medico-hygienic counseling and that of legal, social and spiritual counseling. The medical counselor can study such questions for the most part in an informative manner by tending to send them to competent centers. It is these very borderline questions which indicate the necessity of including medico-hygienic marriage counseling in a larger organization of universalistic marriage counseling.

a) EXTREME SOCIAL CONDITIONS

A sphere of marriage counseling which should not be neglected pertains to problems resulting from critical social conditions due to the times.

Among these are the following: lack of a dwelling place, unemployment, uprooting arising from the loss of fatherland and citizenship; loss of patrimony, loss of home and household furniture through war and bombardment damages; impossibility of leading a normal conjugal life because of restriction of dwelling space; alcoholism due to a lack of orderly domestic environment, etc.

A definite social problem of our day has been established by the numerous precarious marriages among students contracted without the minimum security regarding the fundamental means of life. In order to overcome such difficulties even in only a partial manner there is need of the organized cooperation of all the centers of social aid, welfare, charity, etc. The present era places us in the face of tasks that overcome even the united forces of large organizations and so will more easily break the power of a single person.

b) PSYCHOLOGICAL DIFFICULTIES

At times during conjugal life problems arise which should have been considered before marriage in the course of premarital counseling. We have already stated that we do not expect miracles of a psychological examination with tests; so we should not underestimate the value of psychological counseling prior to marriage solely because it is not able to impede the occurrence of all difficulties.

Prescinding from the already indicated differences of the rhythm of life, marriage can always be endangered by the deep differences regarding the concept of life. In this regard, marriages of mixed religion and marriages of mixed social status can be more dangerous than "biologically mixed marriages" resulting from race differences.

The problems which we have mentioned indicate the necessity of collaboration between marriage counseling and a serious and scientifically unobjectionable psychological counseling. This can manifest its true worth in the settlement of differences between married partners. Here the psychology in relation to the spiritual adviser is indicated more than that of the lawyer. The latter should in every case desire to be more than a "divorce lawyer." In the interest of *"favor matrimonii,"* he should, in union with the spiritual adviser, the doctor and psychologist, be of service in the preservation of marriage as such and not to the desires and orders of one of the parties.

c) CASES OF INFORMATIVE COUNSELING

Counseling can be simply informative in cases that are beyond the competency of the doctor and which pertain to the sphere of the psychologist, teacher, lawyer and spiritual director. Informative counseling can, for example, take place in cases pertaining to matrimonial right, in cases of separation demanded by one of the parties; in cases of eventual nullity of marriage and appeal for a dispensation from a *matrimonium ratum non consummatum.* In these latter cases the doctor fulfills a very important role as an expert legal doctor in the canonical matrimonal process.

An informative examination is not incompatible with subsequent acceptance of the role of adviser, whereas private medical treatment does indicate incompatibility. Rigorous limitations are placed on a marriage counselor, at least on public counselors. He should only exercise counseling and not execute treatment.

III. BIRTH DECLINE AND MALTHUSIANISM

One of the most diffused evils of our times is the abuse of matrimony (*abusus matrimonii*). It is not our task here to take a position from the moral standpoint. The Church has always pronounced the moral aspect and this has been done in a very decisive manner by Pope Pius XI in the encyclical *"Casti Connubii."*

What had to be said from the hygienic standpoint has already been stated in the chapter on marriage counseling and eugenics and is summarized in the general basic principle of pastoral medicine, according to which nothing can be hygienically correct that is morally false. In order to complete what has already been considered, it is necessary to consider two problems: birth decline, as a mass phenomenon of the present social life, and the ideology of Malthusianism as the ideal basis of the so-called mass suggestion.

A. Birth Decline

Birth decline is the result of birth prevention arising from the mass phenomenon and from the consequent general abuse of marriage.

1. Historical Aspect

It is an historically proven fact that the decadence of ancient people is primarily attributed to birth decline. It is at times assumed that the decadence of people is a natural process of becoming old and of dying and hence a necessary and inevitable biological process as old age and death of the individual. That this is not true is proven by the example of the most ancient people, as the Chinese and Jewish people who, despite the extremely unfavorable conditions of life to which they were subjected from time to time, have survived other people by thousands of years; and the Egyptians, Babylonians, Greeks and Romans have perished.

Burgdafer was induced to give the following verdict: "People do not perish through death but extinguish themselves through lack of birth." It is proper to hold that it has been historically confirmed that the death of people is caused by the intentional limitation of births. The modern birth decline encountered in European people (western) is a social phenomenon which is very similar to the historical examples which we have stated. Ideological factors concur and confer a special character on the same.

Not even history univocally proves that people extinguish themselves biologically. Social and ethico-metaphysical elements represent an essential part besides the biological elements. The very history of the Jewish people shows the decisively determining action the metaphysical factors have on the fate of the people. It is a fact that the Jewish families are large and hence immune from the ideological influences of birth decline as long as they are religious, and, on the contrary, became prey to birth decline as soon as they are emancipated from the religion of their forefathers. The difference in birth rate between the orthodox Jew and the "emancipated" Jew is quite evident. At least this is true that old age and death of people do not necessarily arise according to the same biological law as is the case in the individual person. In the process of becoming extinct the birth decline occupies the leading position. The process is no longer reversible when it reaches a definite terminal stage.

2. Demography

The demographic statistics confirm the fact that in western-culture lands there is verified a constant regression of the number of births in the last thirty years of the nineteenth century. Especially impressive is the comparison between the number of births and deaths.

This comparison is, therefore, the basis of demography. The surplus and the deficit of births represent the balance of the biological movement of the population, prescinding from the social movement, that is, the increase or decrease due to migration (emigration, immigration). The statistics given in regard to the demographic movement are typical of all people of western culture. They manifest the gravity of the situation.

The simple comparison of the absolute number of births and the number of the deceased seems to offer a more favorable picture than that which corresponds to the real situation, since these data do not take into account the structure of the population in regard to age. It is a known fact that there can exist a surplus number of births even when the birth decline has already deeply altered the physical structure of the population. We have here the phenomenon of the abnormal distribution through the age of the population.

In the first place, there is the fact that the average age of man has become notably higher than it was formerly. This does not mean that men live longer as was hastily believed and ascribed to the progress of modern hygiene. The fact that the old generations are scarcely replaced by the newly born with their high rate of mortality is sufficient of itself to make it appear that an increase of the average age is verified without even a single person having lived by this a day more. Hence this phenomenon is verified even prescinding from the successful contributions of hygiene which are indicated indubitably in the diminution of infantile mortality rate in the first years of life. To this is added the fact, also incontestable, that a greater number of people attain a higher age level. The persons who live to an advanced age, from 70 to 75, from 76 to 80, and from 81 to 85 years of age are more numerous than those of the past.

The center of gravity of the population mass shifts, therefore, from the wide base of young classes always more toward the older classes. Thus the decimating effect of birth decline is postponed for a certain time and the real situation is concealed; it appears more favorable than it really is. Only with the gradual dying of the old will the "mortgage of death" (Burgdofer) be due and all the import of birth decline will be revealed. (Grotjahn.)

In order to obtain a clear idea of the demographic situation, Burgdofer requires, as useful values of comparison, "purged figures of births," obtained in relation to the distribution of the old groups.

In order to maintain a constant population the figures of births should correspond to that of the maintenance of the content. In absolute figures that would mean that theoretically, as a maintenance of the content, 2 children would be sufficient for marriage provided that all would marry, that all the marriages would be fertile and that all the children would continue to live. Since this supposition does not correspond to reality, a minimum of 3.7 children for a marriage is necessary for the maintenance of the content (Grotjahn).

Taking into consideration the actual average age, there results, as "a figure of the conservation of the content" referred to a thousand inhabitants: With an average age of 50 years, a percentage of births of 20 for a thousand (50 x 20). From this there further results:

Average age expressed in years	Number of births necessary for every 1,000 inhabitants
50	2.0
60	16.6
75	13.3

Granted that the average age of 75 years represents the maximum limit of the capacity of increase (here it matters little whether the life of the individual is prolonged to 120 or 150 years), a percentage of births amounting to 13.3 for a thousand would represent the extreme limit of the "debit side of births." (In 1954 there was estimated for Berlin a "credit" of births of nine and, for Vienna, of seven for a thousand, with an average age of about 52 years).

In recent years the demographic situation was even worse. It has been asked whether this situation should instead be considered favorable. In particular, attention has been placed on the dangers of a threatening overpopulation, on the threat of famine, world economical crises, unemployment, etc. It was therefore concluded that birth decline was nothing else but a necessary socio-biological reaction and an adaptation to the "vital space," which has become more restricted; the inevitable consequence of the constant conflict of the interests between the preservation of the species and the preservation of the individual, and hence only a natural process of self-regulation.

In 1960 the earth was inhabited by 2,850,000,000 individuals. Every year 34 persons are born for every 1,000 inhabitants, and 18 persons die for every 1,000 individuals, from which is deduced an increase of population of 1.6%. The world population actually increases by 34 millions of individuals every year. According to the calculations of O. N. U., the earth will increase by 3 billion in 1962, 4 billion by 1977, 5 billion in 1990 and 6 billion in 2,000. It would be absolutely necessary to practice a control of births on a large scale before overpopulation becomes catastrophic. This danger would primarily threaten economically and culturally underdeveloped lands.

It is, therefore, important to examine first the close ideological associations between the "theory of vital space" of Malthus and the Darwinian theory of the struggle for life. But we must first formulate clear ideas concerning the causes and effects of birth decline.

3. Causes of Birth Decline

a) REVIEW OF THE THEORIES

(1) The Theory of Well-Being

The theory of well-being (Mombert, Brentano), is based on the hypothesis that the primary cause of birth decline consists in the increase of well-being and consequently the increase of the demands of life.

(2) Theory of the Critical State

The theory of the critical state (Max Hirsch) sees, on the contrary, the principal cause of birth decline in the popularization of the great masses and, above all, in the large families.

(3) Theory of Industrialization

The theory of industrialization (Oldenberg) sees the principal cause of the phenomenon in the increasing industrialization of the city with the concomitant migration from the country.

(4) Theory of Concurrent Pleasures

The theory of concurrent pleasures (Brentano) approaches the theory of well-being very closely. It rests on the hypothesis that the increase of cultural pleasures (theory of culture) offers people a greater pleasure than does the raising of children.

(5) Theory of "Social Capillarity"

The theory of "social capillarity" (Dumont) arises from the idea that social rise is comparable to the rise of liquid in the capillary tubes: the narrower the tube the higher the liquid will rise. Thus the rise in the social scale is payed by the renunciation of children.

(6) Theory of the Surplus of Women

The theory of the surplus of women (Hiwerth-Franken) holds that the primary biological cause of birth decline consists in the increasing numerical disproportion of the sexes.

(7) Theory of Rationalization

The theory of rationalization (Grotjahn) supposes that the primitive "naive type of reproduction" is little by little becoming supplanted by the "rational" type. This process is irresisitble, inevitable and irreversible. This opinion is similar to the theory of civilization of Spengler.

(8) Theory of Biological Degeneration

The theory of biological degeneration is held by certain authors who posit the primary cause of birth decline in the mitigation of the natural power of biological reproduction (Wagner-Manslau and others). It is similar to the theory of domestication of Zeiss and Pintschovius.

(9) Theory of Moral Degeneration

The theory of moral degeneration (V. Ungern-Sternberg) perceives the primary impulse of birth decline in a deep change of internal feeling. Thus Julius Wolff speaks of the "new sexual morality" as the primary cause of birth decline and V. Ungern-Sternberg, of the "ambitious feeling."

b) CRITIQUE OF THE THEORIES

The theories concerning the causes of birth decline which we have mentioned have all a grain of truth. But it is a matter of partial truth depreciated by a unilateral generalization.

Thus the theory of well-being is as correct as the theory of the critical state. Both have justly recognized the existence of an economical factor but they have erroneously considered it as the exclusive or at least primary cause. Both well-being and need are concomitant factors and, according to the times, the one or the other assumes the predominant position. If at one time well-being and the desire of pleasure were decisive, later the critical conditions of the masses held, in a secondary manner, the predominant position. The socio-biological cause of birth decline can be traced back to the formula of a conflict of interests between the preservations of the individuals and the preservation of the species. It is not always easy to determine which factor is concretely the more active, that of luxury or that of need.

Birth decline is a complex phenomenon. The most diverse driving forces in the biological, social, moral and religious realm concur in causing this problem. Without doubt even in this matter the primacy of moral power prevails. The original and decisive driving force rests in the moral-religious sphere: the emancipation from the religious bond, the diffusion of a materialistic philosophy of life and a purely earthly concept of life are the primary driving forces of birth decline.

The theory of well-being is correct insofar as birth decline began in the circles of the prosperous and has become a general phenomenon among the very rich (England, France, United States, Scandinavia, Switzerland). But even the theory of critical conditions has rightly realized that the social conditions of misery have later become quite prevalent. They have taken on the ascendancy in a secondary manner. The diffusion among the people of birth prevention which has been verified in recent years, especially in the large cities but also among the needy country folk, is predominantly caused by the social conditions of hardship. These, in turn, arise from the unjust distribution of earthly possessions and from the violation of social justice. The primary cause of the economic conditions of hardship is, therefore, the violation of moral law. The individual causal factors are closely united and increase reciprocally. One evil generates the other. This is demonstrated very clearly in the study of the effects produced by birth decline.

4. Effects of Birth Decline

As the causes, so also the effects of birth decline are found in the biological, social (economic) and in the moral-religious sphere.

a) BIOLOGICAL EFFECTS

Every species of birth prevention is *per se* associated with damage to individual health. The fact that harm to individual health becomes a phenomenon of the masses constitutes a damage to public health.

The reason why birth decline has been able to assume such great dimensions is attributed to the development of the technique of prevention. The knowledge of the technique of prevention has been largely diffused among the people through an extensive propaganda (under the pretext of "enlightening the people"). The preservative means were set up for sale as "protective means" (against venereal infections). Thus the occasion was presented, especially to the youth, of extramarital relations, and this was also suggested to them.

It is to be noted that this mode of procedure is not justified even from the sexual hygienic standpoint; it has been statistically demonstrated that, as a result of the lack of restraint, the number of cases of venereal infection does not diminish but increases with the increase of the number of contraceptives that are sold. Hence, if the knowledge of contraceptive means is not the true cause of birth decline, it has become the supposition of the diffusion of contraception.

There has been an attempt to present the effects of birth decline as favorable: if less children are born, the quality of the new generation will be better. The lessening of the infant mortality rate seems to confirm this point, but one seems to forget that infant mortality was not lessened in those years in which the birth rate reached its lowest level.

The supposition that, with quantitative regression, a qualitative betterment is associated is an illusion and deception. In fact, the very opposite has taken place: the offspring of the hereditary healthy has been limited while the hereditary tainted have multiplied without restraint. A differentiated reproduction with disastrous eugenic effects has resulted from this situation. In the course of a few generations it has led to a dangerous displacement of the population: to a regression of the hereditary healthy and an increase of the hereditary tainted. In time this process will inevitably lead to a diminution and degeneration of the population. This is the known dysgenic effect of birth decline.

The quality of an organism can be improved only by a copious quantity: *"Pour avoir la qualité il faut la quantité"* (Bertillon). Birth decline, as a mass phenomenon, causes a deep change in the entire structure of the population. This is demonstrated most clearly from the statistics of the structure of the population according to age. Represented in a graph, the distribution of the classes of age present, in a normal population that increases naturally, a pyramid with a large base which terminates toward the top in a point. The base is formed by the young groups, the point by the older groups.

The form of a stationary population presents, in the part corresponding to the older groups which little by little pass away, a flat point in its high part. In the lower part the base is no wider than the median part.

In a decreasing population a reversal of the normal form appears little by little. The base becomes narrower than the median part; the point is completely flat and the rejuvenation of the population vanishes.

These structural changes are of the greatest practical importance. The phenomenon of the aging of a population causes disastrous effects not only from the biological, but also from the social and economic standpoint. The dysgenic effect of the differentiated population has already been mentioned. It also leads to a heavy social and economic burden: the decreasing healthy group of the population must carry the burden for the hereditary tainted group.

b) SOCIAL AND ECONOMIC EFFECTS

In the phenomenon of mass birth-prevention there is present the paradox that even under the social and economic aspect it produces an effect contrary to that which was promised. Just as the possibility of improving the quality of the offspring at the expense of quantity has proven itself an illusion, so also has the possibility of mitigating the social conditions by means of birth-prevention and thus resolving the social question proved itself to be erroneous and illusory. Even in this matter the opposite is the case. In the majority of cases certain individuals can procure advantages at the cost of others in the struggle for existence. In general, the disastrous social conditions would thus be perpetuated: instead of obtaining means in resolving the social question there is a regression toward birth-prevention.

The structural changes of the population sharpen the social conditions of misery. There arises an increasing disproportion between those who are capable of making a living and those who have need of support. The social burdens increase and fall upon the shoulders of those who are less apt to support the same.

The disproportion between the old who are in need of sustenance and the young who are able to work affects perniciously the will to procreate.

Unemployment is not mitigated through birth decline as is erroneously held. The most serious economic crises are those caused by under-consumption. Birth decline causes a constant shortage in large groups of consumers. It is in the first years of existence that the individual is only a consumer. The shortage that is verified in young generations produces effects that are greatly disadvantageous in many branches of economy.

Birth decline favors only the luxury industries. However, these require high capital but little labor. The production of consumers' goods which requires great labor is thrown into a severe crisis through birth decline. This crisis is intensified through the contemporary increasing urbanization, the flight from the country, the abandonment of house work on the part of women and, above all, by the academicism of youth connected with birth decline to which is added the proletarianism of the universities.

Therefore, the promise to "raise the standard of living" manifests itself as illusory. The very opposite takes place: there is an increasing aggravation of the social contrasts. At the onset of this process, the fact that the family maintains itself small still permits a small segment of the population the assurance, in the struggle for existence, of an advantage at the cost of the greater segment of the population. A betterment of the standard of life favors only this segment, while it increases the misery of the masses. With a further progress of this phenomenon the general standard of life is lowered too, except for a small segment of people who know how to live according to a higher standard at the expense of others. The general social conditions of misery are not eliminated by birth decline, but are intensified and perpetuated. The means which could remedy the situation, as the just distribution of social products, are instead frustrated by a small but influential group of profiteers. In compensation the great mass of people are referred to the more convenient form of birth-prevention.

Birth decline does not eliminate national tensions or social pressures; rather it intensifies the same. The password of "people without space" incites a people to penetrate into a "space without people."

The fear of births proper to certain people merely transforms itself to the advantage of expansion on the part of people who are more vital. Hence it is also illusory to hope from birth decline that a lessening of international tension will arise; the danger of war complications is increased rather than diminished.

The demographic politics will be abused as a means of political expansion toward power and militarism. The history of our times has dreadfully confirmed what prudence had previously warned. The fundamental law of pastoral hygiene, that whatever is morally false cannot be economically just, is also confirmed in the social and economical sphere.

c) MORAL EFFECTS

Being a product of a materialistic orientation of life, birth decline cannot but produce a materialistic mentality. Thus arises a further vicious circle. Nothing can alienate people from religion more effectively than the giving over of oneself to the systematic abuse of matrimony. The emancipation from religion was the primary impulse of birth decline; this leads to further emancipation and finally to complete apostasy. One will no longer listen to the voice of conscience or support the announcement of the commandment of God which daily and hourly intervened in all the manifestations of life. To which are added the destructive effect of marital abuse, the disintegration of marriage and the family, the increase of divorces, the deleterious effect upon the education of children, and a general sexual libertinism. If this process continues, it will lead to that promiscuity which the evolutionistic theory affirmed was the initial stage of the sexual relations of human society. But even in this regard the contrary is true. In the original primitive society marriage was considered sacred; promiscuity, on the other hand, is the final stage of the decadence of a society which has removed itself from every form of the natural order of life, after having been emancipated from the moral supernatural law. How far these evils have infiltrated western society and destroyed it is clearly manifested by the much-discussed report of the American biologist Kinsey, which we shall treat critically and in detail.

But we shall first consider in greater detail the ideological basis of birth decline, the theory of Malthusianism and its close spiritual association with selectionism.

B. Malthusianism

1. The Theory of Malthus

The theory of Thomas Robert Malthus (1766-1834) is expounded in his principal work *An Essay on the Principles of Population* (1798). In connection with the theory of Charles Darwin concerning the struggle for existence *(Natural Selection, Struggle for Life)*, he presents the ideological basis of the principle of birth-prevention.

In 1798 Malthus invoked the intervention of the State against the incumbent danger of overpopulation and a universal famine. The Malthusian ideology is based on the notion that the population tends to multiply in geometric progression while the "means of subsistence" can multiply, at the same time, only in an arithmetic progression. If, therefore, the quantity of the means of subsistence increases from one generation to another in proportion to 2, 4, 6, 8, 10, 12, 14, 16, the population increases in the same period of time in proportion to 2, 4, 8, 16, 32, 64, 128, 256. There thus results an irresistible increasing disproportion: the "relative proportion between population and food" would therefore become definitely restricted. For this reason Malthus suggested, as the only remedy, the limitation of reproduction, and this through "moral abstinence" (moral restraint).

From the fact that Malthus, an Anglican minister, recommended moral restraint and rejected the immoral means of birth prevention —then little known—an antithesis has been constructed between Malthusianism and Neomalthusianism, which latter does not reject matrimonial abuse, but propagates the same.

We hold that this differentiation is not exact. It is proper instead to distinguish between theoretical and practical Malthusianism. The latter results from the former as its inevitable practical consequence. What Malthus had taught was nothing else but the theoretical basis from which the extreme practical consequences were later taken. The theoretical basis is, however, exactly the same in both Malthusianism and Neomalthusianism. The attempt to remove

Malthus from the responsibility of Neomalthusianism is, therefore, misleading.

Darwin was close to Malthus, and both Selectionism and Malthusianism are based on the same ideological foundation. The point of contact between the two theories results from the apparently clear formula: it is preferable that less people are born but that there be a good selection; quality instead of quantity.

The basic premise of the theory of the decreasing alimentary space is, without doubt, definitely to be declared false. Even its starting point, that is, the theory of the geometric progression of the population and of the disproportion which results with the increase of the alimentary space is absolutely erratic. If this hypothesis were correct, the following would result with mathematical consistency.

If we figure an average of three generations (of 33.3 years each) in a century, then a single married couple, living in the era in which Christ was born, would in 2,000 years have produced a progeny of about 60 generations. There would be, therefore, according to Malthus, a number of descendants amounting to 2^{60}, that is a number that would reach the enormous class of a quadrillion. In reality there are about 2 milliard people living on earth.

Malthus himself realizes well that the calculations do not correspond to reality since there are natural impediments to multiplication ("checks of population") which effect a natural selection through elimination: wars, epidemics, famines, etc. In spite of this fact, he holds firm by way of principle to his demographic law of geometric progression.

2. Critique of the Theory

Now any further argumentation concerning Malthusianism is based on the foundation of an initial scientific error. Moreover, Malthus has overlooked a fundamental fact: man is not, as the animal, merely a consumer of foodstuffs, but also a producer. He is the most valuable productive element in nature and is capable of producing a greater quantity than he consumes during his life. Hence the alimentary space does not necessarily have to lessen with the increase of the number of men but is susceptible to an unsuspected extension.

How little justified is the anxiety of "overpopulation" is seen from the statistical fact that the entire population of the earth which, before the Second World War, was calculated at about 2 milliard of men, closely arranged (4 persons for a square metre), could be placed on the surface of Lake Constance which is 538,5 sq. km.

Even without any technical progress, the earth could have offered, even before the last World War, sufficient vital space for all. According to the opinion of outstanding representatives of agrarian science, the earth, in view also of the perfecting of the economy and commercial technique, could nourish a greater number of people than those existing today.

This opinion, held, among others, by Aeroboe up to 1910, was fostered by the majority of the most illustrious representatives of the science. Malthusianism which is the object of mass propaganda in Anglo-American lands found in recent times an energetic propagandist in the person of Charles Galton Darwin, nephew of Charles Darwin. Sir Galton Darwin accepted essentially the theory of Malthus concerning the geometric progression of the increase of population. He reduced the same in form insofar as he declared that ("according to a prudent calculation") humanity doubles itself in a century; in these conditions only a small segment of the people could survive. After 3953 it will be impossible for the majority of people to survive.

Galton Darwin expressed, at the same time, a very pessimistic opinion concerning the possibility of opening new sources of means of sustenance by means of new sources of energy. According to him, the standard of life must lower itself continually.

He holds that it shall be necessary to breed a "new species of men," constituted by a type corresponding to the "workers" of the bees and termites which would be desexualized by means of antihormones; a type of warrior and a few individuals destined for reproduction, the proportion of which among the sexes could be regulated at will.

Sir Galton Darwin summarized the ethical consequences of this theory in the following words: "The doctrine of the sanctity of each man must be subjected to a revision." In regard to medical ethics he states that "the duty of the doctor to conserve human life will have no value in the future world." This brings to light the ethical import of Malthusianism and its close association with Selectionism. But even in this matter both Galton Darwin and Malthus overlook the fact that man is a living being endowed with reason and capable of modifying the natural world which surrounds him and of enlarging the confines of alimentary space. Man is not enclosed as gas in a rigid container.

3. Overpopulation and World Famine

Malthusianism has been transformed into a world movement to which the authority of Sir Galton Darwin has given a new impetus. The basic argument of the propaganda of this movement is the panic arising from the danger of world famine. We must, therefore, take a position in regard to this point of argument.

In order to justify the necessity of a world propaganda in favor of Malthusianism, special attention has been directed to the over-population of India, China and Egypt. In this manner the attention is distracted from the true cause of the social conditions, and the indigent population are directed toward the use of birth-prevention. Humiliating for the western world is the answer that was given by a Chinese statesman to a European when the latter recommended that China study and apply, as India, the European-American methods of "planned parenthood." The Chinese gave this wise answer: "It is the white man's answer to the yellow peril!"

In this matter we should briefly indicate some recent facts. In the U.S.A. for every farmer there is a number of consumers main-tained by him which is three times that of the year 1900. In fifteen years the production of grain has increased about 80-90%.

In India, the scarcity of land is not due to the overpopulation but to the irregular distribution of the population. Only a third of the land is utilized. Production can be increased by means of irrigation, as is the case in Palestine.

De Castro (Geography of Hunger) states, contrary to Malthus, that overpopulation is never the cause of famine, rather that the dying-out of people is the real cause.

The combating of the danger of world famine by means of birth-prevention is the worst prescription that can possibly be given. The basic truth is that the earth offers sufficient nourishment for all. The real problem consists in the fact that the workings of human society are based on extreme injustice, and the limitation of birth will distract attention from the solution of this problem. Contrary to the opinion of Malthus, the limitation of birth does not constitute the way toward survival but that leading to definite decadence (De Castro).

In this regard, problems concerning the amelioration of the soil are studied: struggle against soil erosion and the loss of humus caused by inundation; methods of fertilization and utilization of refuse. Moreover, attention should be directed to the extensive potentiality of nutrition, for the most part not yet utilized, that exists in the fish kingdom of the sea. The production of fish could easily be doubled. Only seven per cent of the surface of the earth has been cultivated.

Incalculable are the resources arising from the immense multiplication of energy from yeasts and fresh-water alga chorella; and further, of the possibility of directly producing energy from solar heat, radioactive isotope, etc.

Our actual system of exhausting the soil of nature is characterized by the brutal destruction of the natural supplies, especially of the forests and of the vital element of water. The rotation press of the entire world consumes in one day the wood of an entire forest. The scarcity of water has always been a severe hygienic problem.

4. Total Critique

In summary and in regard to the criticism of Malthusianism the following can be said: the anxiety of overpopulation and world famine is the greatest deception imposed on mankind for almost two centuries. It has accomplished a victorious march throughout the world in unison with the theory of Darwin, and this triumph represents nothing else but the triumph of the forces of destruction and ruin.

Birth decline, even if couched in euphemistic words as "planned parenthood," does not render humanity richer, but poorer, and completely destroys all the moral and cultural values which even two world wars have not destroyed.

The Malthusian theory is one of the theories that disturbs and destroys the world. More than once in the course of world history theories which later shattered the world have been concocted by theoretical thinkers. Often the ideology which appears harmless is often the most dangerous. Even such French Encyclopedists as Didérot, Montesquieu, Rousseau and Voltaire cannot be completely absolved from the responsibility of the bloody sacrifices of the revolution.

Malthusianism has developed in our times into a system and an ideology. The close idealistic affinity of this system with the rejecting methods of Selectionism, with which we have become acquainted in negative eugenics, manifest the reproaches made by Sir Galton Darwin concerning medicine because it preserves the life of men instead of allowing it to perish. These currents of thought are not new since we encounter them in Plato.

According to Nietzsche, we find them in the notorious maxim of Tille who called the miserable quarters (slums) of the Oriental section of London the "National Sanitarium" of the British nation, since there all deteriorating existences unsparingly perish. "That which is about to fall should be pushed"; this is the way in which Nietzsche expressed the ideology of brutal Selectionism. Already in 1907, O. Hertwig called attention to the destructive effects of biological, social and political Darwinism.

From the religious and moral standpoint we conclusively observe that the propaganda of Malthusianism exercised a deeply destructive effect since it spread the idea that it is impossible to live in marriage according to the commandment of God. We have always learned that God never commands what is impossible *("Deus impossibilia non iubet")*.[1] If Malthus is correct, then it is actually impossible to follow what the law of God commands. The most insidious aspect of the ideology of Malthusianism is this, that it leads into error even the believers concerning the possibility of following the commandment of God.

We have already observed that the greatest danger contained in the indiscriminate propaganda in favor of the method of Knaus is that it avails itself, with a certain right, of the fact that it is not *in se* illicit, not even according to the most rigorous Catholic morality. Through this propaganda it has been able to manifest its influence among Catholics so that it has annexed this circle to the mentality of Malthusianism. The comparison of this propaganda

[1] Cf. *"Casti Connubii,"* n. 62.

with the "Trojan Horse" is very precise. Formerly, Catholic families represented the last and most solid bulwark against Malthusianism. The undermining of this bulwark is the work of the propaganda in favor of the Knaus-Ogino method.

Nothing can be changed in regard to this judgment, not even the fact that, at the world congress of the Neomalthusian league held in Rome in 1954, P. Lestapis declared that the Vatican, in view of the threat of a world overpopulation agreed that the "rhythm" method (periodic abstinence) be applied and propagandized, above all, among the "underdeveloped" people. The Neomalthusian propaganda immediately took hold of this and interpreted it in the sense that the Vatican, in view of the world danger of overpopulation, "yielded" in the question of birth-prevention.

On the contrary, it can be observed that the Sixth International Congress of Catholic Doctors (Dublin, 1954) established, with the greatest decision, that Malthusianism represents a universal false doctrine which lacks a scientific basis. In regard to the "rhythm" method, the Church has always declared that it is *in se* not illicit, but this does not mean that she approves its propaganda among the people. A declaration of the indicated matter can very easily be taken up and abused for the purpose of their propaganda.

The Church could not and would not recognize Malthusianism, much less approve of it. If Malthus is right, then there could not be a God or, at least, there could not be a wise, good and merciful Father who protects the destiny of man and constantly conserves the universe; at most there could exist only a shadow god as is acknowledged by English Deism to which Malthus was manifestly very close. If, on the one hand, the extreme logical consequence of evolutionism is that a Creator does not exist, since the universe developed "of itself," on the other hand, Malthusianism leads to the denial of a personal God, since a personal God could not have created the universe in such a manner that it is impossible for man to fulfill His commandments.[2]

The heresies of our times clothe themselves in the garment of profane science. "Science," or, better, that which passes off as scientific, has become the idol of our times. It is the task of a universalistic genuine science to unmask this idol and reopen the way that leads to an effective knowledge of truth.

[2] Cf. Council of Trent, Section VI, Chapter 11.

IV. THE RELAXATION OF THE SEXUAL LIFE

The possibility of impeding the effects of sexual commerce by means of protective means has contributed, in lands of western civilization, to a relaxation of the customs which in the history of mankind is without example.

But this does not mean that, in the course of history, similar conditions among all the people of the earth and at all times have not been verified. The basic difference is merely this, that in other times and in other places men were aware of the lapse as such: they were aware of the fact that every lapse disturbs a sanctioned order.

This awareness is today practically lost, and the relaxation of the sexual instinct is no longer considered a disturbance of sanctioned order but as something "natural."

The feeling for the "taboo" of the sexual sphere is lost and there is the demand that the formerly constituted order be changed since it no longer corresponds to nature and is merely "fastidious." A typical example of this tendency of the inversion of the natural order is the report of the American biologist, Kinsey, concerning the sexual behavior of men and women.

A. The Kinsey Report

The Kinsey report consists of two parts: 1) *Sexual Behaviour in the Human Male;* 2) *Sexual Behavior in the Human Female.*

It is very significant that Kinsey does not use the terms "man" and "woman," but the zoological designations of "male" and "female."

1. Sexual Behavior in the Man

This first report of Kinsey was treated by the following contributors;

1) Geddes, Donald Porter, "New Light Concerning Our Knowledge of Sex"
2) Ford, Clellan, "The Sex Life of Primitive People"
3) Ginzberg, "The Behavior of the Classes Regarding Sexuality"
4) Gilbert, G. M., "The Sex Life of Students"

5) Montagu, Ashley, "The Understanding of Our Sexual Desire"
6) McIver, Cobert, "The Orientation of Society and Sex"
7) English, Spurgeon, "Love and Sex"
8) Fromm, Erich, "Sex and Character"
9) Gruenberg, Benjamin, "Who Teaches Our Children?"
10) Dickinson, Robert, "The End of Hypocrisy"
11) Kuether, "Sex, A Gift of God"
12) Llewellyn, Karl, "The Limits of Sex Legislation"

The report begins with the thesis: "In the last two millenia we have developed something that we call *western culture.*" The report affirms still further that in the course of these two millenia the human sex instinct has remained constant, but that the public orientation and the individual expression of it has undergone a profound change. The instinct, as such, has remained basically constant, but, as we have observed in the introduction, there has been a relaxation which not only infringes the most ancient sanctions, but also demands the abolition of the same. The traditional mode of behavior is designated as deceitful and hypocritical: one acts externally as if one recognizes a "sex ideal," but one does not have the confidence in the possibility of realizing this ideal.

Public opinion and private behavior are completely different. The fact of "repression" and its effects has been known by the psychoanalyst for a long time. The actual deviation from the "ideal," from a representation which does not correspond to reality, renders man insincere.

The report declares that Kinsey wants to be considered a researcher and a moralist. Kinsey further declares: we do not practice what we preach. The sex instinct begins early and lasts for a long time. We have reason to suppose that the sex instinct, as an important aspect of human nature, does not change; but it cannot be denied that the behavior of men changes, as a rule, through changes of the so-called social order.

Always and at all times there have been forms of sex behavior which have been approved by society and forms of sex behavior which have been condemned. "This does not mean that a recognized sexual behavior remains the same for all times and that it is equally right and valid for all lands." With this negation of universally obliging norms, the Kinsey report has placed itself clearly and unequivocally in the realm of ethical Relativism.

The statistical material of the Kinsey report includes about 16,000 persons of the male sex and 5,940 of the female sex. In answering the questionnaire the women definitely manifested a greater reserve than the men.

The Kinsey report first analyzed, on the basis of answers given to a complete and detailed questionnaire, the rise and frequency of orgasm, subdivided into six forms of sexual release:

1) Through ipsation (here designated as "onanism")
2) Through pollution
3) Through heterosexual caresses ("petting")
4) Through heterosexual sex relations
   a) before marriage
   b) during marriage
   c) outside of marriage
   d) after marriage
5) Homosexual acts
6) Animal contacts

Kinsey begins with the statement that in the past one was not aware of the precocious awakening of sexual activity; this was "taboo," at least up to the time of full maturity. It could appear as if Kinsey was the first to discover infantile sexuality. One could consider him correct if he wanted to say that every sex education should be directed toward the control of sexuality until the attainment of full maturity. But this is the very thing that is denied in every line of the report. Kinsey directly blames theology for having merely considered the control of sexuality and of having directed her teaching and support solely to this point: "The laws were formed and applied according to this opinion"; "Every sexual activity outside of marriage was declared sinful and for the most part even illegal." The only exception was that of pollution, but this was considered "unaesthetic."

Prescinding from the erroneous judgment as to value, pollution cannot be considered a species of sexual activity since it occurs passively, without the cooperation of man. On the fact that it has absolutely nothing to do with an *actus humanus* rests its moral indifference.

The general statements concerning the sex life of primitive people can be misleading. We know from the research of the school of Wilhelm Schmidt and W. Koppers that monogamy prevailed among the primitive people and that sexual activity was strictly prohibited to the adolescents before the rite of initiation and consecration of puberty. It was the authentic primitive people who scrupulously observed the sex "taboo" and severely punished its infraction.

The Kinsey report calls upon the testimony of psychiatrists, psychoanalysts, marriage counselors, social workers, etc., according to whom numerous people continually transgress the prevailing norms of sex life. The opinion that these individuals are "sinners," delinquents or psychic deviants is designated as "superficial." It is this very statement that denotes the frivolity with which the Kinsey report, by passing over the establishing of facts, motivates judgments of a general nature.

Kinsey states that all modes of sexual behavior found among the "primitives" can also be found among Americans: the manner of obtaining an orgasm is the same:

Ipsation (masturbation) is a largely diffused habit which is only rarely admitted. Kinsey affirms that in the U.S.A. over 90 per cent of men give in to masturbation from time to time. (In this regard it is, however, important to distinguish accurately whether it is a matter of the temporary masturbation of the adult, eventually also of marriage).

Homosexuality, according to Kinsey, is found in about one third of the men of America.

Sodomy (*ratione generis,* that is, with animals) is also, according to Kinsey, the most infrequent form of obtaining an orgasm; yet always often enough that it can be included statistically.

Seventy per cent of the American youth between the ages of 16 and 20 are already involved in sexual cohabitation before marriage.

Kuether, after having correctly observed that in sexual problems there is also present a religious problem, holds that our civilization demands impossible things of youth; that society refuses to acknowledge precocious activity and prefers to condemn it as unhygienic, immoral and reprehensible: "A constructive religious conception must take into account the fact of human life." The jurist K. Llewellyn asks how low must the respect of law sink when the action of law finds itself in conflict with the fact of human nature.

The Kinsey report reaches its peak in the statement that 95 per cent of the entire male population in the U.S.A. could be put in prison or in an institution because of some sexual activity contrary to law.

Llewellyn declares that "we have to set an end that will direct humanity forward and, once this end has been established, we have to formulate laws that will promote the realization of this end."

There are a series of unofficial lifelong habits that are contrary to law, religion and "with rules of life that should be observed." Just as men are differentiated among themselves according to weight and stature, so there are differences regarding the intensity and direction of the sexual instinct. In this respect not all men are to be judged in the same manner.

Dr. Eli Ginzberg, professor of Columbia University, declares that the lower and the middle class are divided one from the other by a philosophy of life that is completely different.

Kinsey believes that he has offered convincing proof of the affirmation that the difference between the higher and lower class, in regard to sexual behavior, depends on their diverse conception of life.

Ginzberg, however, concludes his observations with the point that no society can exist if its citizens do not sacrifice for the future their momentary pleasures. This will be possible only on condition that the content of life is constituted of meaningful labor. Only a society capable of resolving definitely the problem of labor can also resolve the sex problem and, with it, also the problem of human society in general.

We could agree with the last thesis of Ginzberg by inverting it in the following manner: only when men overcome their sexual problem can they also overcome the major problems of society and, above all, the social question.

As long as the uncontrolled desire of sexual pleasure indicates the direction, then one will tend toward the procuring of the greatest quantity of pleasures. In this way social justice can never be realized.

Taking into consideration these observations one can see under a new aspect the close connection that exists between the two great encyclicals, *"Casti Connubii"* and *"Quadragesimo Anno."*

The Kinsey report promises to overcome all difficulties by means of timely and full sex instruction which should be imparted from the early days of youth (cf. articles by Gruenberg and Dickinson). On the contrary, we have always held the opinion that a purely rational instruction is an inadequate means. If it is not at the same time associated with a deep religious formation, it is not able to impede any harm. That which is decisive is not the simple instruction, but a finality of sex pedagogy which corresponds to the true nature of man. But it is not possible to understand the true nature of man if one is imbued with positivistic, biological and evolutionary prejudices which deny the difference between man and animal; but is possible only on the basis of a universalistic complete knowledge which includes both the lowest and highest aspects of man as well as the fact of man's fallen nature and of the sole possibility of elevating the same.

The fundamental error of the Kinsey report is just this: Kinsey transfers indiscriminately to man the biological concepts acquired by Kinsey in his capacity as a zoologist.

We consider as worthy of consideration and partly as right the opinion of Dickinson that the Kinsey report is the most discussed book of the twentieth century, and, because of its social effects, is to be compared to the works of Karl Marx *(Das Kapital)* and of Charles Darwin *(Origin of Species)*. We have no reason to consider the destructive effect of the Kinsey report as less than that of the revolutionary effect caused by the works of Marx and Darwin.

Moreover, we subscribe to the opinion that, as atomic energy, so sexuality is a force that can be utilized for either the betterment of human society or for its destruction. We have nothing else to add except that what matters is the right use or abuse of the same. And if the Kinsey report should lead only to the realization that the abuse of sexuality has upon human society the same effect as the abuse of atomic energy, we cannot but agree.

That to which we object in the Kinsey report, from the standpoint of pastoral hygiene, is not the establishment of facts, though they can be deplorable (as the fact that 95 per cent of the male population of America transgress in sexual behavior against moral and penal law), but the conclusions from these facts: that moral law and the law of justice should be modified; that the institutions of society, the Church, State, law, and the family should make concessions to the new factual data; if laws are to be formulated, morality must adapt itself. On the contrary, we declare that "men should change themselves" and not the laws, with this reservation however: *"quid leges sine moribus?"* The report of Kinsey concerning the moral defection of 95 per cent of the men was first of all considered in the feminine world as the proof of the moral inferiority of man.

The indignation was greater in the feminine world when, in 1953, the second part of the Kinsey report was published and this had as its object the sexual behavior of the woman.

2. The Sexual Behavior of the Woman

This second part of the Kinsey report was treated by the contributions of the following collaborators:

Pomeroy, Wardell (Psychologist)

Martin, Clyde E. (Statistician)

Gebhart, Paul H. (Anthropologist)

Kinsey and his collaborators studied the sexual behavior of women with the same method of statistical involution. They arrive essentially at the following conclusions:

If it is possible to demonstrate that 85 per cent of men have had premarital relations, this percentage is reduced in women to 50 per cent. Conjugal infidelity was established in 50 per cent of the men and in 40 per cent of the women.

"Petting parties," that is, amorous rendezvous with sexual excitement, are generally frequent among girls and boys. Two out of five girls under 15 years of age have had the experience of "petting." Around 20 years of age the percentage is 91 per cent and around 35 years it is 99 per cent. Only 10 per cent of these have had experience with only one man. The remaining 32 per cent have had experience with 2 to 5 men; 23 per cent with 6 to 10 men; 35 per cent with more than 10 men.

Among the married women, one out of five have, at the age of 35, already committed an act of adultery; one out of 4 at the age of 40. The complete percentage of infidelity amounts to 40 per cent. In the younger generation, 50 per cent of the youth had lost their virginity before marriage; of the unfaithful wives, 41 per cent had committed adultery with only one partner, and 32 per cent had only transitory relations.

Homosexuality was found to be present in 20 per cent, and masturbation in 62 per cent of the women. Frigidity was seen to be widely diffused; the confirmation that 10 per cent of the women in sexual relations do not reach a "climax" (orgasm) is not yet a definite proof of the existence of true frigidity.

Even in this report Kinsey emphasizes the fact that it is not his task to judge what is right or wrong; he deserves to be merely a researcher who limits himself to the establishment of truth. But his argumentation goes much further:

1) Man is an animal.
2) Many animals behave themselves in such a manner that human society condemns them as abnormal or pervert.
3) If these animals act according to their nature, their behavior is natural. The concept of "biological normalities" should, therefore, take the place of a moral judgment of value or worthlessness.

In its second part the Kinsey report is on the same plane as the discovery of Freud regarding the deep strata of the subconscious. Kinsey has become celebrated as the "Columbus of Sex": he has accomplished for sex knowledge what Columbus accomplished for Geography.

On the other hand, it has been justly objected that Kinsey based his judgment of women exclusively on the questionnaire that only one part of those that were questioned answered. But this is not all the women. He has overlooked, above all, the fact that for the majority of women the true element of feminine life is found in maternity and love.

The public reaction to the second part of the Kinsey report was more violent than the first. The presumptuous illusion of the American feminine world as being substantially better than the "morally inferior men" was destroyed. Hence it happened that the Kinsey report was denounced most resolutely by the very American group of women who approved most agreeably the first part of the report.

As matters now stand, neither of the two sexes has anything with which to reproach the other. In both reign a similar thirst for pleasure, a hunger for life which has degenerated into an addicted inordinate desire and unbridled sexuality which has assumed a malignant character inasmuch as it rejects any law that tends to set limits, destroys the concept of failure and, with it, annuls the concept of sin.

The fact of a widespread relaxation of the sexual life in the sphere of modern civilization has found in the Kinsey report a confirmation which could surprise only those who did not realize the real state of affairs and their proportions.

We are now to examine to what degree the emancipation of women and feminism itself have contributed to this relaxation of sexual life.

A change of the forms of life which has no equal in history has taken place in our time. It was believed that feminism overcame prostitution, the shame of civilization. In reality it has only modified its forms: prostitution, which at first was placed outside of society, has penetrated society with its evident consequences. This is without doubt one of the lessons that one can learn from the reading of the Kinsey report.

B. Feminism and the Sex Problem

1. Concept

We have first of all to distinguish between feminist movement, emancipation, and feminism.

The feminist movement comprises the aspirations of women in assuring themselves of the participation in the economical, spiritual and political life. In the feminist movement three aims are distinguished:

1) Social (movement in favor of the rights of women).
2) Cultural (movement in favor of the culture of women).
3) Political (movement in favor of voting by women).[1]

The feminist movement, in its entirety, is further divided into politico-philosophical groups:

1) Civil-liberal.

---

[1] The encyclical *"Casti Connubii"* distinguishes between social, economical and physiological emancipation. The latter refers to the aspiration of the woman of deciding herself whether she desires to become a mother or not.

2) Socialistic.

3) Christian-social.

Emancipation implies the aspiration of the woman toward her liberation from the predominance of the man, toward an equality of rights in the political, social and cultural sphere. The first objective toward which the movement tended was the request of the right to vote politically.

By feminism we mean the sum total of all the mentioned interests toward an ideological unity, toward a radical politico-philosophical tendency whose ultimate scope was no longer the simple equality of rights, but the pre-eminence of women in all the spheres of life. Feminism is, in a special manner, the logical consequence of the radical tendency of the feminist movement of which the opposite with a Christian social tendency is characteristic.

2. The Impetus of Feminism

Evolutionism has given impetus to feminism toward radical demands by applying the ideology of a general progressive evolution even to sociology (cf., for example, the theory of matriarchy of Bachoften). The feminine question of our day constitutes a part of the general social question. The definite solution of this question will also resolve the feminine question.

When it is a matter of considering the feminine question from the purely economical standpoint, many authors indicate the basic biological cause of the surplus of women to be that of the displacement of the normal "proportion among the sexes."

The normal proportion among the sexes, that is, the relationship between the birth of males and that of females, is for the newly born 106:100. Because of the higher mortality rate of the males and the more precocious mortality of men, the proportion became gradually more unfavorable for them. The surplus of women became more acute through wars, especially in the age of reproduction and of marriageable age. The surplus of women, especially of those in middle age, constitutes a notable advantage for the woman. Where such a surplus exists in too great a degree, it produces disastrous effects.

The effects of the surplus of women manifests itself in a special unfavorable manner in the sphere of sex life. In courtship and in its means the natural order can easily be inverted. There arises a depreciation of virginity which, in turn, brings about a deleterious vicious circle in the social and moral sphere. Hand in hand with this depreciation of virginity, there arises the exaggerated evaluation of sex attraction which the woman exercises upon the man ("sex appeal").

It would seem that the surplus of women would result in favor of the man, but the contrary is true both from the psychological standpoint, since the woman always desires to be courted and conquered, and from the economical and social standpoint, since the women who cannot find a husband are forced to get on alone and thus acquire with independence a realization of their capacity in professions which at one time were reserved to men.

The war, with the calling of men to arms, brought it about that women had been called upon to participate in work that was once exclusively taken care of by men. And it cannot be denied that under difficult circumstances women have shown themselves to be equal to men in labor performance. That has strengthened their position exceedingly.

Feminism has promised to free the woman from the dominion of the Church, kitchen and children.

That the emancipation from the Church has not been a benefit but, rather, a misfortune for both man and woman is quite evident. Concerning this fact we shall comment later. Whether the liberation from the kitchen is a blessing for the woman, let the women themselves judge, who after a strenuous work day return home tired, and let the men judge, who likewise return home tired and do not have a home that offers them peace and relaxation. Whether the liberation from the children is a benefit for the woman, for the children themselves and for society, let the children themselves judge, who, instead of being educated in the bosom of an ordered family are, in the majority of cases, educated in a public children's home at the expense of the community, as "children of the State."

It is certain, if the family is systematically disrupted, that one can easily affirm that it has lost its qualification to educate and its educative power. The fact that it has reached such a point is due to radical feminism. One might feel that it had its day and that its ideology is a thing of the past. It could be that a great part of women and definitely the best of women have completely overcome the same. But its effects are not yet subdued, as has been clearly demonstrated by the Kinsey report. Little has feminism been subdued in the U.S.A. while the women of Latin countries have manifested themselves relatively immune to it.

In treating of pastoral hygiene we cannot ignore a phenomenon in our time which has produced such deep social consequences.

3. Effects on Sex Morality

Sex libertinism, developed in a deplorable manner as the first fruit of the new "freedom," has perhaps reenforced the position of women externally, but her interior position has become undermined and corrupted. The woman is and remains the victim of all the attempts to procure greater sexual freedom or of interjecting her more definitely in the labor process.

At the Austrian Congress for spiritual directors held in 1953 an expert representative of women stated that feminism has become a "boomerang" which has fallen back upon women.

The evolution above described has had the effect that the woman does no longer enjoy only the right to independent labor, but, willing or unwilling, is constrained to it. This has given to women a certain material independence from men, but not really an economic autonomy, for this results rather in an increased and oppressing dependency. To this is added the collision of duties which is insoluble, due to a double burden arising from the tasks associated with profession, home and family. The collision is, for the most part, "resolved" to the detriment of the home and family.

Hand in hand with this process, a catastrophic devaluation of housework is verified, which leads to a phenomenon that is analogous to that of the flight from the country, a phenomenon which we call the flight from home to the progressive exodus from the domestic economy.

The phenomenon of birth decline and the diffusion of the ideology of Malthusianism are closely associated with this social transformation. Besides the primary causal factors of birth decline which pertain to the moral sphere, the social relations which have become pre-eminent in a secondary manner represent an important role. A contributing factor in this regard has been the shaking of the man's position as head of the family and home caused by the social conditions after the war.

Unemployment caused the husband to lose his position as supporter of the family and established the situation whereby the wife was taken away from the home to work for the maintenance of the children and, in many cases, also for the maintenance of the husband.

It would be of utmost importance for the woman to return to her natural position in the home, but this is not as simple as it appears. It must be a true home in which the wife can find internal and external security by occupying anew the position of a queen who reigns by serving.

And the husband should maintain the family by his physical or mental work, by occupying the position of "head" of the family, not in a fictitious manner, but solidly based on authority. In order to attain this end, it is necessary that the husband first understand the deepest reasons for his actual loss of authority.

The wife is neither a slave nor a breeding animal. This depersonalization is the worst degradation of women. But the wife depreciates herself when, from a desire for an individualistic life, she declares that she wishes no longer to be a "generating machine." Inasmuch as an extreme paternalistic concept tended toward "rendering the woman a slave," it also brought about a "double sex morality." This means that for the man there is unlimited freedom, for the woman the assumption of all burdens.

In the just struggle against "double morality" or the "lordly morality" of the man, the representatives of feminism have gone too far. They not only demanded that the commandment of morality in the sexual sphere be equally obliging for the man and woman which would be understandable, but they would give to men, who would have more often broken the commandment because of their aggressive sexuality, the awareness of the guilt and to the woman a justified feeling of superiority. Instead, feminism demanded an "equal justification" in the sense that henceforth the woman could make use of the same "right" of "living her sexual life to the full." But with this demand the feminist movement has done nothing but threaten the position of the woman. Today the woman "rules" more than ever before, and her lust for power often destroys marriages. She does not rule as formerly by serving in love and does not even rule in the sense of the position of power of a matriarchate. She is more properly on the way toward a gynecoc-racy which already manifests characteristics of degeneracy: a control by which the woman rules the man only through sex. Thus the glorification of the "sex appeal" in the new woman type which the present era has produced. The Kinsey report concerning the sexual behavior of the woman is a shaking document of the situation of this epoch. This must be said once and for all with the greatest clarity. It was this same feminism, with its depreciation of virginity and its demand of equal rights even in the sexual sphere, that has created this situation.

This evolution has led to an enormous increase of homosexuality among women. Lesbian relationships are more frequent than is believed. It is a matter in many cases of single women who do not want to give up sexual relations, but who have no intention of "giving," of surrendering themselves physically to man. We find among them those who desire maternity, but reject men.

Female homosexuality (tribadism) is on the increase. The virile intersexual types (the virago type) are primarily so inclined. They are the same types to which the majority of female guides and champions of militant feminism belong, those types which Mathes has compared to "the form of the future," to the feminine and maternal "youthful form."

It is this militant type that has coined the phrase, "battle of the sexes." This type is now being cultivated through planned and domineering demands of fashion which has intimated the struggle against the natural maternal bodily form of the maternal type in favor of an intersexual "beauty ideal." This is also the type against which the intersexual type is willingly submissive to man and gives in freely to sexual bondage and intercedes in favor of feminism. This development leads to an effacement of the sexual character.

In this regard one has perceived a definite "decline of the masculine leading power" (Petterson); on the other hand, in it has been seen the decline of civilization (Eberhardt).

4. Questions Relating to Professional Work of Women

It is not possible to perceive the solution of the feminine question in the fact that the woman is always more inexorably dragged into the process of extra-domestic professional work. This process has not brought the desired and promised independence to the woman; and insofar as it has done so, it must be asked at what a price and in what relation is the advantage with the sacrifice. The "liberation of the woman" has led her only into the oppressing servitude of professional work. We do not allude here to those women who have chosen a profession as a true vocation and who exercise the same with joy and dedication. Inasmuch as this has been freely chosen, this kind of professional activity can be approved. There are numerous feminine professions in which the woman can truly unfold her maternal disposition.

The constraint of professional work as imposed by social conditions constitutes instead a heavy yoke for the woman, and especially when the married woman and mother is constrained to exercise a profession without any internal obligation but only because the earnings of the husband are not sufficient in conveniently maintaining the family.

The extra-domestic professional work is a more seriously physiological burden for the woman than for the man. And if she still has to fulfill the duties of housekeeper and mother, she then has to carry a double or triple burden which she cannot sustain for a long time.

She will either try to fulfill as much as possible all her duties— and then in time will necessarily suffer in health—or will attempt to lighten her burden in one direction; but since this is for the most part not possible in the professional sphere, she will tend toward the direction of "least resistance," that is, she will sacrifice the household duties and the duties of motherhood. The latter will be avoided through birth-prevention. But even this cannot be pursued for a long time without harm to health and danger to marriage.

Hirsch has rightly formulated the "fundamental law of maternity welfare": "Maternity and extra-domestic professional activity are two antithetical terms which in time become incompatible."

There has been an attempt to lighten maternity and professional activity with laws for the protection of mothers, with rest prescribed by law before and after parturition, and by social contributions in the same measure as insurance for sickness.

The representatives of radical feminism have rejected such facilities by stating that because of these the woman would find herself in a disadvantageous position in the concurrent struggle with man since feminine work would impose greater social burden upon the contractor or the one giving the work (open-door movement).

Thus the women themselves have become the most radical opponents of the "protection of the mother" inasmuch as they interpret the principle of parity in a manner that is unfavorable to women: the woman can produce the same results as man, and hence must work under the same conditions as man.

The professional work of women has become a mass phenomenon. The social and hygienic effects that arise from this are incalculable. The manifold burden associated with it is one of the most serious hygienic-social disasters. For the woman who is not married, professional activity is often only a necessary evil; but for the woman who wishes to be also a wife and mother, it constitutes a real tragedy. Its effects manifest themselves even in the general structure of the population.

For social hygiene the question is not whether the woman can do what is required of her, but rather whether she should do it. In certain circumstances she can accomplish the same as the man, but the question is whether she can do this for a long time without harm to her health or to her efficiency. This does not mean that the woman should not exercise any profession; but her natural profession—the government of the home, maternity, the rearing of children—requires the participation of her whole personality. To such an occupation belongs the acknowledgement of a true profession, even from the standpoint of social legislation.

Although certain professional first-class achievements on the part of women can be of supreme value as a single phenomenon, as a mass phenomenon they produce effects more harmful than advantageous. They lead to a destruction of marriage and family and, with it, to the destruction of human society in general.

5. Social and Juridical Questions

The meaning of professional work by women from the standpoint of social hygiene has already been mentioned in the reference to the "law of incompatibility" (Max Hirsch). Pregnancy welfare represents the principle part of prenatal maternity welfare. In unison with marriage counseling it occupies the central position in the entire social and hygienic welfare system. From the preceding chapters we can easily see how much the problem of extra-domestic work on the part of women is closely connected with questions of birth-prevention, birth decline, and also with the problem of the so-called social indication for abortion. We must now consider the enormous task which social legislation must in great part still fulfill in the sphere of maternity protection, social welfare for the pregnant, birth and childbed. It should, moreover, resolve the questions of family compensation and compensation of burdens and should bring a sufficient renewal of social insurance in its entirety. Tasks of supreme hygienic-social importance should be fulfilled not only in the sphere of social justice, but also of family justice.

Above all, the socialistic tendency of feminism under the slogan "Reform of family justice" strives to obtain a radical assimilation of the juridical position of the woman with that of the man. The principle of parity should be realized completely. These aspirations do not have as their purpose the equality of rights of the woman. Insofar as it regards the human right of freely unfolding one's personality, this equality does not constitute a problem and is no longer seriously contested by anyone. It is rather a case of obtaining a degree of equality which practically leads to a predominance of the woman and a diminishing of the authority of man.

Thus the struggle tends rather toward the abolition of fatherly power and the substitution of the same by a power exercised in common by both parents. Certainly there can be situations—and these are not rare today—in which the father fails in this task, and the fartherly power is taken from him and must be transferred to the mother. It is the purpose of courts for the protection of wards to take care of such dispositions.

The *a priori* division of the fatherly power by bestowing the same on both parents is erroneous and contrary to the natural order. The demand to abolish the obligation on the part of the wife to follow the husband when he establishes a change of residence constitutes a tendency toward the destruction of the family and is also the case when the wife no longer automatically acquires the citizenship of the husband; when the wife is authorized to keep in every case her maiden name and eventually to have the husband assume that of the wife. This last disposition would institute the law of succession in the maternal line, of the matrilineal descendancy, and this would basically constitute matriarchy.

Radical feminism has amalgamated the demand for the reform of family justice with that of the revolutionary sex reform. It has demanded the absolute equality of extramarital maternity with legitimate maternity without considering to what point this demand would be compatible with the stability of marriage and the family as juridical institutions. Where there has been an attempt to resolve the tragic problem of illegitimate children in this manner, it had to be admitted that the price of this solution was very costly.

The education of all the children as "children of the state"—that is the extreme and inevitable consequence of the radical actualization of the principle of parity, which is contrary to all biological and physiological data; the extreme consequence of the disregard of the differentiation posited by nature and the division of labor between the sexes.

Every juridical order must correspond to natural law, that is, to the law that results spontaneously from the nature of things and from the conditions of life.

A consideration of further details concerning the reform of family justice would take us too far. In conclusion we can recall the words of Pius XI in the encyclical *"Casti Connubii"* explaining the natural and supernatural order, which fully recognizes the equality of the rights of women and which takes into consideration the natural difference of the tasks associated with both sexes: man is the head; woman is the heart of the family.[2]

6. Ethico-Metaphysical Viewpoint

If one wishes to discover the kernel of truth contained in the theory of Freud who sees in God only an "image of the father," one must invert the relationship and realize that the position of the father of the family is derived in the last analysis from the authority of God and that the father represents a species of the *"imago Dei,"* an image of that God of whom "all paternity is named."[3]

The systematic struggle against paternal authority is, therefore,

---

[2] *"Casti Connubii,"* n. 27.
[3] Epistle of St. Paul to the Ephesians 3, 15.

in a certain manner also a reproduction of the struggle against the authority of God the Father.

It is obvious the woman is not the sole cause of the loss of authority on the part of man. It was man who, in the great revolutionary movements of our times, was the first to rebel against the authority of God and pronounced his *"non serviam."* As the flesh disobeys the spirit and rises against it when the spirit of man disobeys God (*"Tu Deo, tibi caro,"*—St. Augustine)[4] so the woman had to rise against man after he had risen against God, the Creator, Lord and Preserver of every life. It is serious, but true, that the struggle of the sexes also poisons the source of the natural life after having been first directed against the original source of every supernatural life.

The diabolism raging from this struggle—one can almost speak of an erupted pandemonium of our times—is nothing else but the choir of the Erinyes which executes the vengeance of the offended divine order upon the present humanity.

In order to recover the way from this diabolical problem to the just order of things and peace, there is no other way than that indicated by St. Augustine by the words, *"Tu Deo, tibi caro":* in the measure in which humanity returns to submit itself willingly to the will of God, the flesh will return to a sweet submission to the spirit. In the measure in which man will return to the observance of the order established by God, his companion whom God has given him will also submit to him "in all that is just," and husband and wife will fulfill together the great tasks assigned to them by the natural order and together will also participate in the blessings of the supernatural order.

One can speak of a true social hygiene only when the fundamentals of human society correspond again to the natural order which on its part should be an analogy of the supernatural order. As the present state of affairs stands, every effort made toward the confirmation of social hygiene can signify nothing else but the following: in the majority of cases we cultivate hygiene in small matters, but antihygiene in greater matters.

[4] *"Casti Connubii,"* n. 102.

V. SPIRITUAL DIRECTION AND FAMILY HYGIENE

A. Concept

Modern spiritual direction should be entrusted with problems concerning the protection of the family. If the deterioration of marriage and family is one of the most serious symptoms of our sick times, then its cure can arise only from these fundamentals of human society. The questions of family politics are therefore among the most important of social hygiene.

By family politics we mean the sum of all legislative, social and economical means which have as their object the stability and welfare of the family. In this sense family politics signifies more than demographic politics. Demographic politics is primarily concerned with the numerical increase of the population; if, beyond the purely quantitative increase, it concerns itself also with the qualitative betterment of the population, then its end is united with that of eugenics which tends to favor hereditary health.

Eugenics is only a partial sphere of social hygiene. Race hygiene tends toward the numerical, biological, social and political prevalence of a dominant race even with means of an eliminative selection. If demographic politics is united with it, it is transformed into an instrument of tendencies which becomes a power and militaristic politics: the increase of the number of births signifies for it an increase of military power; otherwise it has no signification.

The mercantile demographic politics of the eighteenth century perceived in the increase of population merely a question of maternal welfare and an active commercial balance; more men, more labor forces, more riches.

At that time Malthus had not yet formulated his disastrous "demographic" principle: the idea that in the problem of births there is a moral problem—the problem of the purity of marriage and the problem of social justice, for the family can acquire value only when one is freed from the *"rage du nombre"* of demographic politics.

Even in our times such divergent tendencies as collectivism and individualism are encountered in family politics.

Extreme individualism is an enemy of the family since it does not consider the individual as a member of a social community, as a "social animal," and hence favors egoism of the individual.

Collectivism is an enemy of the family since it neglects the fundamental fact that the individual person, as a personality, is the unique and irreparable expression of the species man and is the bearer of an immortal soul. From the denial of the latter and from its system of dialectic materialism (which is derived from evolution) there arise errors of collectivism with its destructive effects.

Collectivism fails to recognize the fact that the family is the basis and the root of human society. It proposes as a means of progress a "society without the family," in which the children belong to the community, and only the community should provide for their education. For these reasons collectivism favors any movement which tends to remove the woman from the home and encourages extra-domestic professional work.

For a decade collectivism has propagated theoretical and practical Malthusianism. Only in recent times have its supporters become aware of the fact that the consequences of birth-prevention endanger the future of social security, especially old age and pension provision. For that reason it has recently also orientated itself toward a planned "family politics." The manner in which this should be formulated betrays the collectivistic tendencies which hide behind it—tendencies which, in fact, tend toward a deterioration of more than the welfare of the family.

B. Natural Law Concept and Collectivistic Concept

Collectivistic family politics rejects the compensation of familial burdens in the form held by us and proposes in its place the absolute assumption of family burdens by the public administration. Thus, the duty of maintaining the family is taken from the head of the family and is taken over by the State. This signifies nothing less than the collectivism of the "rearing of children." This system contradicts the natural right of the family which rests on the right and duty of the head of the family to maintain the family, a right which cannot be assumed by any human power: the rights of the family are older than those of the State, and human society has its origin in the family.

C. The Principle of "Subsidiarity"

One of the basic principles of Christian social doctrine is that of "subsidiarity" which has been defined in the encyclical *"Quadragesimo Anno."* It establishes that the greater or greatest social groups as, for example, the State, should never take on themselves tasks which can be fulfilled satisfactorily by the minor or the smallest groups. Hence, that which the family should and can do should not be taken over by the State except in the case in which the family refuses or is materially and morally incapable of fulfilling its tasks. It is the common opinion of collectivism that the family is not capable of fulfilling its task of the maintenance of children and their education and, therefore, this task should be removed from the family and should be undertaken by public administration. But, in effect, this would lead to the abolition of the family. This example demonstrates the disastrous effects arising from the infraction of the principle of "subsidiarity."

D. Legal Argument

If it is asked from what legal basis the claim of family aid is deduced, collectivism can give no answer other than that each individual has in relation to society the right of being maintained according to his needs (the principle of alimentation). The fact that this principle leads to an extension of a general assistance even to those who do not have a need and that thus the "state of absolute welfare" leads *ad absurdum* is yet far from being universally recognized. Natural law prescribes that each individual mobilize his powers in order to procure the means of sustenance for himself and his progeny and to contribute in providing for the old who are unable to work and for the sick members of the family. Herein lies the natural-law root of the social institutions. Every individual has, through natural law, the right to marry and the right to establish a family. But he must, through the right of natural law, be given the opportunity of earning through his work enough to establish a family of average size and to be able to live in frugal comfort.

E. Family Wage and Compensation of Burdens

In the natural economy the welfare of the family increases automatically with the increase of the number of workers in the family. In a progressive economy based on the division of labor this is no longer verified. Yet the right of a just wage for every adult individual who is completely occupied either in manual or intellectual labor still holds.

A just wage, even in relation to natural law, can never be such as to guarantee only the minimum of existence for the individual; but a just wage must be such as to allow the worker to contract marriage as well as to establish and maintain a family of at least average size. A wage which corresponds to the requirements of a "just" compensation indicated by natural law we call a "family wage." It is a fatal error and a conceptual confusion when one misinterprets the meaning of "family wage" so that a wage is understood to be that which, in the so-called "children aid," increases with each child—following therefore from the first child on—and which with every further increase of the family is progressively increased. Such remuneration is not a family wage and has nothing to do with it; in fact, it rather produces antifamilial effects, and lacks a legal basis.

According to justice, the worker receives a wage only for his production (production wage), that is, according to the principle: "equal production, equal wage." The raising of children is a social production and because of this the relative compensation rests on a legal basis different from that on which labor compensation rests. The legal basis for labor compensation is pure and strict commutative justice: the wage must be equivalent to the production (principle of equivalence). In order to be equivalent—that is to say, just—the retribution must therefore be a "family wage" in the sense already indicated; it should be sufficient not only for the minimum of existence for the individual (individual retribution), but, as a family wage, it should be sufficient for the establishment and maintenance of a family of average size. A year after the encyclical *"Rerum novarum"* (1891), the family wage was defined in that way at the first social Catholic Congress ordered by Pope Leo XIII (1892). That definition of the family wage is still valid at the present time; it has been neglected only by those who have intentionally obscured the concept of the same.

On this basis we can develop the legal basis for the compensation of family burdens. If a family increases beyond the average size, then a compensation should be given by society and its institutions.

The rearing of a greater number of children is indisputably a social production. As such, it should not, in a social community, lead to a pauperization of the family; it should not lead to the condition whereby single persons and childless couples acquire an advantage over families with numerous children in the struggle of life.

Social justice is also the legal principle upon which the compensation of family burdens rests. He who has to rear a greater number of children than that corresponding to the average size with the full family compensation is not yet compensated through his social performance. He is, however, considered "father of a large family" and is authorized to raise claims against society and the institution designated for this purpose.

On the other hand, he who is single or who does not have children or has less children than that corresponding to the average size receives by his family retribution more than that corresponding to his social production. He is obliged, however, to contribute to the compensation fund on the basis of social justice.

This is, therefore, the common legal basis for the contribution obligation and for the legal claim. It is implicit in the nature of the family wage which is based on strict commutative justice. Commutative justice and social justice complement each other, so that even the principle of "subsidiarity" is preserved.

F. Further Associations with Problems of Social Hygiene

If family politics constitutes at present one of the primary problems of social politics, we must consider it in relation to the entire problem, that is, in relation to the numerous, vast and interrelated problems. These associations can be studied only in the light of social hygiene.

1. Associations with Questions of Social Security

It would be an error to combine family compensation with social security according to organization. The idea appears obvious, but it is erroneous. We can show how, in the modern structure of the population, the relationship between persons subject to contribution and those having a right to compensation is favorable to family compensation and unfavorable to social security. An organizational unity of both would bring it about that a surplus of the compensation funds would be used to keep not the family, but social security which finds itself in difficulty. The threatening situation in which the insurance against sickness and old age can find itself because of birth decline cannot be averted at the expense of the family burden compensation. In fact, only this can in the long run also improve the situation of social security.

A substantial improvement of the situation in which social security finds itself can take place only through a complete and basic reform through which it would be liberated from the structural basic errors.

A reform based on the principle of "subsidiarity" would transform social security in a manner that this could without difficulty be extended even to independent workers under the form of "independent security" and thus to the entire population ("general popular security").

Such a transformation of social security would become the most effective weapon against that unpleasant phenomenon which we designate as social parasitism.

2. Protection of Motherhood

Since the extension of the professional woman worker is enormous, the protection of labor for these as well as for the independent workers by means of a new law for the protection of motherhood should be extensive. In relation to this proposal the profession of the housewife should be recognized in its fullest sense together with that of the woman of independent affairs.

It is important to remember that, with such an ample protection of motherhood, with the recognition of the profession of the housewife and with the actualization of a family wage and compensation, the obligation and necessity of participating in extra-domestic work would cease for many women. The extra-domestic work by women would thereby be reduced to a tolerable proportion. In this manner the status of the husband, as provider for the family, will be restored, which, when lessened, become precarious for the position of the entire family as such.

3. Health, and Questions Regarding the Family

The former development would lead to a complete socialization of the health system including therapeutic treatment, that is to say, it would lead to a "total welfare state."

Thus the doctor would, in giving free help to anyone in need, become a functionary, and his moral responsibility toward the sick would be limited to the observance of the disposition of law. This is possible in public health service, but not in the personal relationship between the doctor and the patient during therapeutic treatment.

But even if all that is concerned with health constitutes an integral part of the general welfare and is closely associated with all the branches of the social administration, yet it is well that the relationship between the doctor and the patient remain on the basis of personal trust.

It falls upon a rightly orientated universalistic social hygiene to play a directive role. If hygiene, as a hygiene of human society, is intent on obtaining a life worthy of man, it cannot lose sight of the fact that only an unobjectionable moral life, above all in marriage and the family, is truly worthy of the dignity of man and is one of the essential and absolutely indispensable conditions of human health.

These are considerations which have a basic importance even for the spiritual director, especially those questions of the family which today constitute one of his most vital problems. For this reason the indicated problems are also basic problems of pastoral hygiene.

VI. DAMAGES CAUSED BY CIVILIZATION

A. Concept

A man forms his own environment and modifies it in great measure. This is a great advantage to him, but it can also become a disadvantage. The disadvantages to health resulting from the alienation from nature are called damages caused by civilization.

Sellheim defines it in the following manner: "Culture stands between man and nature." This formula can with equal right be inverted: "Man stands between nature and culture." It is he who transforms nature, who cultivates the land and who through planning of food provision and provision for the future can also render possible the formation of a culture.

Civilization is that modification of the original natural environment which makes it possible for man to protect himself from the hardships of nature and to form an artificial environment. The original elements of this artificial environment, which we call civilization, are residence and common settlement, clothing and food as well as labor.

According to Spengler, the concept of culture is to be strongly differentiated from that of civilization. If culture comprises, above all, the spiritual values of the interior life which make it possible for man to attain his innate striving toward knowledge (science) and imitation of nature (art), civilization contains the technical and material progress which render the external life more facile. Up to this point we can accept the distinction of Spengler between culture and civilization. But we cannot agree with him when he states that culture is the primary activity which is gradually transformed into civilization through unilateral technical progress. This process is, according to Spengler, irreversible and leads to the inevitable decline of old civilized notions as soon as they have entered into the final stage of civilization. According to him the western world at present finds itself at this stage.

We use the expression of "damages caused by civilization" in a sense similar to that in which Zeiss and Pintschavius have spoken of "damages" imposed on man "by civilization." By this expression they allude to the damages imposed on man by civilization as such.

B. The Problem of Domestication

We cannot agree with the authors cited when they identify the indicated damages imposed on man with that state which, in the case of domestic animals, is called domestication.

Domestication brings about in trained domestic animals a diminution of the biological force of resistance in relation to that possessed in the "wild state."

It is an evolutionistic and selectionistic idea to compare the civilization of man with the domestication of animals especially in regard to the effect. The evolutionists are firmly convinced that the suppression of the natural struggle for existence effects a degeneration.

Domestication is a state which man, as trainer, has artificially provoked in the animal. In order that an animal be domesticated, it must be directed by man in its natural tendencies. Of itself, it could not modify its life conditions to the point of transforming itself from wildness to domestication.

Man, on the other hand, can form his own environment. No one has "domesticated" him, and he has no need of "trainers" to change his conditions of life. He has been capable from the beginning of forming himself by means of his reason and action.

It is, therefore, absolutely inadmissible to compare or to consider as parallel the conditions of human culture and civilization with the state of domestication of animals. To declare that man has "domesticated" himself is nothing more than a play on words to justify the application of a zoological concept to anthropology.

C. A Survey of the Problems

A great number of social hygienic problems can be comprehended under the concept of "damages caused by civilization." We shall select only those problems which are of importance also to pastoral hygiene.

The following problems are included:
1) Influences exercised by large cities
2) Cultural overload, alienation of life
3) Tourism
4) Addictions
5) General neuroticism

1. Influences of Large Cities

The rise of large cities is closely connected with the process of industrialization of the nineteenth century. The first half of the twentieth century introduced this process, under the title of "national autarchy" even in lands which, as agricultural lands, had been the granary of the entire continent (Hungary, Rumania, Ukraine, Argentina, etc.).

Industrialization brought a great number of people to the industrial centers of large cities, and this factor brought on the urgent problem of space. A scarcity of dwellings, the squalor of homes and the formation of miserable quarters in large cities (slums)— hotbeds of criminality and prostitution—arose from this situation. The modern tasks of renewal and social home-building have been realized only in part. The growing cities continue to press back the rural environment more and more.

The characteristic proper to the large city is its increasing distance from nature. Large buildings and stone or asphalt pavements place a separation plane between man and the natural soil. The ever-increasing traffic, especially of motor vehicles, causes an intense modification of that vital element of the air. The air of the large city is filled with dust, smoke and exhaust gas from industrial factories, from masses of people, and, above all, from the combustion gas of motor vehicles. These substances which are found in the air cause the rays of the sun, especially the short-wave ultraviolet rays, to be so sustained and absorbed that they no longer reach the ground. The long-wave heat rays penetrate more easily and this causes life in the large city greater heat so that the temperature within the city is higher than that registered outside the city. During the summer months these conditions provoke notable harm to health through accumulation of heat and intestinal illness especially frequent with infants. It can also be held that the increase of lung cancer encountered in the large city is due partly to the corruption of the air caused by exhaust gas. To this is added the enormous noise of the large city due primarily to motor vehicles.

Further harm to health arises from the increase of traffic through motor vehicles. Notwithstanding all the indicated traffic laws and regulations, the death rate has attained a higher proportion than that arising from the most serious diseases. The street traffic is so intense during the highest point of traffic (8-9, 12-1, 5-6), that the motor vehicles are a hindrance to each other.

Life in large modern cities tends to effect a depersonalization which threatens to suffocate every form of individual life. To this is added the indescribable quantity of stimuli which incessantly attack the nerves and sense organs of the large city-dweller; noise, street traffic and traffic signals which demand constant attention; exhibits and billboards; advertisements over the loudspeaker or in lighting effects—usually in constant movement in order more effectively to attract attention. It is a complete whirl of sense impressions which rush in continually. The result is that only imagery impressions are perceived. The written or spoken word loses its efficacy. Man loses the receptive capacity for all that is not imagery and is transformed more and more into an eidetic type (Jaensch). His memory and capacity for concentration slackens in the measure in which his capacity of rapid reaction is constantly demanded.

Thus, because of constant exposure to always changing sensory stimuli there arises a need for a variety of "distractions," a desire for excitement which easily degenerates into real inordinate desire for experience while the incapacity for interior experience increases.

This, united with the damaging effects of the large city, no longer allows repose and reflection to modern man. His personal life is completely lost; he can exist only as a member of a collective mass and feels well only in this collectivity. The paradox lies in this, that the greater the collectivism of life, the greater the isolation of the individual person. He is isolated in the midst of a crowd, but he hurls himself into the frenzy of the crowd. This also explains the mass activity in the so-called places of recreation in the large cities in which a restless whirl of impressions again envelops the individual. The cinema, radio and television are the adequate expression of this milieu of civilization. To this is added the consequences of night life in the large city, leading to the inevitable reversal of the rhythm of life. A great number of business activities and professional duties are so arranged that the center of gravity of life in the large city is shifted to the late hours of the evening and night.

All this concurs in forming a new type of individual. He lives only externally, and his interior life is stunted. The spiritual director must be aware of the fact that this type of person is incapable of reflection. A sermon concerning the simple truths of Christianity is too much for him. He is incapable of concentrating his attention for more than ten minutes and is attracted only to the "sensational." There are certain famous preachers in the large cities who profit from such a particular disposition and exercise a great attraction over the masses. They have become "stars" and are listened to only because of personal fascination, and not because of what they say.

This is the psychic terrain that the spiritual director will encounter in the large city and which he must cultivate, and this is the terrain that the doctor must heal—a terrain that is hardened and even poisoned.

2. The Overload of Culture

The externalization of life is increased by the overload of culture which overwhelms the individual's capacity of supportability.

One need only recall the great number of lectures, concerts, art exhibits and other cultural performances which are offered during the course of a "season." It is truly too much! Every evening would be occupied even if one wanted to pursue only the more important engagements. One kills off the other and, in order to attract attention, each must overshoot the other. The billboards are expressive monuments of this situation.

Even "art" and "science" are drawn into this type of operation. Scientific societies, especially the medical, are frequented by journalists in search of "sensations" to present to the public in the morning editions. The mania for conventions no longer permits a real scientific depth. The very abundance of external arrangements impedes interior reflection.

The literary production presents the same disintegration found in the arts, exemplified in sensational, glaring titles. A book is considered old after, at the most, two years. Only the "latest" is sought, and so no one is interested in writing a work of lasting worth. With this in mind, many books are written merely to make a great deal of money. The "best seller" is the drive of every ambition. Many more books are written by unqualified rather than qualified writers. The result is the clouding of the spirit, the loss of every clear orientation of life. Notable is the fact that a book has greater "sale success" when it corresponds to the spirit of the times and to the intellectual orientation of the masses. What attracts the glance of the public in the windows of bookstores merits no other name than that of "intellectual refuse." This applies especially to that phase of literature which speculates exclusively on the erotic sensational desires of the masses.

From the standpoint of cultural hygiene, the concern is not only the inferior quality of the published books; the quantity is so enormous that the cultural overload constitutes a danger to the spiritual health of man. All this engenders in many a tiredness which tends toward a cultural tiredness and a general displeasure with life *(malaise générale)*.

In analyzing the causes of the cultural *malaise* Freud rightly considered general neuroticism as a result of the constant conflict between the deep subconscious strata of the personality and conscious man. But Freud has unfortunately not succeeded in discovering the deepest causes of this cultural malaise and in indicating the manner of eliminating the same.

3. Tourism

Since tourism constitutes an acceptable source of revenue for every land, it is easily understandable how it represents, in the economical sphere, a conspicuous factor of prosperity, and that all possible means are used to encourage the same. The desire to travel has become an essential characteristic of modern man and has assumed such proportions as to become a concern from the hygienic standpoint.

Modern man is no longer satisfied in renewing his strength by spending his vacation time in a quiet and restful place close to nature. He no longer desires to remain quietly for a few weeks in one place, but is anxious to see new places and experience new interests.

One who lives a superficial life is constantly in flight or escape from oneself. The demand for travel is, accordingly, always increasing, and the trips cannot be extended far enough. For this reason travel has taken on a different character. It no longer implies the comfort of former times. The means of transportation are so crowded during vacation time that, instead of being a pleasure, traveling has become a burden. Moreover, the individual character of travel has also been lost: individual trips are supplanted today by the less expensive collective trips. Under the title of social tourism, such trips are thought to make the pleasures of life accessible to many more groups of society.

All of this gets us farther from the solution of the true social question. Excessive demands are cultivated and these manifest themselves as incompatible with the duty of maintaining a family and the education of children. And so the matter ends in dilemma: whether to dedicate oneself to his family or spend the financial resources and time on tourism. And often the decision is made in favor of the latter, and the thought of having children is put off to a later date.

The influx of travelers presents as great a problem for the spiritual director as it does for hygiene. Some time ago, a pastor of a famous tourist center in Tyrol, Austria, brought attention in a written work to the fact that a community, formerly strongly rooted in religious tradition, was, from the time of its "discovery" as a center of tourism and winter sports, completely transformed in its internal structure. The influx of tourists had made the people avaricious for money. The "dance around the golden calf" was set free and everyone was anxious to earn money easily and quickly.

The religious life of the sector had taken a rapid and terrible regression. A contributing factor to this sad phenomenon was the circumstance in which numerous quests, removed from the religious life, ridiculed before the people of the place the processions and ancestral customs. The local people were ashamed in the presence of these visitors whose "superior culture" they greatly respected. To this fact was added that of an excessive relaxation of the sexual life encouraged by the visitors especially in the winter sport centers.

Bad example quickly made disciples, and all these innovations were associated with the "higher culture" of the large city. This, in turn, provoked a catastrophic flight from the land, since it was promised that life in the city would be as good to them as to the city-dwellers who were seen merely as tourists. Because of the increasing tendency to leave the land, the rural element of the population, so precious for culture, lost its stability and native characteristic only to be transformed in the large city into a fluctuating proletariat.

In recent times, however, favorable impressions seem to be made as a result of tourism. In certain international health resourts one can observe an increased number of tourists who, from the religious standpoint, give magnificent example to the local people. However, it will take a long time before this process of renewal will be able to produce its proper effects, especially in those places in which the state of relaxation and abandonment of traditions has reached a high point. The same can be said of those places in which the local people have been drawn into an intoxication of pleasures and into an inordinate desire for experience. But even in these cases the influence that can be exercised by individual example is quite evident.

Briefly, in regard to tourism and travel, it would be a misunderstanding of our viewpoint if·one were to interpret our cautions in the sense that we reject this phenomenon in its entirety. We wish to evaluate its positive worth and, in particular, we desire that the benefit of true culture be accessible even to the great mass of people and thus not remain a privilege merely of the rich.

Man must have an inner middle point in his life which is his foundation and which signifies for him not merely habitation, but a true home. But only the religious person, who remains conscious of the fact that he has "no lasting place on earth" and that his true home is in the next world, can live in earthly space as one living in his homeland. Modern man, exclusively attached to this world, has in great measure lost this center of earthly gravity; he feels at home "everywhere and nowhere." Our serious considerations are directed against tourism only insofar as it is a phenomenon characteristic of our time and where it can result in a serious external superficiality of life. The result is that the benefits of culture offered to all are enjoyed by none.

Practically all who participate in these collective trips return home dissatisfied and burdened down with "photos." The eidetic type has done nothing but take photographs and has thus completely lost the capacity of "seeing." Certainly, a good photograph can be a beautiful souvenir. But the mania for photography can terminate in distraction—one does not want to think, feel or experience internally. It is only this kind of traveling which we reject from the standpoint of mental hygiene. The task of mental hygiene rightly understood can be summarized in the following manner: the renewal of the interior life for the whole humanity.

4. Addictions

We have already considered in another section the habituation to stimulating and pleasurable means transformed into addiction. Narcomania (morphine, cocaine, hashish, marijuana, etc.) is, in our time, widely diffused. Moreover, the use and abuse of medicaments (analgesics, soporifics) has assumed great dimension. The thirst for medicines on the part of the insured (panel patient) has become an object of concern both for the hygienist and for social insurance. All the elements which we have already treated in the chapter entitled "the damages caused by civilization" concur in increasing the diffusion of addictions.

Even the mania for narcotics is a symptom of a neurotic flight from reality, an escape from oneself and from reflection. When someone wishes "to relax," he does not seek quietude, but reaches for the injection syringe; when he wishes to be "stimulated," he stretches for a cigarette or a drug from the series of "awaking amines" (pervitin, cola, etc.,); when he wishes to be "entertained," he frequents the bars or forms a "cocktail party"; and, finally, we must call special attention to the enervating effect of strongly mixed alcoholic drinks.

Even the mania for medicines has assumed grotesque proportions and is of great concern to hygiene. Partly responsible for this is the competition of the chemical-pharmaceutical industries with their unscrupulous soliciting methods. We have known of cases in which the recommendation of hormone preparations and means for the "regeneration" of nerves and for the "strengthening of sex potency" has led old patients to such an unrestrained consumption that a premature collapse followed.

The diffusion of addictions and the difficulty in combating the same go hand in hand with a relaxation of the sexual life. One can declare that even sexual activity has already degenerated and has been transformed into an addiction. All this is the expression of a general neuroticism of immense proportion.

5. Neuroticism

The increase of neuroses and mental disturbances is, in our day, one of the principal problems of social hygiene and especially of mental hygiene.

The basic symptom is that of anxiety—a pronounced and general anxiety of life which pursues man everywhere and does not permit him to concentrate: the "flight from himself" incites his thirst for excitement by causing him to seek new sensations until the pursuer either lands in a clinic with a nervous breakdown or ends his life by suicide as the conclusion of a neurotic development.

The "psychological balance of civilization" is negative. The eradication of the existential basis of life leads to mental illness

(Kraeplin). Only healthy, robust and balanced personalities can endure to be suddenly elevated to a higher and more complicated degree of civilization.

The increase of excitability and sensibility, as effects of civilization, determine the relation between civilization and neurosis. If adaptation to the demands of civilization is not fully accomplished, the psycho-physical tensions produce chronic spasmodic states, and these manifest themselves in neurotic symptoms. This explanation alone cannot satisfy us. It would indicate that the "adaptation to the demands of civilization" would be the criterion of mental health.

Neurosis is, instead, an erroneous behavior, a disturbance of the conduct of life. Therefore, our concentration must penetrate deeper than that in which the factor of the "damages caused by civilization" is found. The correct behavior of life presupposes a proper orientation of life itself.

In regard to this point, we can refer to Caruso and Daim who, concerning the origin of neurosis, have gone deeper than any other authors in seeking the causes of neuroticism. Daim observes that when man is removed from the motives of life and existence which are proper to him, he creates an "idol" around which he orientates his life. And this orientation toward a false purpose of life, even toward this "idol," gives a false direction to the entire life, and, in following this direction, the neurotic finally suffers a breakdown.

The problems of depth psychology which we have indicated have equal importance both for the doctor and for the priest. A more detailed research of this pertains to the sphere of mental hygiene.

VII. CULTURAL HYGIENE. MENTAL HYGIENE

A. Concept

To the sphere of cultural hygiene we include all the questions concerning human health which are related to the cultural life. But since the entire human social life pertains to culture in the widest sense, there is no distinction between social hygiene and cultural hygiene. Nor should the separation of the damages caused by civilization from the sphere of cultural hygiene cause any difficulty.

Hence, for practical reasons, we shall restrict the concept of cultural hygiene to the realm of culture according to the meaning of Oswald Spengler, that is, to the consideration of the psycho-spiritual values of the interior life; while to civilization belong the activities of technical and material progress.

We agree with Spengler that a too technical, materialistic civilization can lead to a terminal stage of degeneration from which a regeneration is no longer possible. We cannot, however, agree with him concerning the historical series of culture and civilization, with his representation of a linear lapse of both and of an irreversible process which leads irresistibly to a decline. We are rather of the opinion that culture and civilization are mutually conditioned and rhythmically act and react on one another. The development of superior culture presupposes a certain degree of external civilization. Civilization acts favorably as long as it does not deteriorate its purpose by suffocating cultural values. Spiritual culture can flourish only on the basis of an authentic religiosity. If this diminishes, then culture will perish and civilization will degenerate into a gross materialistic and inordinate desire for pleasures. The eradication and alienation of basic religion—that is the essential problem that manifests itself in the degeneration of culture and civilization.

For the creation of cultural values a certain material well-being is desirable and a definite vital space is indispensable for the unfolding of the personality. But in no case is culture merely an "ideological superstructure" constructed on economical conditions. If, because of restriction, the space required for life does not allow the necessary unfolding of the personality, this restriction suppresses the values of the personality. Again, if too much is required of man in a given unit of time, if "too much is demanded of him," the value of production is affected by the restriction of time. Both factors are definitely harmful for cultural production. A true cultural production is possible only in freedom and creative inspiration.

In order to attain such an end, a certain calm and "leisure," the so-called "creative pause" which guarantees the spirit restoration and renewal of energy is necessary.

The sphere of personality that man needs for the conservation of his existence is called the sphere of conservation. A certain surplus of the same renders possible the free configuration of existence.

Then we speak of the "sphere of configuration." The optimum of the conditions of existence which renders possible the free unfolding of the powers and dispositions can be called the "sphere of expansion." Over and above this, an increase of the vital space through an increase of the demands on life would be harmful: we attain in this manner the sphere of the consumption of luxuries and the sphere of degeneration.

The zone of decadence, of the minimum of existence, of oppression and atrophy begins under the sphere of conservation. In this sphere the damages are still reparable. A further fall leads to the zone of destruction. The damages have become irreparable, the social fall is definite, and destruction is sealed.

These fundamental concepts indicate that cultural fulfillment is possible only in the formative and unfolding sphere. The sphere of degeneration, which is that of luxury, no longer permits any cultural fulfillment. It only acknowledges material values or, for the most part, a vitiated aestheticism without inner strength. Under the sphere of conservation there exists only the conservation of mere existence: *primum vivere, deinde philosophari!*

B. Summary of the Problem

Even here we can select a few of the many problems. In regard to the problem of neuroticism the following are to be considered:

a) Neurosis and cultural activity
b) Spiritual culture and spiritual life
c) Spiritual and material culture
d) Order of precedence regarding spiritual and cultural values
e) Dissolution of formation and possession
f) Revolutionary "revaluation of values"
g) Anxiety of life and philosophy of life
h) Orientation in the highest values of life
i) Psycho-hygiene of old age
j) Suicide and prevention of suicide

We can consider only a few factors concerning the various points.

1. Neurosis and Cultural Activity

Neurosis has not only a negative aspect, but it can be shown that even important creative forces can be found in the cultural sphere.

Without doubt, in the majority of neurotics, neurosis exercises a harmful influence on all the activities of life. In particular, the cultural value of the activity is generally seriously affected by neurosis. Yet there are cases in which neurosis deepens rather than impedes creative activity in the cultural sphere.

Not all cases of this type can be explained by the Adlerian formula of "overcompensation of the inferiority complex." Certainly, the inferiority feeling can present a strong impulse in regaining, through an increased performance, the disturbed consciousness of self-worth. But this social-psychological explanation is, of itself, often insufficient: we must understand the deeper metaphysical background of the "problem of neurosis and genius."

In neurotics and psychopaths, in general, a cultural activity which is above average bears a negative sign, inasmuch as the psychopath—because of "ressentiment"—is, for the most part, orientated negatively in regard to the highest cultural values. But when the relation with the supernatural is not disturbed, that is, when grace is built on nature and when it elevates, completes and perfects it *(gratia implet et perficit naturam),* then the neurotic and psychopath can penetrate the depths and reach the heights of life that are less accessible to the "normal individual":

> "And when man, in his torment, is silent,
> A God has me say what ails me."

Thus does Goethe allow the insane Torquato Tasso (who suffered from schizophrenia) to speak of himself.

It would be an injustice to the neurotic to deny him cultural value and to designate him as "inferior." As the example of Tasso shows, it is not permissible to consider the psychopath in this manner. There are works which manifest the artistic ability of the schizophrenic. On the other hand, history impressively shows the culturally destructive works of asocial and anti-social neurotics who are negatively orientated.

The question of the custody of criminal psychopaths in special institutions of detention has already been considered in another chapter.

2. Spiritual Culture and Spiritual Life

When we limit the concept of culture to the sphere of psychic-spiritual values of the interior life, an association between spiritual culture and religious life automatically arises. Modern civilization has led to an externalization of life through an exaggerated activism. We have already seen, in another section, that the penetration of this activism in the modern methods of spiritual direction is a serious matter. From the purely religious standpoint, we notice, in this phenomenon, a compromise with the methods of the "world" and the danger of a deviation from the *"unum necessarium."*

The *vita activa* and the *vita contemplative* are two forms of life which are necessary in their own individual way (cf. the rule of life: *ora et labora*). But when the *vita activa* demands exclusively for itself the justification of existence, then the harmony of the order of life is disturbed.

In another chapter we have also indicated the importance that the liturgical life has for the harmonious formation of the rhythm of life.

The history of culture shows clearly that the periods of greatest success coincide with the highest points of the religious life. Recall in this regard the era of Gothic culture with its cathedrals and philosophical *Summae;* the era of Baroque culture with the magnificence of its courts, with the flourish of the arts and sciences under the illustrious patrons, with its greatest flourish of philosophy and theology, especially of moral theology.

The Baroque culture began its ascent immediately after the Thirty Years War and overcame with surprising rapidity the devastation that this war left behind both in the spiritual and economical sphere. This fact can also fill us with hope after the devastation following the two world wars of 1914-1918 and 1939-1945.

Thus there are many reasons for holding that such a spiritual reconstruction must proceed hand in hand with a total renewal of the spiritual life. As we have already shown in the relationship between culture and civilization, so there are manifold reciprocal relations between spiritual and material culture.

According to its nature, hygiene belongs primarily to material culture at least insofar as it has, for its object, the material presuppositions of health. Just as the concept of health, besides the physiological, also includes the social and moral welfare, so moral hygiene and psycho-hygiene essentially pertain to cultural hygiene.

Mental hygiene has, above all, psycho-spiritual health as its object: the preservation of mental health and the recovery of health for the mentally ill. To psycho-hygiene and cultural hygiene further belong the maintenance and reestablishment of a just hierarchy of values.

We have already referred, in another section, to the hierarchical order of Scholastic philosophy regarding the *necessarium,* the *utile* and the *iucundum* as well as to the hierarchical order of the *bonum privatum, bonum publicum* and the *summum bonum.* The *necessarium* of the conditions of life is guaranteed in the sphere of conservation; the *utile* in the sphere of formation and the *iucundum* in the sphere of greatest development. If the material values are overestimated; then it is not possible to avoid the transition into the sphere of degeneration through dissipation.

Individual hygiene is of service to the *bonum privatum* of health, and social hygiene to the *bonum publicum.* True cultural hygiene should not lose sight of the supreme value of the *summum bonum.*

Thus the hygienic requirements of material and spiritual culture, of spiritual and religious culture unite with each other in the formation of a harmonious unity.

3. Inversion of Values

A revolutionary "inversion of all values" (Nietzsche) has torn asunder this harmonious unity of material, spiritual and religious culture. In the first place, there has been a separation of "formation" and "possession," and this has produced disastrous effects upon society and culture.

In the natural order, human society has the form of a pyramid which, resting on a wide base, terminates upward into a small point. Without a hierarchical order human society cannot exist. If the pyramid is inverted so that the higher point is found at the lowest and vice versa, it is then very difficult to maintain a stable balance.

This "inversion of values," has also entered into the spiritual and moral and especially in the religious sphere.

The bond of *re-ligio,* of the rejoining of the natural with the supernatural order, has been broken; in place of the living relation with God, the Cause of all being, there is substituted the relation, extremely problematic, which each individual establishes with one's own "idol" (Daim), and, thus, even the relation of individuals among themselves is disturbed.

In the U.S.A., psycho-hygiene has acknowledged the establishment and regulation of human relations as one of its important tasks. "Human relations" has become a mode of expression and has been almost misused as a slogan. For the establishment and regulation of human relations, the words of St. Thomas should be directive: *"Non est alia coniunctio hominum inter se nisi coniunctio hominum cum Deo."*

In this confederation *(religio)* are found the powers which protect man from isolation—which can lead to psychosis—and, at the same time, from collectivization, since it makes him conscious of the immeasurable value of every individual human soul. In it alone lies the strength capable of overcoming "existential anxiety," which is one of the basic causes of neuroticism.

4. Anxiety of Life and Philosophy of Life

Existentialism uses, with preference, the term "existential anxiety" in indicating the anxiety of life which torments modern man. If by this is meant that anxiety is at the basis of existence, we can then accept this designation. But since Existentialism is wont to indicate, by the concept of "existence" and the corresponding adjective "existential," essential being (that is, the mode of being specific to man), we must protest against this abusive equivocation of philosophical concepts consecrated by tradition. In this case we are faced with the falsification of fundamental concepts.

"Existentia" signifies, in the terminology of Scholastic philosophy, existence without any other determination, the simple existence. But essential being, the mode of being, is called *essentia.* Only God is the Being of whom it can be said that His existence is, at the same time, His essence, His mode of being; the only Being in which existence and essence are identical: God is the fullness of being in its totality; He "is His own being" (ἐστὶν εἶναι). He says of Himself: "I am Who am" (the Being without any determination, Jahweh, Yahweh, also Jahveh, Jahve).

If, therefore, existentialism understands by "existence" a specifically human mode of being, then it uses, for man, an expression that is proper only to God. This is the basic conceptual falsification of Existentialism which has arisen from an unprecedented hybridism.

The second basic conceptual confusion pertains to the nature of anxiety. Existentialism perceives man as "cast" into an existence of insecurity and concern. Hence anxiety is defined as the "fundamental condition of human existence" (Heidegger).

On the contrary, it must be most clearly stated that anxiety as such is not the "fundamental condition" and is not the primary, but rather the secondary, effect of the "fundamental condition": the fallen nature of man *(natura lapsa seu vulnerata)* which one strives to deny. How deeply anxiety is rooted in the essence of fallen nature is manifested very clearly by the biblical account of the behavior of the first human couple after original sin.[5]

This is the true basis of every human anxiety. The "basic condition" of this anxiety is not the fact that man was "thrown" into an existence of concern, but the fact that he has fallen: this is the "basic condition" of human nature. This is the essence of man in the order of nature and not in the order of grace. The separation of the two orders is certainly a consequence of fallen nature.

Existentialism is a false philosophy of life. It cannot and does not wish to overcome anxiety as such; it can only pretend to conquer this anxiety in the face of nothing, "heroically" looking at nothing in the face. It is, therefore, a philosophy of absolute nihilism. That is the greatest reason why we cannot see in existential analysis (Frankl) the last redeeming word of psychotherapy as long as this analysis represents only a practical application of Existentialism.

A universalistic psychotherapy capable of establishing, in conformity with the totality of human nature, the positive values of all directions, is conceivable only on the basis of an authentic philosophy of life, in the sense of the *philosophia perennis*. It can overcome anxiety only through genuine fear of God.

A universalistic psycho-hygiene should, therefore, embrace all

---

[5] Cf. Genesis 3; 7-13: "and when they perceived themselves to be naked, they sewed together fig leaves, and made themselves aprons. And when they heard the voice of the Lord. . . . Adam and his wife hid themselves from the face of the Lord God. . . . And the Lord God called Adam and said to him: Where art thou? And he said: I heard Thy voice . . . and I was afraid, because I was naked . . ."

the values of life, the *bonum privatum* as well as the *bonum publicum,* in an arrangement and subordination which gravitate toward their proper center and which are, at the same time, an elevation which gravitates around the proper center when the lower values of the hierarchical order are orientated according to the highest value, the *Summum Bonum.*

5. Psycho-hygiene of Senile Age; Prevention of Suicide

It now remains for us to consider two important problems of psycho-hygiene: the hygiene of old age and the prevention of suicide. Both problems are closely associated: old age represents the natural conclusion of life, and suicide the unnatural conclusion of life.

It is statistically confirmed that old age is today greatly exposed to the danger of suicide. Psycho-hygiene has, therefore, a special interest in the hygiene of old age, especially the research concerning the physiology and pathology of old age (gerontology and gerontopathology); further, the therapy of the diseases of old age (geriatrics), among which mental disturbances assume an essential part.

The psychopathology of old age consists in regressive organic changes; vascular changes and circulatory disturbances in the brain; formation of centers of softening *(encephalomalacia),* which finally produces the clinical picture of *dementia senilis.* To this is added the complication which is proper to old age, namely, mistrust especially toward younger people: sensibility and sensitivity and the feeling of no longer being of any use and hence put in the background; the increasing isolation and inclusion within oneself (egocentric); and, finally, the limitation toward purely vital self-preservation (excessive or voracious eating, *polyphagia*).

Notwithstanding all the vascular therapies, we are not yet capable of preventing with certitude *dementia senilis.* When this disease manifests itself with uncleanliness, lack of interest and loss of contact, often there is nothing left but care in an institution, although it would often seem as if there were a lack of piety. The care of patients with *dementia senilis* at home is, however, very difficult and even the most careful help will not always prevent sudden suicide of the old which follows in the manner of a reaction of a short circuit. If for no other reason than that of prevention of suicide, hospitalization of such patients is very often indicated.

To the premature decrease of mental powers is essentially attributed the circumstance in which today, especially in industry, one who seeks work is refused as being "too old," despite the fact that he is only in his forties. On one side, there is the attempt of artifically prolonging the duration of human life; on the other hand, the duration of activity is shortened without necessity. Thus nothing more is done than prolong the duration of a premature sterile old age.

By this practice of allowing the older workers to go prematurely, even the economy itself is often robbed of most valuable powers. In almost all the professions, the most advanced employees, because of their long experience and acquired efficiency, constitute the most useful power; and in regard to their performance, they have by far a greater resistance than the younger persons. The removal of the older employees appears to be advantageous since others can take their places sooner. But they can sense the disadvantage of such a practice since they find themselves at the peak of their capacity and performance. And thus, even for the economy, there is a loss of inestimable value.

Moreover, it is very important that the feeling of uselessness be removed from the aged. It is of great psycho-hygienic importance that they have a pleasant occupation, even if this represents nothing more than a hobby. This does not mean that a hobby can take the place of a true element of life; for the most part, it can be only a substitute. The more an occupation can give the aged person the feeling of fulfillment and the more he can be convinced of his self-worth, the more will he be guarded against the danger of suicide.

All the authors are in agreement regarding the point that religion constitutes the most efficacious factor in the prevention of suicide. This is as true for senility as it is for youth and middle age. If man, on becoming old, sees in death not an extinction into nothingness, but the entrance into a new and perfect life and, moreover, the perfection of his life, he will overcome the terror of death and will face it with that calm serenity that one experiences in returning to the home of the soul. And he will not lose this hope even in the most difficult situations. But for him who sees behind the curtain of death only nothingness, there is no rational argument that will convince him not to flee from the needs and pains of old age and to seek death in order to remove himself from these difficulties, especially when they are associated with material needs.

The greatest number of suicides in old age arises from material anxiety and extreme needs, from anxiety concerning painful suffering, and especially from isolation and abandonment which the old person experiences when he does not have a deep and close relationship with God.

Suicide in old age, however, is a serious accusation against a society which often allows most worthy men, after a life of sacrifice, to fall into such misery and abandonment. In their desperation such men see no other way out than an escape into premature death, even though in suicide advanced age is not regarded by the world as "premature."

Concerning itself with the problem is one of the indisputable merits of psycho-hygiene. In this manner it also contributes to the elimination of the problem of euthanasia and the exclusion of the same from the mind of modern man.

VIII. DEATH AND BURIAL

In regard to the problem of death we shall discuss only certain questions that are of importance to hygiene.[1]

The following problems are considered:
a. General questions
   a) Sudden death
   b) Confirmation of death
   c) Death and apparent death
   d) Absolute and relative death
   e) Putrefaction and decomposition
   f) Preservation of the cadaver
b. Questions of social hygiene
   a) Burial, cremation
   b) Capital punishment

[1] This problem has been treated in detail in *Compendium of Pastoral Medicine* (translation), Joseph F. Wagner, Inc., New York, N.Y., 1960, but not from the present viewpoint of hygiene.

A. General Questions

1. Sudden Death

Sudden death seldom takes place without some demonstrable cause, even if it is not always a case of a pathological change of definite organs. A disturbance of correlation between the various organs can also exist; for example, the persistence of the thymus glands beyond infancy *(thymus persistens)* and, respectively, the disturbance of correlation between the thymus and the lymphatic system (status thymicolymphaticus).

Prescinding from accidents and violent death, sudden death occurs in cases of severe cardiac diseases: so-called "death of the heart in a few seconds" (cardiac apoplexy), in cases of coronary infarction, angina pectoris *(stenocardia), myodegeneratio cordis,* in embolism of the pulmonary arteries (pulmonary apoplexy); in cerebral hemorrhages following a rupture of the sclerotic cerebral arteries, the so-called *apoplexia cerebri.*

There are also cases of the suspension of the heart's action that are of purely psychogenic origin and arising from severe fright and psychic emotions.

The sudden death of the heart was at one time considered the type of death characteristic of the worn-out old priest: *"improvisa mors—sacerdotum sors."* This is, however, also characteristic of the excessively burdened doctor; with like reason it can therefore be designated as a *"medicorum sors."*

Prescinding from cases of *mors subitanea et improvisa,* there are almost always evident signs of the imminent end: agonal and terminal symptoms.

An infallible sign of imminent death is not yet known with absolute certitude. Some authors have considered the cadaveric odor of the expiratory air as the infallible sign of imminent death. But this symptom is only rarely established, above all, in cases of seriously advanced disease with premortal phenomena of approaching death.

The following symptoms can be considered as agonal or terminal: the emaciated look (sunken eyes, pinched nose), the so-called *"facies hippocratica";* the sudden and considerable drop of temperature after a high fever *(algor mortis);* the cold sweat *(sudor mortis);* the rattling breathing *(stridor mortis)*—this latter being characteristic of pulmonary edema. None of the symptoms here indicated is, of itself, a proof of the definite imminent end.

There is an essential difference between death preceded by a long consuming disease and a long agony and that which occurs suddenly and immediately in an organism of good health (accident, battle injury, etc.) The difference manifests itself in the premortal and postmortal processes, the so-called necrobiotic processes. The premortal processes of approaching death, which can be observed in a slow death, are anticipated processes of decomposition *in viva*. These differences are important in distinguishing between relative and absolute death.

2. The Verification of Death

a) INDEFINITE SIGNS OF DEATH

The definite verification of death is often more difficult than it is generally considered. We distinguish between definite and indefinite signs of death.

The following are considered indefinite signs of death: cadaverous pallor *(livor mortis);* the growing cold of the body *(algor mortis);* rigidity of death *(rigor mortis);* standstill of the heart and respiratory arrest. These signs are considered indefinite since at times they are also present in states of "tonic convulsions," as, for example, poisoning of those addicted to narcotics. In so-called "apparent death" there is consideration, for the most part, of cases of this kind. The "broken glance" is on the border of definite signs of death: when the cornea already manifests signs of maceration, it is a sign of cadaverous changes.

In order to demonstrate the presence of death, certain "proofs of death" (tests) are used, but these have only a relative and subsidiary value, and not a proving value. Even the electrocardiogram can be used to demonstrate the existence of very slight currents of cardiac action in the *vita minima*.

b) DEFINITE SIGNS OF DEATH

The definite signs of death are only those which constitute a proof of cadaverous changes and hence the beginning of the process of decomposition. These are:

1) Maceration of the cornea
2) Parchmentlike dryness of the skin *(parcheminement)*
3) Death spots
4) Odor of decomposition and phenomena of putrefaction.

The changes that take place at death cause a deformation of the body which assumes a frightening antiesthetic sight. In persons of deep spirituality there often appears at death a spiritual beauty which up to this time had remained hidden. The mask of death, therefore, manifests a picture of perfection.

3. Necroscopy and Autopsy

Necroscopy, or postmortem, constitutes a serious responsibility for the doctor. He must evaluate the primary and secondary, the definite and indefinite signs of death, and establish the difficult differential diagnosis between real and apparent death.

Where the obligation of medical necroscopy exists, the doctor's conscientious fulfillment of the same requires great care in avoiding the error of not recognizing apparent death. When necroscopy is obligatory the doctor writes a certificate indicating the diagnosis and the therapy given as well as the time of death and its clinical cause. The municipal doctor, or the doctor who is obliged to fulfill the inspection of the deceased, fulfills the official necroscopy and, in case there is no suspicion of criminal action, writes out the certificate of definite death. From this point on, the corpse is free to be buried. But in doubtful cases an autopsy is demanded by the sanitary police and, when there is a suspicion of crime, a judiciary autopsy is required.

The distinction between real death *(mors realis)* and apparent death *(mors apparens)* is also important for hygiene.

4. Real and Apparent Death

The fear of being buried alive has not been completely conquered, although it no longer has the character of a mass psychosis as was the case one or two hundred years ago. If all the prescriptions are conscientiously followed, the fear is basically unfounded. This fear was practically gone and recurred only after certain extraordinary events that followed during and after the war.

Certain states of cataleptic rigidity (in which a differential diagnosis between real and apparent death could be difficult) can at present be revealed with certitude by means of very sensitive apparatus which registers even the slightest currents of action. Thus the slightest traces of *vita minima* can be indicated in due time, that is, before burial. This confirmation constitutes the greatest guarantee against the danger of being buried alive in cases of unrecognized apparent death. In any case, apparent death is not so frequent as many believe. The casuistry of former times contained only exceptional cases.

The most important measures for the prevention of apparent death are those which tend toward an exact differential diagnosis. Among the oldest tests of death, besides the sealing wax and cupping glass, mention should be made of the mirror and downy feather tests which reveal the slightest trace of breathing. The lead acetate test is based on the fact that a piece of paper, soaked with this substance, blackens under the action of sulphuretted hydrogen ($H_2 S$), which develops in putrefaction.

The apparatus of Karnice used in mortuaries sets off an electrical sound at the slightest movement. But because of its size and complication, it is no longer in use. The selenium-radar and infra-red technique is of greater simplicity. The opening of the veins and puncturing of the heart *(punctio cordis)* tend to effect definite death before burial and serve to calm excessively anxious relatives. But since it is a matter of using means which can cause death to a living person, a conscientious doctor could never use them unless he is morally certain of death. In such a case, the means would be morally licit but superfluous.

5. Absolute and Relative Death

Even in the case of sudden death the extinction of the vital functions is not sudden, but, for the most part, gradual. Even after the moment of the confirmation of death, that is, after the cessation of respiration and cardiac activity, vital processes still continue and may last for several hours. The average time element is about two hours, and this may be considered a minimum limit.

Halluin and other French authors distinguished, therefore, between *"mort rélative"* and *"mort absolue."* Such a differentiation is not synonymous with that between *mort réelle* and *mort apparente*.

By relative death is indicated the more or less prolonged stage of the cessation of life during which an artificial reanimation is still possible. This state should not in any way be confused with the latent life which is always present in apparent death; otherwise, it would not be treated as apparent, but as real death. Latent life is not completely identical with *vita minima* which is present in certain biological states of repose (permanent forms, spores, etc.). Relative death which is an arrest of the vital functions *(arrêt de la vie)* represents a "constant etage" which is verified in every case before absolute death intervenes. We can imagine that the soul *(forma corporis)* has not completely left the body, but continues to exist for the duration of some hours in a more or less close contact.

Even in real death life is not immediately extinguished in all the tissues and cells of the body. We can hold that there is a partial persistence of vital functions in the cells and tissues for some time after real death. This fact is of notable importance from the pastoral standpoint in regard to the possibility of administering the sacrament of Extreme Unction even after death.

6. Putrefaction and Decomposition

Once absolute death has taken place and the soul has definitely separated from the body, then the processes of the destruction of the organic substance bring on decomposition *(corruptio)*. The first cadaveric phenomena (cadaveric changes) are the dryness of skin and death spots. The processes that follow pertain to putrefaction.

Fetid putrefaction first takes place with the development of gas: the cadaveric spots become a diffused discoloring; the skin assumes a dirty gray-green color; the epidermis is covered with blisters and, when these are opened, the true skin *(corium)* is exposed. The gases of putrefaction provoke a strong tumefaction (face, genitalis, stomach), and the stomach can finally burst. When the gases of putrefaction are freed, fetid putrefaction is transformed, little by little, into the process of dry putrefaction. The liquid components are absorbed more rapidly than the solid components and the blood vanishes from the blood vessels.

The process of decomposition follows putrefaction. It is a matter of two distinct processes: putrefaction takes place through anaerobic bacteria under strong gas development. Fly larvae and other animal organisms consume the oxygen and create conditions favorable to anaerobic life. Putrefaction lasts for about three months, but the process of decomposition lasts much longer. Putrefaction is favored by the exclusion of oxygen and the process of decomposition by the supply of oxygen.

The process of decomposition is principally a process of oxidation, that is, of slow combustion. In porous, air-containing terrain, decomposition lasts from six to eight years; in clay soil, from nine to ten years and more.

When dry circulating air enters freely, instead of putrefaction a dehydration of the body, a mummification, takes place. But in very humid conditions it can instead lead to a formation of adipocere. Then the soft parts no longer undergo putrefaction but are transformed into fat which turns to soap. This process is favored by the existence of abundant subcutaneous fatty tissue.

Different living organisms participate in the process of decomposition in various degrees. In the first place, bacteria of putrefaction concur in fetid putrefaction. Then insect larvae (fly-maggots) settle very rapidly within the cadaver. Among these the most active are the necrophile chafers (chafers of the genera staphylinus, silpha and necrophrous), ants, cockroaches, etc. A corpse that is in dung can quickly be reduced to a skeleton, whereas normally in the earth the process of decomposition to complete skeletonization requires a length of eight years.

Finally the cadavers are also attacked by rodents and above all, by rats. To these gnawing effects is added the consumption brought on by worms, especially by those belonging to the class of nematodes. Thus a sepulchral fauna has been grouped and described.

Among the vegetal organisms which partake in the process of decomposition, those that are principally mentioned are the mould fungi (Aspergillus, Mucor, penicillium, etc.). At times, especially in crypts, the mycelium of superior fungi (Ascomycetes, basidiomycetes) can form, like the fungi that grow in mines, into bizarre vegetal formations, which grow out of the base and wall of the crypt (so-called *cadaver fungus*). They can also form permanent mycelium *(sclerotium)*.

7. Preservation of Cadaver

If the biological meaning of the processes of decomposition for the economy of nature were rightly understood, it would not be denied that, from this very standpoint, there could be a preoccupation concerning cremation as well as certain methods of preservation by means of formalin and other germicidal methods.

Whatever can be justified by way of exception should not be diffused in general manner. It should, therefore, be considered an aberration when, for economical motives, the propaganda in favor of preservation and cosmetic preparation of cadaver is diffused. It has become customary, especially in the U.S.A., to remove the blood from the cadaver immediately after death and to fill the cardiac cavities and the blood vessels with formalin and other preservative preparations which exercise an action contrary to putrefaction and decomposition. Thus, the cheeks of the deceased are rouged, the lips and eyelashes tinged; in short, the cadaver is subjected to a "make up," in order to give it a brilliant look glamor).

The attempt toward the preservation of the corpse because of a repugnance toward disfigurement and decay is nothing but faint-hearted aestheticism. Apart from the fact that the most noble spiritualization can manifest itself in the very feature of a corpse, it seems to us irreverent and unnatural to throw away the blood extracted from the blood vessels by mechanical means—that blood which has been the bearer of life and partly an instrument of phychic functions—instead of returning to earth the body in its integrity; and to impede the organic life from nourishing itself on the organism of decomposition, which in turn serves for the nourishment of higher living beings. The circulation of the organic life of nature is arbitrarily interrupted by such means, so that this cannot be approved from the standpoint of a universalistic hygiene.

B. Questions of Social Hygiene

1. Burial

The deformation, aesthetically disgusting, undergone by the cadaver following the process of decomposition has furnished a point of hygienic objection against ground burial. The fear of the "cadaveric virus," at times transformed into mass suggestion and representing the basis for this anxiety, is not justified and is the result of a gross exaggeration.

It can be calmly affirmed that a specific cadaveric virus, that is, a virus characteristic of the cadaver as such, does not exist. But this fact does not exclude all the effects of the virus and of infections; these do not arise from the cadaver as such, but from specific infectious agents of different types, as for example, tuberculosis verrucoss, anthrax and sepsis. This, in turn, presupposes that the body of the deceased was infected by specific agents when it was still living.

It is very questionable whether infections of cholera, pestilence, poliomyelitis and meningitis are still possible through a cadaver that is already cold; it must rather be assumed that these agents, extremely parasitical, perish rapidly as the corpse becomes cold. The transmission of anthrax and sepsis always presupposes a lesion through which the agent can enter. The transmission of syphilis should not be feared since the spirochetes perish rapidly in a cold cadaver. The toxic poisons, such as arsenic, sublimate, hydrocyanic acid, cannot be absorbed through simple contact with the cadaver.

Apart from the hypothetical "cadaveric virus," there has been, on the hygienic basis, an appeal to a series of arguments in favor of cremation, above all, that of greater cleanliness and, with this, the avoidance of "antiesthetic" and "antihygienic" processes of decomposition.

Concerning the latter, it has already been shown how important these biological processes are for the circulation of life in nature. Purely aesthetic sentimental elements have nothing to do with scientific hygiene; but it is, above all, the philosophical elements that exercise an influence on the position taken in this matter. The Freethinkers have transformed the question of cremation or burial in the earth into a question of principle since the Church, faithful to the revealed truth that man is dust and into dust he shall return *(quia pulvis es et in pulverem reverteris)*, holds firmly to burial in the earth.

In regard to the mode of burial, we shall consider the same solely from the standpoint of social hygiene.

The defenders of cremation hold that the accumulation of decayed cadaver in cemeteries, especially in large cities and during an epidemic, is dangerous to health. But if the prescriptions concerning the depth of the grave is observed, there is no reason to fear any danger. The fluids of decomposition, penetrating into earth, undergo a rich filtration. The pathogenic microorganisms that can be dangerous during an epidemic perish in the cadaver. They are, moreover, stifled by the bacteria of putrefaction and inhibited in their further development.

It has not been possible to demonstrate a sole case of transmission of infection, even of the most dangerous kind (cholera, pestilence, typhus, anthrax) by a cadaver buried in the earth. The most dangerous pathogenic agents are the severe aerobes. The anaerobic infections as, for example, gas-bacillus, which are possible through contact with a cadaver by hands having lesions, has practically no importance.

The danger of transmitting disease is, instead, greater in the very process of cremation, not through the process of combustion in which all the pathogenic microrganisms would be destroyed with the corpse (if any were alive), but through the inevitable preliminaries of cremation itself.

Naturally the crematories exist only in the larger cities and in the larger commercial centers. This circumstance often requires a certain necessary transportation of great distance and particular prescriptions concerning the same and, moreover, more accurate norms regarding necroscopy, in order to exclude any criminal intervention. All these norms concerning the putting of the corpse in a coffin for transportation, the removal of the same from the coffin and putting it back in the place of cremation—all these repeated manipulations can be hazardous during an epidemic.

To the objection that cremation is more expensive, it can be answered by recalling the fact that in the concentration camps the crematories with very great capacity functioned very "expediently." Certainly, for such mass operations, these crematories functioned "suitably": it was of particular interest to remove every trace of illegal action. But this very thing is one of the most important arguments against cremation in general.

Here the considerations of social hygiene are united with those of legal medicine. It has been proven that criminal actions have been revealed even after years, by means of the exhumation of a cadaver. Legal medicine and criminology have the greatest interest in rejecting cremation in the most resolute manner.

If, from the hygienic standpoint, there has been an anxiety regarding the danger to the water supply caused by cemeteries, such an anxiety is without foundation and can easily be subdued if, in the construction of cemeteries, one conscientiously fulfills the norms of law. These prescribe that cemeteries are not to be constructed in an entry zone of a water supply system and that they should be situated in a place of subterranean running water. The deepest point of the grave level should be a distance of at least three meters from the highest point of the level of the subterranean water.

From the standpoint of the hygienist, Kollath has stated, regarding cremation vs. burial, that the anxiety concerning burial is unfounded when the required norms are observed.

The problem is not so much one of hygiene as that of one's philosophy of life. Ethical and aesthetical factors are also associated with these elements.

The objection that extensive land set aside for cemeteries removes precious land for the purpose of cultivation and building is a matter more of social economy than social hygiene. Since selfish land speculation is the basis of this argument, it does not merit consideration. In reality, the loss of space used for cemeteries is so small in proportion to the land that can be cultivated that it is of little importance for the nourishment of the people. If the use of land for cemeteries is considered a loss for humanity, it is necessary to realize that the cemeteries themselves represent, from the standpoint of social hygiene, a precious acquisition of a verdant section. Abandoning the same would be a serious loss for the large cities and the building up of the same would do nothing else but favor land speculation. In this connection it is sufficient to recall the cemeteries of Latin countries which are of notable value not only from the aesthetic, but also from the public hygienic standpoint.

2. The Question of Capital Punishment

The problem of capital punishment pertains indisputably to the scope of social hygiene and also to pastoral hygiene, inasmuch as it is of interest to the priest.

It seems paradoxical to speak of hygienic standpoints in regard to capital punishment. It is evident that it is rather a matter of humanity to consider how the inevitable severity in execution can be removed of all possible cruelty and that the victim will undergo the least possible suffering. Nevertheless, hygiene is interested in the most rapid and definite mode of justification.

a) THE EXECUTION OF CAPITAL PUNISHMENT

The question concerning the most humane manner of executing the capital sentence has not yet been univocally resolved. The execution of punishment in ancient and medieval times took place in cruel forms (*"ad muraenas";* a bag with serpents or rats; impalement and being buried alive; death by fire, wheels, etc.). However, in modern execution, the principle is observed of not having anyone, even the worst criminal, suffer any longer and more intensely than is inevitably necessary.

Decapitation is one of the most brutal and bloody forms of death. In the head, quickly removed from the body, a trace of consciousness can still remain so that the moments immediately following execution can be even more terrible than those that precede execution.

Fusillade, specifically military, is likewise cruel and bloody. The sudden intervention of death depends solely on the precision of the executioners. In recent times, recourse has been had to fusillade by individual shooters (so-called "shot in the back of the neck"), which deforms the countenance as to make it unrecognizable.

The electric chair is only an apparent humane mode of execution. The criminal visibly suffers dreadful moments and, moreover, it is possible that only apparent death with cataleptic rigidity may be provoked.

Poisoning (by means of gas) is also a cruel mode of death, the more so since the condemned is taken by surprise because of humane consideration. But such a mode of execution, in which the condemned is not given the opportunity of preparing for death, is anything but humane and is incompatible with human dignity. It brings to mind certain unworthy forms of "euthanasia."

Although there has been strong emotional aversion toward hanging, yet, from the hygienic standpoint it can be considered the most humane form of execution. Hanging is only apparently cruel since from the condemned person's face one receives the impression of deep suffering because of the persistent convulsive movements. But, in reality, at the moment in which the noose tightens, a sudden loss of consciousness takes place, and this is due not only to the detachment of the carotids, but also to the disarticulation of the atlanto-occipital joint and to the breakage of the medulla oblongata and, hence, to the sudden blockage of the respiratory center.

The objections posited against hanging are more of an emotional rather than of a rational nature since they are not directed against capital punishment itself, but against the type of death of the "common criminal." It is the same error as that in which crucifixion was considered the most ignominious death.

Recent medical research (Hynek, Barbet) has shown that crucifixion is one of the most cruel and painful among the forms of execution. This research has proceeded from the study of the Shroud of Turin (Sacra Sindone). It has been shown in a most convincing manner, both from the anatomical and physiological standpoint, that the nails must have been driven through the wrist and not the palm of the hand and, on the basis of the traces of blood, it has been shown that, through the weight of the body, the arms, originally extended horizontally, tended always more obliquely upward and toward the point of a very accentuated obliquity and that death must have been caused by spasms of the respiratory musculature.

b) QUESTIONS BASED ON PRINCIPLE

From the standpoint of law, the justification of capital punishment is derived from the supreme power of the State over life and death, that is, from the *"ius vitae ac necis."* This right of State power is considered as delegated from God Himself. In the patriarchal era it belonged to the father of the family (pater familias) as the expression of supreme regal power. Christ Himself recognized this supreme power. When asked by Pilate: "Knowest thou not that I have power to crucify thee, and I have power to release thee?" he answered: "Thou shouldst not have any power against me, unless it were given thee from above" (John 19; 10-11).

A divine derivation of capital punishment can also be taken from the words of Genesis: "Whoever shall shed man's blood, his blood shall be shed: for man was made to the image of God" (Genesis 9,6). The justification: "for man was made to the image of God" points to a supernatural motivation and, hence, not merely to the law of "Talion" of the Old Testament.

The arguments against capital punishment are not based on the point that the State does not have the right, but on the fact that man is never capable of exercising such a right with justice and of not abusing it.

One of the most serious arguments against capital punishment is, without doubt, the fact that in case of judiciary error, the punishment is irreparable. The other basic argument against capital punishment is that it romoves from the repentant criminal every possibility of conversion and reparation.

If the question of capital punishment is perceived from the purely "earthly" standpoint, one cannot posit any argument in its favor. But if in it is seen nothing but a provision of social security (of general prevention) or of intimidation (of special prevention), then experience teaches that not even this means of itself is sufficient to reduce the number of capital crimes.

Finally, the possibility of abuse for political purposes has placed upon capital punishment such discredit that it appears absolutely inadmissable, even considering other viewpoints which can give it meaning.

But these viewpoints pertain exclusively to the supernatural order. Among these we recognize only the punitive power of earthly authority as a participation of the punitive justice of God. This places upon the one having the power a tremendous responsibility before God. Only this point of view can cause capital punishment to appear justified and to confer upon it meaning as a defence of society against the unjust aggressor. This presupposes that the criminal accepts death as an expiation for the violation of the right to life of an innocent party: that he accepts the sacrifice of his own natural life in order to save his supernatural life.

To modern juridical positivism these considerations of legal and moral philosophy have become strange, since positivistic thinking regards no life other than physical life. For the person in the Middle Ages who possessed faith, these factors were completely understood. But the naturalism and positivism of our day have made a problem of capital punishment and have not been able to resolve the same. One cannot, however, abolish capital punishment in theory and execute the same indirectly through forced labor and cruel regulations of concentration camps. The capital judgment pronounced by an ordinary tribunal on the basis of rigorous dispositions of law, even if at times it can appear as an act of justice, violates the supernatural order because it sheds the blood of man made to the image of God.

3. Task of the Spiritual Director

To a morally clear execution of capital punishment belongs, as absolutely indispensable, the preparation and spiritual assistance of the condemned person. The prison chaplain should so direct him as to have him consider his punishment as an expiation; he must assure him that through repentance and penance, he can save his eternal life. Thus capital punishment itself can be transformed for the criminal into the last "good deed" that he accomplishes on earth in that, in place of a "ruined life," he opens through the "purifying power of death" the way which will lead him to supernatural life.

IX. THE CARE OF SOULS AND HYGIENE. OUTLOOK

A. Basic Problems

In this compendium we can only briefly mention some of the more important associations of hygiene with the care of souls. The considerations of social hygiene have led us from the question concerning preparation for marriage, marriage counseling and protection of the mother, through the relaxation of sex life and the damages caused by civilization, to the ultimate problems of death and capital punishment. We have constantly found ourselves faced with problems that cannot be resolved from the standpoint of a purely positivistic science but can only be solved from the universalistic viewpoint by considering man in his totality and also as a member of a supernatural community.

Since social hygiene goes beyond individual hygiene, because it has as its object not only man as an individual but also as a member of a human society, pastoral hygiene goes even further and considers man as a citizen of two worlds. Only then can we, even as hygienists, acknowledge health as the greatest among earthly values without losing sight of the fact that it is not the supreme, ultimate and absolute value; only then can we hold, even regarding the problem of capital punishment, that the surrender of earthly life—death—does not signify the destruction of "being," but that it can rather save the very "being" from perishing. Viewed in the light of these considerations, death does not speak the last word. Death, seen in its true sense, does not represent the victory of matter and decomposition over the spirit, but it is rather the victory of the spirit over matter and its decomposition. It loses its terror for him who perceives it as a passage to true and safe being.

The inscription found over the entrance of an anatomical institute—"*Mors ianua vitae*"—signifies for young students an admonition to reflect more deeply on the remote background of their study. To teach hygiene in the light of this knowledge—that is the essence of pastoral hygiene!

B. Care of the Soul and Care of the Body

Hygiene was formerly considered and taught to be merely the care of bodily health. It was, therefore, limited to the mere "care of the body." A characteristic expression of this idea was an old student song in which it was said of the priest that he "reproached the sinful soul" and, of the doctor, that he "repaired its house which was falling into ruin."

An absolute separation of the spheres of activity, an extreme dualism between body and soul—this was the basis of the separation between hygiene and spiritual direction; the doctor for the body, and the priest for the soul: a clear and apparently definite distinction. There was no mode of communication between the two; for the majority of cases, the relationship between them consisted in a benevolent tolerance (coexistence), but it was never a matter of a comprehensive cooperation. These relations have undergone a substantial modification.

Psychotherapy has begun to pull down the frontiers. At one time it was considered a violation of competency if the doctor participated, in any way, in the function of modern spiritual direction. Since that time we have made notable progress and have overcome the conflicts of competency.

The competencies are again clearly distinguished: to the priest, that which pertains to the priest and, to the doctor, that which pertains to the doctor; but in such a way that each complements the other and both work hand-in-hand and, in case of necessity, each intervenes as a subsidiary of the other. This is the tendency that has undergone a profound and promising evolution. From this standpoint it is proper to say that hygiene can offer much to the care of souls, but that even spiritual direction can render great service to hygiene.

Our striving toward a mental hygiene would be devoid of meaning if we were not able to utilize the inestimable value which spiritual direction can offer for the purpose of hygiene. Mental hygiene would remain an expression without meaning, a sphere of confusion and without definite limits, in which the incapacity of formulating clear ideas would predominate, if hygiene and spiritual direction would not extend a helping hand to each other; if, by indicating their limits with clarity, they did not tend, even through different ways, toward a common end. The common goal is the re-establishment of the deeply shattered bodily and mental health of our sick age.

C. Sanctity and Sanity

If we realized the pagan background of our times, it would be evident to us that the renewal of the natural order cannot be actualized without the recognition of the supernatural order. If the health of body and soul is the purpose of hygiene, then sanctity —that is, the highest possible concordance with the norm of life prescribed by God—represents the ultimate purpose of spiritual direction.

We have at various times had occasion to bring attention to the fact that the principle, *"Gratia supponit naturam,"* should not be misunderstood in the sense that grace "presupposes" the integrity of nature; rather it must be understood in the sense that grace builds on nature as its basis, that it elevates and perfects it *("implet et perficit naturam").*

Goldbrunner has, in a short and precise literary work, studied the relationship between sanctity and sanity.[1] He starts with the principle that sanctity, as an "heroic degree of virtue," can very well be present even in a crippled and broken body. The medieval

[1] Cf. Goldbrunner, *Heilikeit und Gesundheit* (Herder, Freiburg, 1949).

ascetic held that the sick and crippled could be closer to God than the healthy and robust person (St. Hildegarde).

It certainly appears as the highest purpose of every aspiration to pray that in a healthy body there be also a healthy soul *("Orandum est, ut sit mens sana in corpore sano"),* and, hence, the current translation that "only in a healthy body can a healthy soul exist" is completely false and erroneous.

These acknowledgments have nothing to do with the often asserted "hostility of Christianity toward the body." Statements of this kind do not become true through consistent repetition. When we thus understand the purpose of pastoral hygiene, as has been outlined in this compendium, then it can not only contribute much to the pastoral sphere, but can also confer fruitful stimulation in the field of hygiene.

Epilogue

A universalistic research renders possible a vast view of the instinctual forces which have given form to the countenance of our times. From such a research there have resulted aspects which have been of equal importance for both the priest and the doctor. Many of these, as the relaxation of sexuality and the diffusion of birth control, are alarming. They indicate the devastating picture of an epoch that is sick to the very depths of life, but which invokes health with the ultimate resources of a healthy vital force. The doctor alone cannot affect a cure, just as the priest alone cannot do so, if there is lacking the knowledge of establishing a diagnosis and of accurately selecting a therapy. The cooperation of both can fulfill the task. The prognosis is serious, but not hopeless.

For our world that is threatened with ruination we wish to express the hope that by returning to its proper values, which are those of Christian tradition, it will again be capable of a regeneration for, "He created all things that they might be, and He made the nations of the earth for health" (Wisdom 1, 14).

Bibliography

Alexander, Franz, *Psychosomatic Medicine,* New York, Norton, 1950.

Alexander, Leo, M.D., *Treatment of Mental Disorders.* Philadelphia, Saunders, 1953.

Allers, Rudolph, M.D., *The Psychology of Character,* New York. Sheed & Ward, 1933.

Allers, Rudolph, M.D., *Character Education in Adolescence,* New York, Joseph F. Wagner, Inc., 1940.

Allers, Rudolph, M.D., "Sin and Neurosis," *Homiletic and Pastoral Review,* XLII 2 (1942), 637-644.

American Hierarchy, Statement, "The Christian Family," *The Catholic Mind,* Vol. 43 (Feb., 1950).

Anastasi, Anne, and Foley, John, Jr., *Differential Psychology,* New York, Macmillan, 1949.

Anastasi, A., Foley, J. *Psychological Testing.* New York, Macmillan, 1954.

Angrist, A. A., "A Pathologist's Experience with Attitudes toward Death," *Rhode Island Medical Journal,* 63: 693-697, 710, Nov., 1960.

Archdiocese Of Chicago, *Pastoral Counseling and Problem Marriages,* Chicago, 1960.

——, *Archdiocesan Regulations for Problem Marriages,* by Rt. Rev. Msgr. Edward M. Burke, Chancellor.

345

——, *Catholic Family Consultation Service,* by Rev. James J. Murtaugh, Associate Director.

——, *The Study of Psychology in Relation to Pastoral Counseling,* by Rev. John J. Fahey.

——, *Principles of Counseling and Interviewing.*

    1. "Counseling in Personal and Marriage Guidance and Education."

    2. "Some Suggestions from Counseling Skills," by Rev. Charles A. Curran, Ph.D., Loyola University.

——, *The Parish Priest and Problem Marriages.*

Arnold, Magda B., and Gasson, John A., S.J., *The Human Person,* New York, Ronald, 1954.

Arnot, Robert, M.D., "Some Observations on Mental Health Based on the Psychiatric Treatment of the Religious," *Guild of Catholic Psychiatrists Bulletin,* Vol. VII, No. 3, July, 1960.

Aumann, Jordan, "Can Neurotics Be Saints?" *Cross and Crown,* V (1935), 451-469.

Barrow, J. G., Quinlan, C. B., Cooper, G. R., Whitner, Virginia S., and Goodloe, Mary, *Studies in Arteriosclerosis, III. An Epidemiologic Study of Arteriosclerosis in Trappist and Benedictine Monks: A Preliminary Report,* Ann. Int. Med., 52: 368-377, February, 1960.

Bartemeier, Leo., M.D., "Psychiatric Training for Seminarians and Chaplains," *Guild of Catholic Psychiatrists Bulletin,* Vol. VI. No. 2, April, 1959.

Beirnaert, Louis, "Does Sanctification Depend on Psychic Structure?" *Cross Currents,* I (1950), 39-43.

Belam, O. H., "The Holy Shroud of Turin: A Doctor's Meditation," *Catholic Medical Quarterly,* London, 12: 113-126, October, 1959.

Berkowitz, S.J., *et al:* "Diagnosis and Treatment of Marital Problems," reprint from *Journal of Social Casework,* 1949, Family Service Association of America, N. Y. 16.

Bier, William C., S.J., "Goals in Pastoral Counseling," *Pastoral Psychology* (Feb. 1959).

Bier, William C., S.J., "Psychological Aspects of Pastoral Work," in *Proceedings of the Archdiocesan Institute of Ecclesiastical Studies,* New York, St. Joseph Seminary, 1957.

Bier, William C., S.J., "Religious Counseling: The Roman Catholic Church," in R. K. Hall and J. A. Lauwery's (eds). *The Year Book of Education,* Yonkers, World Book Co., 1955.

Bier, William C., S.J., "Psychological Testing of Candidates and the Theology of Vocation," *Review for Religious,* XII, 1953, 291-304.

Blum and Balinsky, *Counseling and Psychology,* New Jersey, Prentice-Hall, Inc., 1954.

Bonnar, A., O.F.M., "The Priest and the Psychopath," *Catholic Medical Quarterly,* 14: 8-19, Jan. 1961.

Bordin, Edward S., *Psychological Counseling,* The Century Psychology Series, New York, Appleton-Century-Crofts, 1955.

Brayfield, A. H., *Readings in Modern Methods of Counseling,* New York, Appleton-Century-Crofts, Inc., 1955.

Breen, W., "Neo-Malthusianism," *Irish Eccles. Review,* Nov., 1931.

Breitenbeck, Gerard R., C.Ss.R., "Counseling Parents of Retarded Children," *Linacre Quarterly,* Vol. 29, No. 2, May, 1962.

Brennan, Robert E., *General Psychology,* New York, Macmillan, 1952.

Broadway, John S., "Some Domestic Relations Laws That Counselors in Marital Difficulties Need to Know," *Social Forces,* Vol. 17, October, 1938, pp. 83-89.

Bruno de Jesus-Marie, C. D., *Conflict and Light,* London, Sheed and Ward, 1952.

Burgess, Ernest, W., "The Family in a Changing Society," *American Journal of Sociology,* Vol. 53, May, 1949.

Byrne, John, T. (Rev), "The Counselor and the Spiritual Director," *The Homiletic and Pastoral Review,* Vol. 59, No. 6, March, 1959.

Carroll, Herbert A., *Mental Hygiene,* New York, Prentice-Hall, 1951.

Carney, Francis W. (Very Rev.), "The Catholic Physician and Premarital Education," *Linacre Quarterly,* Vol. 27, No. 1, February, 1960.

Cattell, J., *Psychology in America,* New York, Science Press, 1929.

Caulfield, Thomas E., M.D., "Impact of the Sick Person on the Religious Community," *Guild of Catholic Psychiatrists Bulletin,* Vol. VIII, No. 3, July, 1960.

Cavanagh, J. R., M.D., *Fundamental Pastoral Counseling,* Milwaukee, Bruce Publishing Co., 1962.

Cavanagh, J. R., M.D., and McGoldrick, James B., S.J., *Fundamental Psychiatry,* Milwaukee, Bruce, 1953.

Cavanagh, J. R. M.D., *Fundamental Marriage Counseling,* Milwaukee, Bruce Publishing Co., 1957.

Cavanagh, J. R., M.D., "Marriage Counseling Is a Problem of Preventive Medicine," *Guild of Catholic Psychiatrists Bulletin,* Vol. VI, No. 4, October, 1959.

Cavanagh, J. R., M.D., "The Psychological Effects of Birth Prevention," *Marriage,* 42: September, 1960.

Chodoff, P., "The Dying Patient," *Med. Ann. Dist. Columbia,* 29: 447-450, August, 1960.

Clemens, A. H., Ph.D., *Marriage Education and Counseling,* Washington, D.C., Catholic University of America Press, 1951.

Clemens, A. H., Ph.D., "Personality, Traits in Successful and Failing Marriages," *Guild of Catholic Psychiatrists Bulletin,* Vol. VIII, No. 4, October, 1961.

Colbert, Edward G., M.D., "Confession, Psychotherapy, and the Problem Penitent," *Guild of Catholic Psychiatrists Bulletin,* Vol. VIII, No. 3, July, 1961.

Connell, F. S., (C.Ss.R.), "Medical Experimentation on Condemned Criminals," *American Ecclesiastical Review,* 140: 199-201, March, 1959.

Cuber, John F., and Harper, Roberta A., *Problems of American Society: Values in Conflict,* N. Y., Appleton-Century-Crofts, Inc., 1954.

Cuber, John, F., *Marriage Counseling Practice,* Appleton-Century-Crofts, Inc., N. Y., 1948.

Crotty, Charles, M.A., "Marriage Counseling and Psychology," *Guild of Catholic Psychiatrists Bulletin,* Vol. VI, No. 4, October, 1959.

Curran, Charles A., (Rev.), *Counseling in Catholic Life and Education,* New York, Macmillan, 1955.

Dailey, Robert H., S.J., "The Dismissal of Religious," *Guild of Catholic Psychiatrists Bulletin,* Vol. VIII, No. 3, July, 1961, Washington, D.C.

Deferrari, Sister Mary Theresa, "Moral Freedom and the Influence of the Emotions," *Guild of Catholic Psychiatrists Bulletin,* Vol. VII, No. 4, October, 1960.

De Lestapis S., S.J., "The Catholic Position as regards the Problem of Population," *Guild of Catholic Psychiatrists Bulletin,* Vol. VI, No. 4, October, 1959.

Demal, Willibald, O.S.A., *Pastoral Psychology in Practice,* translated by Joachim Conway, New York, Kenedy, 1955.

Dempsey, Peter, O.F.M.Cap., *Psychology for Everyone,* Westminster, Md., Newman, 1953.

Deutsch, H., *The Psychology of Women,* 2 vols., New York, Grune and Stratton, 1944.

Dickerson, J., "Religion and Medicine: 'The Healing Team,'" *J.A.M.A.,* 178; adv. p. 132, Dec. 23, 1961.

Dobbelstein, H., *Psychiatry for Priests,* translated by Meyrick Booth, New York, Kenedy, 1954.

Donat, J., S.J., *Psychologia.* Barcelona, Herder, 1944.

Doniger, Simon, editor, *Religion and Human Behaviour,* New York, Association Press, 1954.

Doob, Leonard W., *Social Psychology,* New York, Holt, 1952.

Driver, Helen, PhD., *Multiple Counseling,* Madison 4, Wisconsin, Monona Publications, 1954.

Driscoll, John M. (O.S.A.) "A Note on Psychosomatic Medicine in the Light of Thomistic Psychology," *Guild of Catholic Psychiatrists Bulletin,* Vol. VII, No. 4, October, 1960.

Duffey, Felix D., C.S.C., *Testing the Spirit,* St. Louis, Herder, 1947.

Duncan, Sylvia and Peter, *Bonganga: Experiences of a Missionary Doctor,* New York, Random House, Inc., 1960.

(Editorial) "The Smoker and His Conscience," *America,* 103: 9, April 2, 1960.

English, O. Spurgeon, and Pearson, Gerald, H.J., *Emotional Problems of Living,* New York, Norton, 1955.

Exton-Smith, A. N., "Terminal Illness in the Aged," *Lancet,* pp. 305-308, August 5, 1961.

Fecher, Con P., Ph.D., "Mortality and Morbidity Studies of Religious," *Linacre Quarterly,* Vol. 27, No. 4, Nov. 1960.

Flood, Peter (editor) *New Problems in Medical Ethics,* Westminster, Md., Newman, 1954.

Ford, John C. (S.J.), "Chemical Comfort and Christian Virtue," *American Ecclesiastical Review,* 141: 361-375, Dec., 1959.

Forker, Thomas S. (Rev.), "The Relationship of the Priest Mental-Hospital Chaplain and the Mental Patient," *Guild of*

Catholic Psychiatrists Bulletin, Vol. VII, No. 3, July, 1960.

Foster, Robert G., Ph.D., *Marriage and Family Relationships,* New York, Macmillan, 1950.

Fox, W. G., "Spiritual Needs of Older Persons," *New Physician,* 10: 205-209, July, 1961.

Gabriel de Ste. Marie-Madeleine, "Present Norms of Holiness," *Conflict and Light,* London, Sheed and Ward, 1952, pp. 154-169.

Gannon, T., *Psychology: the Unity of Human Behaviour,* New York, Ginn, 1954.

Gardeil, H. D., O.P., *Introduction to the Philosophy of St. Thomas Aquinas,* Vol. III, *Psychology,* translated by John A. Otto, St. Louis, Herder, 1956.

Gerle, H., Lunden, G., and Sandblom, P., "The Patient with Inoperable Cancer from the Psychiatric and Social Standpoints: A Study of 101 Cases," *Cancer,* 13: 1206-1217, November-December, 1960.

Groves, Ernest R., *The Family and its Social Functions,* Chicago, J.B. Lippincott Co., 1940.

Hagmaier, George, C.S.P., and Gleason, Robert W., S.J., *Counseling the Catholic,* Sheed and Ward, New York, 1959.

Hiltner, Seward, *Pastoral Counseling,* New York, Abington-Cokesbury Press, 1949.

Hughes, Margaret M., *The People in Your Life,* New York, Knopf, 1951.

Hulme, Seward, *How to Start Counseling,* New York, Abington Press, 1955.

Jersild, Arthur T., *Child Psychology,* New York, Prentice-Hall, 1958.

Johnson, John, *Marriage Counseling according to the Principles of St. Thomas,* Gregorian University, Rome, 1958.

Kalthoff, Robert J., M.D., and Gunther, Francis L., M. S., "Collaboration of Psychiatrists and Supervised Psychotherapist in the Treatment of People in Religious Life," *The Bulletin of the Guild of Catholic Psychiatrists,* Vol. X, No. 1, January, 1962.

Kanner, Leo., M.D., *Child Psychiatry,* Springfield, Ill., Thomas Press, 1957.

Keefe, Edward F., M.D., "Successful Periodic Continence," *Linacre Quarterly*, Vol. 29, No. 4, November, 1962.

Kelly, Audrey, *A Catholic Parent's Guide to Sex Education*, New York, Hawthorn, 1962.

Kelly, George A. (Msgr.), *The Catholic Family Handbook*, Robert Hale Ltd., London, 1961.

Kelly, George A., *The Catholic Youth's Guide to Life and Love*, New York, Random House, Inc., 1960.

Kelly, George A., *The Catholic Marriage Manual*, New York, Random House, 1958.

Kelly, G., S.J. (Rev.), *The Good Confessor*, New York, Sentinel Press, 1951.

Kelly, G., S.J., *Guidance for Religious*, Westminster, Md., Newman Press, 1956.

Kelly, G., S.J., *Modern Youth and Chastity*, St. Louis, Queen's Work, 1952.

Kelley, M. W., "Depression in the Psychoses of Members of Religious Communities of Women," *Am. J. Psychiat.*, 118: 423-425, November, 1961.

Kevorkian, Jack, *Medical Research and the Death Penalty: A Dialogue*, New York, Vantage Press, Inc., 1960.

Laforet, Eugene G., M.D., "The 'Hopeless' Case," *Linacre Quarterly*, Vol. 29, No. 3, August, 1962.

Lambert, J., "Attitude of the Chaplain toward Scrupulosity: Psychiatric Point of View," *Laval. Med.*, 33: 194-197, March, 1962.

Leake, C.D., "Aging, and Moral Judgments," *Geriatrics*, 16: 499-501, October, 1961.

Lindworsky, Joannes, *Experimental Psychology*, translated by H. de Silva, New York, Macmillan, 1931.

Lindworsky, J., *The Psychology of Asceticism*, translated by E. A. Heiring, London, Edwards, 1936.

Lindworsky, J., *Theoretical Psychology*, translated by H. R. de Silva, St. Louis, Herder, 1932.

Lindworsky, J., *The Training of the Will*, translated by A. Steiner and E. A. Fitzpatrick, Milwaukee, Bruce, 1929.

Lister, J., "Medical Care in Old Age," *New Eng. J. Med.*, 263: 399-400, August, 1960.

Lister, J., "Sin and Crime," *New Eng. J. Med.,* 263: 191-192, July, 1960 (The Wolfenden Report).

Litin, E. M., "Should the Cancer Patient Be Told?" *Postgrad, Med.,* 28: 470-475, Nov. 1960.

Loftus, P. M., "Theological Aspects of the Contraceptive Pill," *Catholic Med. Quart.,* 14: 97-103, October, 1961.

Long, P. H., "On the Quantity and Quality of Life"; I. "Fruitless Longevity," *Resident Physician,* 6: 69-70, April, 1960.

Long, P. H., "On the Quantity and Quality of Life"; II. "Moral, Religious, National, and Legal Responsibilities of Physicians in the Care of the Incurably Ill or the Dying," *Resident Physician,* 6: 53-61, May, 1960.

Long, P. H., "On the Quantity and Quality of Life"; III. "A Discussion of the Prolongation of Life in the Incurably Ill and Dying," *Resident Physician,* 6: 51-53, June, 1960.

Lynch, John J., S.J., "Extreme Unction: Towards a Practical Appreciation of the Sacrament," *Linacre Quarterly,* Vol. 28, No. 4, November, 1961.

Lynch, John J., S.J., "The Oral Contraceptives: A Review of Moral Appraisement," *Linacre Quarterly,* Vol. 29, No. 4, November, 1962.

Magner, James A., *Mental Health in a Mad World,* Milwaukee, Bruce, 1953.

Marshall, John, M.D., "The Psychological Aspects of Family Limitation," *Guild of Catholic Psychiatrists Bulletin,* Vol. VI, No. 4, October, 1959.

May, Rollo, *The Art of Counseling,* New York, Abington Press, 1939.

McAllister, R. J., and Vanderveldt, A., O.F.M., "Factors in Mental Illness among Hospitalized Clergy," *J. Nerv. and Mental Dis.,* 132: 80-88, Jan., 1961.

McCarthy, Raphael C., S.J., *Safeguarding Mental Health,* Milwaukee, Bruce, 1937.

McCormick, Richard A., S.J., "Moral Considerations on Autopsy," *Linacre Quarterly,* Vol. 28, No. 4, November, 1961.

McCready, Robert B., "Premarital Counseling: A Multidimensional Approach," *Obstetrics and Gynecology,* 13: 420-425, April 1959.

McKernan, Louis, C.S.P., "Population in a Changing World," *Catholic World*, 190: 287-293, February, 1960.

McReady, L. L., "Warning the Dying of Their Danger," *Clergy Review*, 44: 295-298, May, 1959.

Meshorer, M., "Medical Research and the Death Penalty," *Postgrad. Med.*, 30: A 46 ff., July, 1961.

Mihanovich, Schnepp and Thomas, *Marriage and the Family*, Milwaukee, Bruce, 1955.

Misiak, Henry K., and Staudt, Virginia M., *Catholics in Psychology*, New York, McGraw-Hill, 1954.

Mohrer, O. H., *Psychotherapy: Theory and Research*, Ronald Press, New York, 1953.

Morison, R. S., "Darwinism: Foundation for an Ethical System?" *Christianity and Crisis*, 20: 120-123, August 8, 1960.

Moore, Thomas Verner, *Cognitive Psychology*, Phila., Lippincott, 1939.

Moore, Thomas Verner, *Driving Forces of Human Nature and Their Adjustment*, New York, Grune and Stratton, 1948.

Moore, Thomas Verner, *Dynamic Psychology*, Phila., Lippincott, 1926.

Moore, Thomas Verner, *Nature and Treatment of Mental Disorders*, 2nd Edition, New York, Grune and Stratton, 1951.

Moore, Thomas Verner, *Personal Mental Hygiene*, New York, Grune and Stratton, 1944.

Moore, Thomas Verner, *Heroic Sanctity and Insanity*, New York, Grune and Stratton, 1959.

Mudd, Emily H., Ph.D., *The Practice of Marriage Counseling*, New York, Assoc. Press, 1951.

Nabors, G. C., M.D., "The Doctor and Ovulation Determination," *Linacre Quarterly*, Vol. 27, No. 4, November, 1960.

Neuberger, K. T., "Some Neuropathological Aspects of Boxing," *Industrial Medicine and Surgery*, 29: 440-441, September, 1960.

N.C.W.C., *Marriage Counseling* (National Catholic Welfare Council), Washington, D.C., 1950.

Niedermeyer, Albert, Ph.D., M.D., J.C.D., *Compendium of Pastoral Medicine*, translated by Rev. Fulgence Buonanno, O.F.M., Ph.D., Wagner, Inc., New York, 1961.

Nix, J. T., M.D., Ph.D., K.S.G., "A Progress Report on Health of Religious," *Linacre Quarterly,* Vol. 30, No. 1, Feb., 1963.

Nix, J. T., M.D., Ph.D., "Health Care of Clergy and Religious," *Linacre Quarterly,* Vol. 27, No. 3, August, 1960.

Nix, J. T., M.D., Ph.D., "Primary Cancer of the Lung in Nuns," *Linacre Quarterly,* Vol. 29, No. 4, November, 1962.

Noyes, Arthur P., M.D., *Modern Clinical Psychiatry,* Phila., Saunders, 1939.

Nuttin, Joseph, S.J., *Psychoanalysis and Personality,* New York, Sheed and Ward, 1953.

Odenwald, R. P., M.D., "The Priest as Counselor," *Conference Bulletin of the Archdiocese of New York,* Vol. XXXIII, No. 2, September, 1956.

Oken, D., "What to Tell Cancer Patients: A Survey of Medical Attitudes," *J.A.M.A.,* 175: 1120-1128, April, 1961.

Page, I. H., "Death with Dignity," (editorial), *Modern Med.,* 30: 81-82, Oct. 15, 1962.

Parker, W. L., and Trifunov, J., "The Sport of Amateur Boxing— Good or Evil?" *The Canadian Medical Association Journal,* 83: 432-435, August 27, 1960.

Pepinsky, H. B., and Pepinsky, Pauline N., *Counseling Theory and Practice,* New York, Ronald Press, 1954.

Pius XI, "Christian Marriage (*"Casti connubii"*), New York, The America Press, 1936.

Pius XI, "On Christian Education of Youth," New York, Paulist Press.

Pius XII, "Allocution to Catholic Mothers," *Acta Apostolicae Sedis,* Vol. 33, Nov. 26, 1941, pp. 450-458.

Pius XII, *Humani Generis,* New York, Paulist Press, 1953.

Pius XII, "Moral Questions Affecting Married Life," New York, Paulist Press.

Popenoe, Paul, *Principles, Techniques and Materials of Counseling,* American Institute of Family Relations, Los Angeles.

Porter, E. H., *An Introduction to Therapeutic Counseling,* Boston: Houghton-Mifflin Co., 1950.

Riesman, David, *The Lonely Crowd,* New Haven, Yale University Press, 1956.

Robo, Etienne, *Two Portraits of St. Therese of Lisieux,* Chicago, Henry Regnery Company, 1955.

Rogers, Carl R., Ph.D., *Counseling and Psychotherapy*, New York, Houghton-Mifflin Co., 1951.

Rogers, Carl R., Ph.D., *Client-Centered Therapy*, New York, Houghton-Mifflin Co., 1951.

Rowley, Francis P., S.J., "The Mental Hospital Chaplain—Religion as Adjunct to Psychiatry," *Guild of Catholic Psychiatrists Bulletin*, Vol. VII, No. 2, April, 1960, Washington, D.C.

Rowley, Francis P., S.J., "The Theology of Dying," *Guild of Catholic Psychiatrists Bulletin*, Vol. IX, No. 3, July, 1962.

Ruff, F. R., "Have We the Right to Prolong Dying?" *RISS* (National Magazine for Residents, Internes and Senior Students), 3: 54-59, 100, November, 1960.

Schneiders, Alexander A., Ph.D., "The Psychology of Dying," *The Bulletin of the Guild of Catholic Psychiatrists*, Vol. X, No. 1, January, 1963, Washington, D.C.

Schneiders, A. A., Ph.D., *Pastoral Counseling*, New York, Fordham University, 1957.

Schwarz, B. E., M.D., and Ruggieri, B.A., M.D., *Parent-Child Tensions*, Phila., Lippincott, 1958.

Segal, Stanley J., "The Role of the Counselor's Religious Values in Counseling," *Journal of Counseling Psychology*, Winter, 1959, Vol. 6, No. 4.

The Human Body, Selected and Arranged by the Monks of Solesmes, Printed by the Daughters of St. Paul, Boston, Mass., 1961 (a series of papal teachings complied by the Monks of Solesmes).

Seminar on the Psychiatric Aspects of Annulment, *Guild of Catholic Psychiatrists Bulletin*, Vol. VII, No. 2, April, 1960.

——, "Introductory Comments," Joseph Deuel Sullivan, M.D.

——, "Mental Disease and the Ecclesiastical Courts," Rt. Rev. John J. Hayes.

——, "Psychopathic Personality and Annulment," Paul E. Kubitschek, M.D.

——, "Schizophrenia as a Consideration in Annulment of Marriage," John W. Higgins, M.D.

——, "Homosexuality as an Impediment to Marriage," John R. Cavanagh, M.D.

Sister M. Aloyse, I.H.M., "Evaluations of Candidates for Religious

Life," *Guild of Catholic Psychiatrists Bulletin,* Vol. VIII, No. 4, October, 1961. Washington, D.C.

Sister Margaret Mary Kinzel, O.P., "A Study of Natural Tensions," *Guild of Catholic Psychiatrists Bulletin,* Vol. VII, No. 4, October, 1960.

Skidmore, Garret and Skidmore, *Marriage Consulting,* New York, Harper and Bros., 1956.

Slatis, H. M., Reis, R. H., and Hoene, R. E., "Consanguineous Marriages in the Chicago Region," *American Journal of Human Genetics,* 10: 446-464, December, 1958.

Snoeck, A., S.J., *Confession and Pastoral Psychology,* translated by Theodore Zuydwigk, S.J., Newman Press, Maryland, 1961.

Stephanie, Sister M., S.S.C., "Chaplain-Hospital Relationship," *Hosp. Progress,* 42: 152, May, 1961.

Stern, Edith M., *Mental Illness,* National Association for Mental Health, 1951.

Swenson, W. M., "Attitudes toward Death in an Aged Population," *Journal of Gerontology,* 16: 49-52, January, 1961.

Synder, Em. U., Ph.D., *Casebook of Non-Directive Counseling,* New York, Houghton-Mifflin Co., 1947.

Taylor, Fred M., M.D., and Borreca, Frank A., M.A., "On Mentally Retarded Children," *Linacre Quarterly,* Vol. 29, No. 2, May, 1962.

The Catholic Counselor, Iona College, New Rochelle, New York.

Thorne, Frederick G., "Principles of Personality Counseling," *Journal of Clinical Psychology,* Brandon, Vermont, 1950.

Towne, Janet E., "Premarital Counseling," *Med. Clin. N.A.,* 45: 53-62, January, 1961.

Trevett, R. F., "The Church and Sex," (Volume 103 of The Twentieth Century Encyclopedia of Catholicism, edited by Henri Daniel Rops), N.Y., Hawthorn, 1960.

Vaughan, Richard P., S.J., Ph.D., "The Neurotic Religious," *Review for Religious,* XVII, 1958.

Vaughan, Richard P., S.J., "Specificity in Program of Psychological Examination," *Guild of Catholic Psychiatrists Bulletin,* Vol. VIII, No. 3, July, 1961.

Vaughan, Richard P., S.J., *Mental Illness and the Religious Life,* Milwaukee, Bruce, 1960.

Van Greunsven, Rev. Norbert, "A Priest Looks at Marriage Counseling," *Guild of Catholic Psychiatrists Bulletin*, Vol. VI, No. 4, October, 1959.

Vanderveldt, Rev. James H., Ph.D., and Odenwald, Robert P., M.D., *Psychiatry and Catholicism*, New York, Mc-Graw-Hill, 1960.

Walters, Sister Annette, and O'Hara, Sister Kevin, *Persons and Personality*, New York, Appleton, 1953.

Webb, B., O.S.B., "Catholics and Family Planning," *Catholic Med. Quart.*, 14: 16-18, January, 1962.

Weisman, A. D., and Hacket, T. P., "Predilection to Death; Death and Dying as a Psychiatric Problem," *Psychosomatic Med.*, May-June, 1961.

Werth, Alvin, O.F.M.Cap., and Mihanovich, Clement S., *Papal Pronouncements on Marriage and the Family*, Milwaukee, Bruce, 1955.

Westberg, Rev. G. E., "The Hospital Chaplain's Contribution to Physician-Clergy Cooperation," *The Pharos of Alpha Omega Alpha*, 22: 217-221, 240, October, 1959.

Wise, Carroll A., *Pastoral Counseling—Its Theory and Practice*, New York: Harper and Bros., 1951.

Wise, Carroll A., "Client-centered Counseling and The Pastor," *The Journal of Pastoral Care*, Vol. VII, No. 3, 1953.

Zimmerman, A., S.V.D., "The Catholic Viewpoint on Overpopulation," *What's New*, 22-26, Spcin, 1959.

Zimmerman and Cervantes, *Marriage and the Family*, Chicago, Regnery, 1956.

Index

359